BIRDS of OXFORDSHIRE

J.W. BRUCKER, A.G. GOSLER and A.R. HERYET

This book is dedicated to
Dr Bruce Campbell who helped to put
Oxfordshire on the ornithological map
and kindled the spark of an interest in
birds in so many, both in this county
and beyond.

BIRDS of OXFORDSHIRE

Edited by

J.W. BRUCKER, A.G. GOSLER and A.R. HERYET

Illustrated by
Martin Elliott, Andrew Forkner and Ian Lewington

Pisces
PUBLICATIONS

The Nature Conservation Bureau Limited

First published by Pisces Publications 1992. Pisces Publications is the imprint of The Nature Conservation Bureau Limited.

British Library-in-Publication Data.
A catalogue record for this book is available from the British Library.

ISBN 0 9508245 9 3

Designed and produced by the Nature Conservation Bureau Limited,
36 Kingfisher Court, Hambridge Road, Newbury, Berkshire RG14 5SJ.

Printed by Information Press, Oxford.

Cover illustration: Great Spotted Woodpecker by Andrew Forkner.

Contents

Foreword

It is now just over a century since Oliver Aplin published ("perhaps rather prematurely", according to his obituarist in *Ibis*) the first book devoted to the birds of Oxfordshire. Little could the author have guessed the upsurge in interest in the birds of Oxfordshire that has taken place in the ensuing century, a period which has already seen the publication of another book (on the birds of both Berkshire and Oxfordshire) and where changes and additional knowledge have been so great that yet a third volume on this subject is now justified.

Aplin might have guessed that changes would continue, because he bemoaned the fact that several species had more or less completely disappeared during the course of the nineteenth century; these included Red Kite, Buzzard, Hen Harrier, Raven, Bittern and Bearded Reedling, all of which he thought had been regular breeders at the beginning of the century. Even then several of these species were probably already much scarcer than they had been, because of habitat destruction. Oxfordshire remained quite well wooded until the mid-1600s, but during the Civil Wars the woodlands were much reduced and were never replanted. This deforestation must have lead to great reductions in the numbers of woodland birds, including species such as the Red Kite, Buzzard and Raven, which, although they needed open country for foraging, depended on large blocks of woodland for safe nesting.

Habitat destruction was not the only problem facing the birds; persecution cannot have helped. In recent times, over-assiduous game-keepers have usually been held responsible for the fact that some species, such as the Buzzard, are not commoner in our area. But in Aplin's time enthusiastic 'naturalists' also made heavy inroads into the bird populations. A great many birds fell to the gun, becoming dusty members of the natural history collections of the gentry. In this, at least, we now may be a bit more civilised; no longer do we indulge in this rather pointless 'stamp-collecting'. Unlike Aplin's book, the current work does not acknowledge the records provided by the taxidermists based in Oxford, Banbury, Chipping Norton and Burford. The mere fact that, in addition to Oxford, three quite small county towns could each support a taxidermist says much about the widespread nature of bird collecting at that time.

Yet despite this fervour for collecting anything and everything, our ornithological predecessors did miss one or two things. For instance, one small brown bird enjoyed its daily life untroubled by the collectors' 'need' for specimens of every kind. Another eight years were to elapse before the Willow Tit was recognised as a distinct species in Britain.

If the woodland is now much reduced, so is the marshy ground. Aplin's descriptions of the extensive wet meadows of the Thames above Newbridge and at Otmoor make today's Port Meadow and Somerton seem very much the poor relations, though at least they are not "affording employment to professional gunners" as were the Newbridge and Otmoor areas in Aplin's day. This, together with the reduction of the riverside vegetation, must have led to the losses of the Bittern and the Bearded Reedling. Nor do these meadows any longer reverberate with the sound of Corncrakes which Aplin described as "commonly distributed throughout the county". Similarly, the loss of the rough meadows has resulted in the virtual disappearance of the Whinchat, and the Lapwing has clearly, and almost unnoticed, declined even more recently.

Aplin's description of the fields as "small rather than large, divided by tall thick hedges studded with an abundance of hedgerow timber, the elm being the most numerous tree, and a characteristic feature of the landscape", reminds us of another element of the landscape that has disappeared only since the advent of Dutch Elm disease and after the appearance of Mary Radford's book on the *Birds of Berkshire and Oxfordshire* in 1966. Much has happened to Oxfordshire in this quarter of a century and there is so much new to report on that already a new book is necessary. Both the avifauna and the habitats have changed and are in the process of changing further still. Amongst the birds, in 1966, Collared Doves were only just appearing and, amazing as it may now seem, the Canada Goose was still an uncommon bird in the county; since then, sadly, Nightingales have dwindled fast. The changes in aquatic habitats has been quite marked; in 1939 W.B. Alexander wrote of Oxfordshire "sheets of still water in the county are comparatively rare". Not much had changed by the late 1940s, but since then many gravel pits have appeared and new ones are being excavated today, with major effects on the aquatic birds. Farmoor reservoir did not exist (and if it had, it would not have been in Oxfordshire!). These areas have added greatly to the sightings of waterbirds in the county. If the proposed, mammoth, new reservoir is built south-west of Abingdon, then we may need another new book at the end of the century or soon after!

Not only have these changes occurred, but so has the standard of ornithological recording. More watchers are watching — and doing so more systematically. As a result, this book not only records the changes that have occurred, and are occurring still, but does so in a much more detailed and quantitative way than has been possible in the past. The tetrad atlas recording that has been done throughout the county has put our understanding of the county's birds on a much more quantitative, checkable and repeatable footing. So, we have here, not only an enjoyable and informative book, but one that, when the time comes for yet another work on the birds of Oxfordshire, will provide the precise and reliable background data, against which to plot the changes that have occurred.

A century ago, in the introduction to his book, Aplin voiced the hope that "the material here collected may prove serviceable as a basis for a fuller account of the birds of this inland county, should another edition be called for." He was proved amply right and it is difficult to believe that this will not also prove true of the present volume in due course; the authors are to be congratulated on another milestone in Oxfordshire's ornithology.

C.M. Perrins,
December 1991.
Edward Grey Institute, Oxford.

Preface

The organisation of this book follows a clear path. It is not intended to be an identification guide to the birds of Oxfordshire nor does it represent the last word on the subject. Indeed we strongly hope that it might inspire greater efforts in the future. Instead, we are attempting to document our current knowledge of the county's avifauna particularly with regard to its populations rather than specific biology and to assess the status of the species which make up that avifauna.

One result of this policy is that the reader will encounter a great range of length in the species accounts, and this is, in part at least, a reflection of local interest and knowledge and not necessarily related to any qualitative judgement of the importance of that species in local, national or international terms. Another result is that we have tried throughout, to include only data that were collected within Oxfordshire. That is not to say that we have tried to isolate Oxfordshire's birds geographically since this would result in artificial and arbitrary constraints on the text. Birds know of no county boundaries and to try to impose such rigidity would be counter-productive; but we have included information from outside the county only when to do so would help to place these populations in a national or international context. Further details concerning the layout of the species accounts appears as a short introduction to that section of the book.

Also, we have tried not simply to re-hash the previous works on the birds of Oxfordshire. Instead, while we have used much of the information which they contained to trace out the population changes which have occurred in the last century, our main aim is to present material collected since Dr Radford's book of 1966, along with any other records which were missed from earlier accounts.

We have tried throughout this book to avoid abbreviation as far as possible. However, some common terms occur so frequently that we have used abbreviations for simplicity. Many

of them will be known to the reader already. Those used are as follows:

BBONT	Berkshire, Buckinghamshire and Oxfordshire Naturalists' Trust
BOS	Banbury Ornithological Society
BOU	British Ornithologists's Union
BTO	British Trust for Ornithology
BWP	Birds of the Western Palaearctic (see References)
CBC	Common Birds Census
EGI	Edward Grey Institute of Field Ornithology
FWAG	Farming and Wildlife Advisory Group
ha	hectare
LNR	Local Nature Reserve
MAFF	Ministry of Agriculture, Fisheries and Food
NNR	National Nature Reserve
NR	Nature Reserve
NCC	Nature Conservancy Council (Now English Nature)
NR(C)	Nest Record or Nest Record Card
OOS	Oxford Ornithological Society
RSPB	Royal Society for the Protection of Birds
SSSI	Site of Special Scientific Interest
WBS	Waterways Bird Survey

There were many powerful reasons for wishing to embark on this work. Foremost is the fact that the face of the county has changed greatly since 1966. The county is now 30% larger than it was then, and rapid changes in land-use have occurred during this period with a profound affect on the wildlife. Attitudes to wildlife have also changed dramatically since 1966. The well documented growth of the local naturalist's trusts, and national organisations such as the RSPB reflect this fact.

As this book is compiled, we have a sense that we have entered a period of growing environmental awareness, with many more people (though far from all) having at least one eye on environmental matters. Also, leisure pursuits, particularly those close to the environment, have developed considerably in the past 25 years and few of them more so than birdwatching. As many as 70 people regularly contribute valuable records to the county bird recorder each month and more than 300 people helped in the collection of data for the Atlas of Breeding Birds in Oxfordshire which features so prominently in this book.

Our brief, to keep this work relevant to Oxfordshire's birds has involved delving through much information presented in books and journals together with the huge quantity of records passed on to the county recorder and/ or published in the reports of the various ornithological and natural history societies in the county. Hence we might have made errors in our interpretation of our avifauna or might have omitted vital points simply because relevant information was not readily available. The point we make is that if we are to learn more about our local bird populations, further their conservation and secure their future, information needs to be collated from as wide a range of sources as possible and filed together, ideally with the county bird recorder. With this plea for greater cooperation in the future we point out that the book is published on behalf of the Oxfordshire Bird Study Group, a body covering the OOS and BOS, as well as other groups and individuals with an interest in ornithology in the county.

Acknowledgements

From its conception, during the course of the Atlas of Breeding Birds in Oxfordshire, and throughout the subsequent research, writing and publication, this book has been a team effort. Many people have freely given their time, effort and advice to enable us to produce this book to such a high standard and a number of individuals and groups deserve special mention.

We are especially grateful to the artists Martin Elliott, Andrew Forkner and Ian Lewington for their splendid illustration of this work; and to Mike Bayliss, Peter Pool, Anthony Roberts, Roger Scase, Jane Sears and Mike Wilkins for writing a number of accounts of species for which they have particular local knowledge. John Campbell, Martin Daniel, John Kearvell, Ted Norvell, Roy Overall and Roger Wiggins also assisted at an early stage of the writing.

We are grateful to C.G. Smith and T.P. Burtt of Oxford University's School of Geography for providing much information for Chapter 3 on the climate of Oxfordshire, and for commenting on an earlier draft of that chapter.

This work could not have been undertaken without the continued support of the two principal ornithological societies of the county: the Oxford Ornithological Society and the Banbury Ornithological Society. Members of these societies have assisted us in many ways, including carrying out the bulk of fieldwork both for the Atlas project and in general recording in the county, and by commenting on earlier drafts of species accounts for which they had a strong interest. We are most grateful to them for their help.

More than 300 people contributed to the collection of data for the Atlas of Breeding Birds of Oxfordshire (ABBO) and every record is greatly appreciated. A full list of contributors appears as an appendix. Further, we should like to thank everybody who has contributed their records over the years to the local societies and county bird recorders. Many of these records have been included in the species accounts of the book, often without reference, but without them our knowledge of Oxfordshire's birds would be very much poorer.

Amongst the contributors to the fieldwork for the ABBO, a number of people deserve specific recognition. The 10 km square leaders, who played an important part in the organisation of the survey and who made life much easier for the project coordinator. They are identified by bold print in the list of Atlas contributors. Guy Houlsby developed the necessary software to allow the atlas maps and statistics to be generated by computer from the enormous quantity of data collected and Jenny Houlsby painstakingly entered these onto the computer. We also should like to acknowledge the help given by local media in publicising the work, and to the local RSPB Members Groups, West Oxfordshire Field Club, Abingdon Naturalists' Society and BBONT for the interest shown and the support given for the work.

The project would have been impossible without considerable financial support and in this respect we gratefully acknowledge the following: Cherwell District Council, M. Rowntree, Oxford City Council, Oxford Ornithological Society, South Oxfordshire District Council, United Kingdom Atomic Energy Authority, Vale of the White Horse District Council and the West Oxfordshire District Council. In addition, The Northmoor Trust provided a fieldworker to work solely on the Atlas, and Oxford County Council Department of Museum Services provided the recording cards necessary for standardised fieldwork.

We are grateful to the BTO for supplying specific information for the species accounts and in particular we wish to thank David Glue for providing details from the Nest Record Scheme and Will Peach of the Ringing Office for the laborious task of extracting all of the ringing recoveries relevant to Oxfordshire. Further useful information has kindly been supplied by local ringers, particularly Andrew Harris, Ross Laugher and Brian Shaw.

Prior to our embarking on the project, so as to pick their brains, and with some considerable cheek, we contacted many other individuals who had been involved in similar county-based projects. The response from these people was wonderful and gave us a much clearer idea of where we should be aiming. We are therefore indebted to Ian Castle, John Clark, Simon Cox, P.K. Holland and Jon Hornbuckle and to Jen and John Scott for their help and advice. Tim Sharrock also offered much advice and moral support in the early days of the project.

Finally we are grateful to our publishers and particularly to Peter Creed and Paul Goriup for having the vision to take on this project and for their frequent and expert guidance in its execution.

CHAPTER ONE
An Introduction to the Ornithology of Oxfordshire

This is a book about the birds of Oxfordshire — a medium sized county (260,942 ha or 643,788 acres) in the south midlands of England. But more than that, it is a book about the relationship between man and birds, for there is no truly natural habitat in the county, most of the area having been cleared and cultivated since before Roman times. For the last 70 years, a period of profound change in land use, the fortunes of bird populations in the region have been documented by the Oxford Ornithological Society (the oldest county-based ornithological society in the country).

Oxfordshire as an administrative unit dates from about AD 911 in the time of Edward the Elder. Hence it was recognised by the Normans in the Domesday Book. This showed the existence of most of the settlements that we recognise today. Except for a few minor adjustments, largely in the nineteenth century, the county boundary changed little between 1086 and 1974 (see Bloxham 1982). In 1974, a major re-organisation took place in local government, which resulted in the inclusion of the Vale of White Horse district within Oxfordshire. This had formerly been part of Berkshire. This event increased the area of the county by some 37% (from 190,209 ha) and, as will be seen, had important implications for bird recording in the county and consequently for the production of this book.

Present-day Oxfordshire is bounded to the north by Warwickshire and Northamptonshire, to the east by Buckinghamshire, to the south by Berkshire, and by Gloucestershire and Wiltshire to the west. It has a human population of about 550,000. The administrative capital is Oxford, established by the Saxons in the eighth century, on the low-lying flood plain at the confluence of the Rivers Isis (Thames) and Cherwell. Before 1974, the southern boundary of the county was formed by the Thames itself, so that Oxford lay practically on it with the Vale of White Horse to the south-west. Today, Oxford lies more or less at the centre of the enlarged Oxfordshire. With a population of about 120,000, Oxford is

also the centre of population and this has tended to bias bird recording toward it. However, the north of the county has been well represented since the establishment of the Banbury Ornithological Society in 1952 (see below).

A fuller treatment of the county's bird habitats is presented in Chapter 2 but a brief description of the county may be of value at this point. With a population density of only 0.2/km², Oxfordshire is still chiefly a rural county in which the principle land-use is agriculture. However, the total area of the county devoted to agriculture has dropped from around 90% in 1886 to about 80% in 1986, and this despite the fact that the Vale of White Horse, added in 1974, is chiefly agricultural. Figure 1.1 presents the relative change in agricultural land-use in the county since 1866. It shows clearly a long-term decline in pastoral farming (mostly termed 'other' in the figure) in favour of cereals.

The rural landscape of Oxfordshire falls into the category that Rackham (1986) terms *planned countryside*, that is, a countryside of regular fields bounded by planted hedgerows that was superimposed during the enclosures of the eighteenth and nineteenth centuries on the

Figure 1.1.
Agricultural land-use in Oxfordshire, 1866-1986.

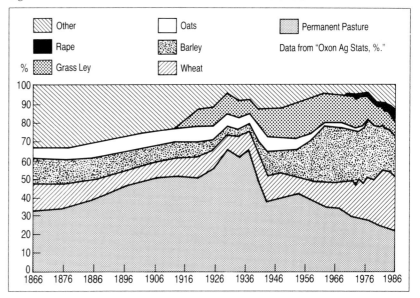

open medieval field systems of ridge and furrow which preceded it. That *ancient countryside*, which evolved naturally from the lie of the land, from the distribution of woodland, heathland and marsh, can still be seen in the winding country lanes skirting embanked irregular field boundaries in counties like Devon and Essex. However, the countryside of Oxfordshire is amongst the most modified, the most derived of any county and, as shown in Chapter 2, there is little left of the original vegetation.

Although there is no true upland in the county, indeed it has been described as "a countryside without extremes" (Bond and Over 1988), the landscape is sufficiently diverse for a range of farming types. In essence, farming in Oxfordshire is mixed, although the mixture varies from sheep, wheat and barley on the limestone uplands to dairy and wheat in the clay and alluvial vales. This mixture arises chiefly from the diverse geology and consequently soils of the county (see Chapter 2).

Yurdan (1988) divides the county into six regions differing in topography and land-use. These regions also provide a useful starting point for an ornithological description of the county. The first of Yurdan's regions is the city of *Oxford* itself which we shall exclude for present purposes. However, it should be acknowledged that several useful accounts of the birds of the city exist such as Warde Fowler (1886) and Bayliss (1982). The latter notes that 208 species have been recorded within the city since 1900 and of these, 88 have bred at some time during this period.

The second region is formed by the *Chiltern Hills* to the south-east of the county, typified by Beechwoods, thin soils and dry river valleys. Yurdan points out that the buildings of the region are of brick, a fact which distinguishes it from the Cotswolds. The region includes the important BBONT Warburg Reserve at Bix near Henley where Long-eared Owls have bred successfully in recent years. The chalk of the Chilterns is geologically continuous with that of the Berkshire Downs which form the third region and which in Oxfordshire constitute the

Vale of White Horse already noted for its annexation to the county in 1974.

What vegetation was natural to the Downs has long been debated. There is much evidence of human activity here stretching back thousands of years as indicated by barrows, hill forts and ancient footpaths such as the Ridgeway. It is almost certainly true that this was the first area of the county to be cleared by Man of its natural postglacial woodlands. However, exactly what that 'wildwood' consisted of is unclear. The woodlands which exist today are dominated by Beech but much of this was planted within the last few hundred years. The open downland of closely cropped pasture is a man-made vegetation derived from many hundreds of years of grazing by rabbits and sheep. When grazing is relaxed as at the height of the *Myxomatosis* epidemic, the vegetation quickly succeeds to scrub and then woodland. Is this the natural vegetation of the region?

Sheep farming is the traditional land-use on the Downs and this provides opportunities for a number of bird species found rarely elsewhere in the county. These include the rare Stone Curlew which hangs on in the county with fewer than five pairs although recent initiatives by the RSPB working closely with sympathetic landowners have given some cause for hope. Other birds of the region include wintering Merlin and Hen Harrier, Golden Plover and Short-eared Owl, and breeding Quail. The Downs and their birds were described in some detail in an essay by E.L. Jones in Radford (1966). Since the 1960s, much of the downland has been brought into cereal production, especially barley and wheat. This has greatly affected the birdlife of the region but a recent renewal of interest in sheep production (as indicated by Figure 1.2) in the county might be viewed with guarded optimism.

The fourth region consists of the *Cotswold Hills* to the west of the county. In contrast to the chalklands of the Chilterns, Cotswold buildings are of the local stone which blends them naturally into the landscape. Nevertheless, the region shares much in common with the Chilterns and the Vale. Again, sheep are an important mainstay of the economy here and this is exemplified by the *Cotswold* breed. The birds of the region also are comparable with those areas, but in addition, the fast-flowing Cotswold streams provide suitable habitat for the only breeding pairs of Dipper in Oxfordshire.

Yurdan's fifth region she terms the *Oxfordshire Plain*. Formed on ironstone deposits in the north of the county, this region has Banbury as its capital and in many respects bears greater resemblance to the Midlands than to the great chalkland country of Thomas Hardy to the south. However, the region is topographically more or less continuous with the Cotswolds and is sometimes combined with them as the North Oxfordshire Uplands. The birds of the Oxfordshire plain have been documented in great detail by members of the Banbury

Figure 1.2.
Sheep and cattle stocking density.

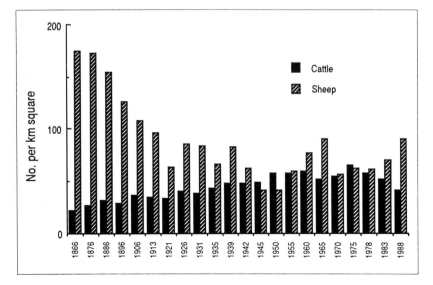

Ornithological Society, and interested readers should especially see Easterbrook (1983).

From this description, it emerges that Oxfordshire is framed by relatively high ground. A central plain is formed from the softer rocks of the Oxford and Kimmeridge Clays of the Upper Jurassic. This corresponds more or less with Yurdan's sixth and final region — The Thames Valley, which she considers to be the best known part of the county. Aplin (1889) described Oxfordshire as one of the best watered counties in the country and this is in no small part due to the Thames which divides it, and whose tributaries drain the upland regions. The vale, which lies mostly at about 60 m(197ft) is punctuated by a line of 'islands' of Corallian limestone such as at Wytham hill (164 m) and of the Cornbrash to the north of Otmoor (140 m). Whilst much is given over to agriculture, the Thames valley itself retains lush water meadows, small riverside reedbeds and extensive gravel workings which provide habitat for the greatest diversity of birds of any of the regions. That this is true owes much to the fact that the city of Oxford, which lies within the Thames valley, still retains much wetland habitat.

Agricultural practice in the Thames valley has changed immeasurably during the present century and the loss of many species of bird such as the Corncrake reflects this (see Chapter 2). However, the creation of new wetlands in the form of gravel workings in the Dorchester area and the lower Windrush valley provides valuable replacement habitat for many birds, compensating in some degree for the loss of natural marshland. Figure 1.3 shows the development of open water in the lower Windrush between 1970 and 1990. Recent developments in planning for an integrated after-use of these pits which will make adequate provision for wildlife conservation now marks a major milestone in conservation development in the county. In Chapter 6, the future for birds in Oxfordshire is considered. Whilst this is of course speculative, recent developments at both national and county level give cause for optimism as indicated above, but it is only possible to make realistic predictions by recourse to the past, and the greater part of this book forms such a review.

Oxfordshire is fortunate in having a major work on its birds published before the present century. The Birds of Oxfordshire by O.V. Aplin, published in 1889 gives both a charming and yet detailed and useful picture of the county's birds 100 years ago. Furthermore, its 22-page introduction gives an equally vivid impression of Oxfordshire's countryside in the days before cars and metalled roads, aeroplanes and agrochemicals. This was a world in which travel was limited by the speed of the bicycle, the horse and the steam engine and in which the sight of Redstarts and the sound of Nightingales and Turtle Doves were a commonplace (though no less welcome) occurrence. However, despite this apparently idyllic scene Aplin tells us that the detrimental impact of Man's activities on the distribution of birds, largely through agricultural development, was proceeding apace by 1889. For example, the draining of major wetlands such as Otmoor and the lower Windrush valley was well under way or was complete. This had considerably affected the livelihoods of local people, many of whom depended on winter wildfowling for additional income.

Aplin's book forms an excellent yardstick against which the distribution and abundance of our present-day bird populations can be judged. On the whole, despite a considerable reduction in hunting and the more effective implementation of bird protection legislation (both existing and new) since Aplin's day, the losses to the county's avifauna greatly outweigh the gains. The latter have resulted from introductions such as the Little Owl (first

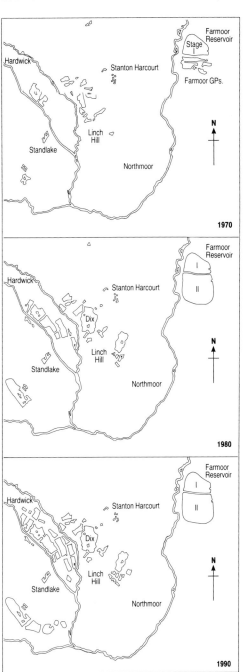

Figure 1.3.
Development of open water in the lower Windrush, 1970-1990.

Table 1.1.

Notes on the number of Contributors to the annual bird reports.

Year	No. observers	Comments
1925	16	covering the three counties
1930	38	. . .
1935	44	. . .
1940	31	. . .
1945	36	. . .
1950	43	(in addition, observations from the three counties were extracted from reports of the Reading Ornithological Society, Middle Thames Natural History Society and ornithological section of the Newbury District Field Club, bringing the apparent total to 111)
1955	85	(38 OOS) covering Oxfordshire and Berkshire
1960	182	(57 OOS) . . .
1965	232	(47 OOS) . . .
1970	235	(59 OOS) . . .
1975	189	(102 OOS) Oxfordshire only
1980	125	. . .
1984	121	. . .
1985	121	. . .
1986	100	. . .
1987	148	. . .
1988	182	. . .
1989	205	. . .

Figure 1.4.
Oxfordshire population density, 1801-1981.

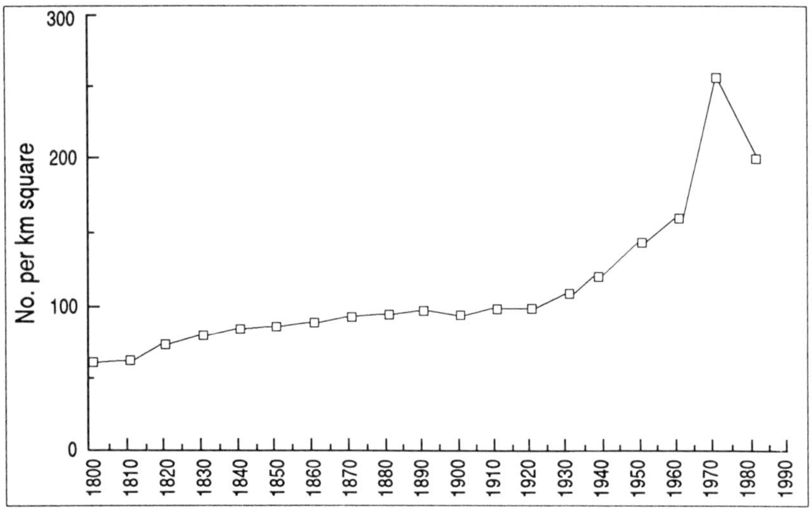

recorded in 1891), from natural colonisation such as the Collared Dove and Cetti's Warbler, and from escapes such as the Canada Goose and Ruddy Duck. Gains of species such as the Yellow-browed Warbler have undoubtedly resulted also from the greater number of knowledgeable, better-equipped observers. The losses have resulted from a combination of climatic change and habitat loss or degradation both here in the breeding grounds and in Africa where many of our declining species spend the winter. Losses and near-losses from the county list include Bittern (although already declining by 1889), Corncrake, Stone Curlew, Nightjar, Wryneck, Woodlark, Red-backed Shrike, Redstart, Whinchat and Stonechat. Many others such as the Redshank, Barn Owl, Turtle Dove, Tree Pipit and Nightingale are very much scarcer now than they were 100 years ago.

Despite the invaluable contribution made by Aplin's book, our knowledge of the changes in Oxfordshire's birdlife that have occurred during the last 100 years is much more precise than might have been possible from a simple comparison of county 'snapshots' taken in 1889 and again in 1989. In 1880 the Ashmolean Natural History Society of Oxford (founded in 1828), had established an Ornithological subsection. In 1916, Francis Jourdain (later to be more widely recognised for his contribution to the Witherby *Handbook of British Birds*) became its president. Between 1890 and 1914, Aplin had published a series of 'Notes on Oxfordshire Ornithology' in *The Zoologist* journal. In 1919, Bernard Tucker (also later to make an important contribution to 'The Handbook') came up to Oxford to read zoology at Magdalen college. The near coincidence of these three events was later to change the face of Ornithology, not just in Oxfordshire but in Britain as a whole.

Tucker was greatly influenced by Jourdain. Together they saw the need for an independent ornithological society, not least as a vehicle to publish an annual report on the birds of Oxfordshire. In 1921 the Oxford Ornithological Society (OOS) gained its independence from the Ashmolean Natural History Society and it is

clear that the report was to be its focal point right from the earliest days. In 1924 Jourdain and Tucker published the *Report of the Oxford Ornithological Society on the Birds of Oxfordshire, Berkshire and Buckinghamshire 1915–1922*. According to their editorial, they had originally intended to cover only the year 1922 and possibly a little earlier, but due to the considerable contribution of hitherto unpublished material from O.V. Aplin, they decided to back-date it. Also, because of contributions from other non-members (in fact Aplin is listed as such) in Berkshire (Reading and Faringdon) and Buckinghamshire (Bletchley and Great Missenden), the greater geographical coverage was possible. In truth of course, that first report did little more than up-date the county list (although very common species were often omitted from a year's report) but it did set a number of precedents which were to be incorporated in all subsequent reports. For example, it listed all 15 of its contributors in full, and assigned each a set of initials by which individual records could be traced to the particular observer responsible for its contribution. It made some mention of the weather during the year, and species accounts were annotated with behaviour and other details rather than simply being listed.

The report has been published annually since 1924. Since 1925 it has included first and last dates of migrants and since 1929 it has included a ringing report. The report still lists its contributors, and this (to some extent) allows one to review the growth of both the OOS and the general interest in the county's birds that have occurred during this century. Table 1.1 shows the total number of contributors cited in the annual bird report over a number of years. Although many of these are (or were) members of the OOS, members' records make up only a part of the total submitted and the reports have not always distinguished clearly between members and non-members.

The figures presented here for 1980–1988 are somewhat misleading. Records are included from the Banbury Ornithological Society and from the Berkshire and Buckinghamshire county recorders (where appropriate) so that, in fact, a considerably greater number of individuals were involved in these years than is apparent from the figures. However, as in 1950, these observers did not contribute directly to the report. Their records were received second-hand. Hence the figure presented in the number of named contributors. Counteracting this, is the fact that some names have been added of people who recorded observations in a bird logbook which is maintained at Farmoor reservoir although these people did not otherwise submit records to the county.

However, whatever their shortcomings, these figures do make the following important points:

(a) the number of contributors has increased some 10–15 fold during the report's 65-year history. This is also encouraging as the population of Oxfordshire has increased only about three-fold during this time (see Figure 1.4)

(b) the increase has been greatest since the Second World War

(c) OOS members contribute about 30–50% of the total number of records so that clearly the report satisfies a greater demand than would be required from the society alone (OOS membership now stands at around 250).

What is not apparent from Table 1.1 is the quality and indeed the historical value of the information published over the years in the county reports. Some impression of this can be gained from the fact that Gosler (1990) was able to trace the history of birds at a single site over some 70 years, largely from information published in the county reports. In fact 50% of 1,072 records included in his historical survey of the birds of Wytham were extracted from county reports and were not otherwise available. Of the rest, the great majority were of observations made after 1975 and therefore covered a much shorter period. One might hope that similar reviews might be carried out for other important areas in the county such as Otmoor, Shotover or the Windrush drawing on the great wealth of material that is undoubtedly present and still untapped in these reports.

Having said this, it must be acknowledged that any report compiled from records which were collected in an unsystematic manner will be biased. First the geographical distribution of records will often reflect the distribution of human population rather than that of the birds. Secondly there is a bias towards particularly favoured sites such as Farmoor reservoir although they are favoured precisely because they tend to attract birds. Thirdly, and perhaps the most difficult to allow for in the interpretation of records, is the bias of observers in what they choose to report. The dedicated local birdwatcher, hoping to reduce the bias of the annual reports may report everything observed on a particular site. Most birdwatchers however, are more selective and have their own subjective idea of what is worth reporting. For example, all would report an Osprey in the county, some would report a Little Owl and few would report a Marsh Tit. Finally, the dedicated twitchers might not even report the Osprey. In an attempt to influence these tendencies, the County Recorder together with the OOS Records Committee has produced a complete annotated species list for the county. Whilst it points out that if possible, all bird records are required, it emphasises the value of records of certain species. A full copy of this list is available from the county bird recorder, c/o the OOS but an abbreviated form appears with the county list in Appendix 1.

The report continued to cover the three counties until 1952 when Buckinghamshire was no longer included. It was inevitable that the number of contributors to the report should

decline after the boundary re-organisations of 1974 since Berkshire also was then dropped from the report's coverage. Since 1974, however, the report on the birds of Oxfordshire has covered the enlarged county including the Vale of White Horse. Since the old county of Berkshire was included in the report from 1924 to 1974, in effect, records are available for the whole of 'New Oxfordshire' during the whole period of the report's existence. Both the figures in Table 1.1 and the bird records presented in the species accounts in this book should be interpreted within the historical framework of the boundary changes although the book covers the whole of the 'New Oxfordshire'.

I suggested above that the coincidence in Oxford of Jourdain, Aplin and Tucker around 1920 had more far-reaching consequences than the establishment of a small county bird club and the publication of an annual bird report. This is true, for it was largely from within the ranks of the OOS in the 1920s and 1930s that plans were made and the foundations laid for both the British Trust for Ornithology (BTO) and the Edward Grey Institute of Field Ornithology (EGI) at Oxford University. It was by no coincidence then, that the BTO's first home was in Oxford. Its first secretary was Bruce Campbell who was to remain in Oxfordshire and have a considerable influence on the development of ornithology both locally and nationally.

Fieldwork was always emphasised by the OOS. Hence it was the first society to organise county-wide atlas-type surveys of particular species. This work was started largely on Tucker's initiative in 1927 and it became known as the Oxford Bird Census. Its results were published annually in the report. In 1930 W.B. Alexander was appointed to run the census on a full-time basis. Between 1929 and 1939 the distribution and status in the county of more than 40 species were documented. These included Stone Curlew, Nightjar, Kingfisher, Wryneck, Red-backed Shrike, Nightingale and Redstart, so giving us a detailed picture of the pre-war abundance of these species. The Oxford Bird Census gave impetus for a national ornithological network, and in 1933 the BTO was founded. Under Tucker and Alexander, the Oxford Bird Census became *Oxford University Research in Economic Ornithology* in 1930 and the *Edward Grey Institute of Field Ornithology* in 1938. The relationships between the OOS, BTO and EGI in those early days were complex. They have been described many times and the interested reader should see Lack (1965), Radford (1966), Hickling (1983), Nicholson (1983) and Gosler (1986).

In 1926, E.M. Nicholson went up to Oxford as an undergraduate and joined the OOS. A year later he organised the Society's bird ringing under the 'Witherby scheme' which was later taken over by the BTO and became the national bird ringing scheme. Since 1929 the bird report has included a county ringing report. There is no figure available for the total number of birds ringed in Oxfordshire since 1926 because the early reports did not attempt to collate data from all sources. The Edward Grey Institute alone has ringed more than 44,500 Great Tits and more than 40,000 Blue Tits since 1947 in its population study of these species at Wytham Woods (formerly Berkshire). The main problem in calculating the total number of birds ringed is that although OOS ringers' records were published annually by the Society, many other ringers also worked in the county and they have not always contributed their data to the report although ringing details were sent to the BTO. But the information cannot be obtained from the BTO because the ringing details are filed according to the ring number and not on a county basis. However, from figures published in the later bird reports it is possible to derive an estimate of the minimum number ringed between 1948 and 1989. This is 367,128 which consists of some 245,091 full-grown birds and 122,037 pulli (nestlings). In recent years, about 11,000 birds have been ringed annually, usually in the ratio 2 full-grown:1 pullus. These totals constitute about 1.7% of all birds ringed in the UK since the British Ringing Scheme began.

While these might seem to be large numbers, ringing is the only means we have of monitoring the rates and causes of mortality in most species so that it is essential that large numbers, even of apparently common species, continue to be ringed each year. This was well demonstrated locally by Holmes *et al.* (1987) who studied the return rates of Sand Martins to a colony at Stanton Harcourt between 1979 and 1983. Through ringing, they were able to show that the sudden decline in population size which occurred there from 1982 to 1983 was due to a drop in both the adult return rate and the rate at which juveniles were added to the breeding population (recruited) and that both of these probably resulted from a decrease in over-winter survival.

There is currently available no complete list of species ringed in the county although one could be drawn up from the county reports. Certainly it is more than 150 species. In most years about 100 species have been ringed. In recent years these have included such birds as Stone Curlew, Little Ringed Plover, and Cetti's Warbler.

Although we cannot obtain a complete list of birds ringed in the county from the BTO, details of ringing recoveries involving Oxfordshire are available since they are accessible by computer. Hence the more interesting recoveries have been included in a short analysis of movements in the species texts in this book.

Since the 1950s the BTO, EGI and the OOS have developed distinctly in their own directions. The BTO is now a major organisation of international importance providing valuable information for conservation at a national level. It employs a large professional staff and is supported by some 10,000 members. The EGI is now a thriving ornithological research group

firmly established within the Oxford University Department of Zoology. Under its former director, Dr David Lack, it had developed from its pre-war 'one-man-band' status to a research establishment with an international reputation and this has continued to the present day although its future was by no means certain for some time following Dr Lack's death in 1973. The library which Alexander established has developed into one of the most comprehensive ornithological libraries in the world and is visited annually by hundreds of researchers from around the world. Indeed it was only the existence of this invaluable resource that made the University Press's *Birds of the Western Palearctic* a workable proposition. The library, which is strictly for reference only, is open to OOS, BTO and BOU members in addition of course to University researchers. Others are admitted at the librarian's discretion. One of David Lack's most important contributions to ornithology was the establishment in 1947 of a long-term population study of tits in the University's newly acquired Wytham Woods estate, and this too continues to the present day (see Great Tit).

After its brief flirtation with the wider theatre of national ornithology, the Oxford Ornithological Society has, since the 1950s concentrated strictly on its local responsibilities. It has to be said that although the OOS's children have become great and powerful and neither (at the time of writing) has moved very far from home, the contribution made by them to Oxfordshire ornithology specifically has been minimal. This is right and proper given their vastly different aims. I mention this simply because it is often expected that given the existence nearby of such institutions, we surely must know all there is to know about the birds of Oxfordshire, and, as will be seen from the pages that follow, this is far from being the case. Nevertheless, by the early 1960s, it became clear that after 40 years of detailed documentation in the annual bird reports, a great deal was known.

Dr Mary Radford undertook the immense task of distilling the information from the bird reports into a readable form, and the result, *The Birds of Berkshire and Oxfordshire* was published by Longmans in 1966. Although chiefly concerned with a simple description of the county's avifauna without making any value judgements, there is an undercurrent of unease running through the book concerning the apparent reduction in the abundance and distribution of many species. However, in those days it was impossible to support otherwise subjective impressions with real figures. Even the BTO's Common Bird Census was too young a project to help in this regard. In the 25 years since its publication, changes in the avian environment of Oxfordshire have occurred both more rapidly and more completely than during the 75 years between Aplin and Radford. It is the sense of urgency which these changes have instilled in the ornithological and conservation communities, together with a new and growing environmental awareness in the public in general, that have given the impetus for this book.

While the OOS is the older society and is responsible for the collation of records throughout Oxfordshire, this review would be incomplete without recognition of the fact that the county today has two principal ornithological societies. For in 1952, independently of the OOS, the Banbury Ornithological Society was founded. Bruce Campbell was strongly involved in its creation, so that it is not surprising that the BOS established a strong leaning towards quantitative field survey methods because these were the very tools which were to prove essential for the national surveys later carried out by the BTO of which he was secretary. In contrast to the apparently random or even arbitrary recording methods adopted (out of necessity) by the OOS, the BOS concentrated on systematic surveys of pre-determined locations on pre-determined dates within a block of twelve 10 km squares centred on Banbury. In many respects, this was pioneering work which was greatly to assist the BTO in the future. Hence in addition to the activities that any birdwatcher might expect to find carried out by a regional society, the BOS introduced a number of innovations. All recording was carried out on a 1 km grid basis. The habitats of the region were mapped in great detail within this grid framework. This has become known as the 'Domesday Survey'. Intensive surveys of one or more pre-determined species are carried out in each breeding season. This is essentially similar to an atlas project (see below) for a different species or set of species each year. These surveys are known as Annual Breeding Season Surveys or 'ABSS'. Another innovation was the introduction of Random Square Surveys or 'RSS', whereby a set of 1 km squares is selected at random each year and surveyed intensively. This system, together with the ABSS, maximises the working efficiency of a comparatively small number of observers who, however dedicated, nevertheless have limited time available. Finally, the BOS have, for more than ten years, used a micro-computer to handle the data collected in the various surveys. At the time that this was introduced, it was certainly a revolutionary approach.

In his foreword to the third decennial report of the society entitled *Birds of the Banbury Area 1972-1981* (Easterbrook 1983), Bruce Campbell reported that "Over these 30 years the B.O.S has earned a reputation for the remarkable amount of field work it carries out year after year...". It would also be fair to say that this work greatly helped to inspire OOS members to embark on an atlas project of the whole county, and the BOS input to this project, both in terms of advice and fieldwork, was essential for its success.

In the late 1970s, with the last copies of Radford's book barely sold, members of the OOS decided that the time was already ripe to publish an updated county avifauna. Such was the pace of change in the county and its bird populations. However, it was felt that due to the biased distribution of knowledge (both geographically and by species) the project would have to be shelved, pending the execution of a detailed Atlas project. Fieldwork for this Atlas, now known as the Atlas of Breeding Birds in Oxfordshire, or 'ABBO' was carried out between 1985 and 1988, and forms a focus for the present book. Indeed, without it, it is doubtful whether a new avifauna would have been undertaken at all. Full details of the Atlas of Breeding Birds in Oxfordshire, including details of the project's history, are given in Chapter 4.

Finally, something should be said of the layout and content of this book. The main body of the book, which will be the focus for most readers, consists of accounts of the principal species recorded in the county since 1900. By principal species, I mean that we have generally excluded species which have escaped from captivity and which have not established viable feral populations. A list of escapes is given in Appendix 2 together with a list of species recorded before this century but not since. The Atlas maps are given in a block immediately before the species accounts, and following Chapter 4 which describes the detail of the atlas project. Each map is cross-referenced to the page on which the appropriate species text appears. The supporting chapters give an overview of the Oxfordshire environment for birds, past, present and future. Finally the appendices give species lists, supporting details referred to by the text, a gazetteer, a list of contributors to the Atlas and a list of important addresses relevant to birds and their conservation in Oxfordshire.

CHAPTER TWO
Bird Habitats in Oxfordshire

This chapter examines the physical and biological context in which birds exist in Oxfordshire today. The birds of any region, like its other animals and its plants, have had to adapt to a physical matrix consisting of its rocks, soils, land forms and climate. This framework also determines their relationship with the other animals and the plants of the region, and to a large extent also their relationship with man, the dominant influence in any long-settled country such as Britain. This is because there are no longer any purely natural habitats in Oxfordshire, and no more than 8% of the county's land surface can be regarded as even semi-natural. Indeed, some two-thirds of Oxfordshire consists of farmland, and another 18% is occupied by towns, suburbs and villages. So the great majority of the county's birds, both by numbers and by species, are those that have been able to adapt themselves either to the close proximity of man, or to modern intensive agriculture, dominated as it is by the use of chemicals which are rarely beneficial to birds.

Oxfordshire is not only one of the furthest inland but also one of the most calcareous counties in England. It lies at the south-western end of the scarplands of the south-east midlands, formed during the two great calcareous geological ages of the Jurassic, laid down 110–140 million years ago, and the Cretaceous, some 65–110 million years ago. The strata that make up these scarplands all run from north-east to south-west, with the oldest, the Lias clays around Banbury, in the north-west of the county and the youngest, the Chalk, forming the Chilterns and the Berkshire Downs in the south and south-east.

Figure 2.1 shows a relief map of Oxfordshire together with the major towns. The three major escarpments of the county are those of the Chilterns in the south-east, the Berkshire Downs in the south and the Cotswolds in the north-west. These hills are almost all below 250 m, with the highest point, 255 m, above Shirburn in the Chilterns. A little further north the Chiltern ridge reaches 246 m above Crowell, but south of Nuffield, as it approaches the Thames, it is much lower, in places not reaching 110 m. Across the river the ridge of the Berkshire Downs is also fairly low, generally about 200 m, but from Letcombe Bassett to Rams Hill it attains 230-240 m, rising to 242 m at Sparsholt, and further west to 261 m at Whitehorse Hill above Uffington. The Cotswolds, which reach

Figure 2.1.
Relief map of Oxfordshire.

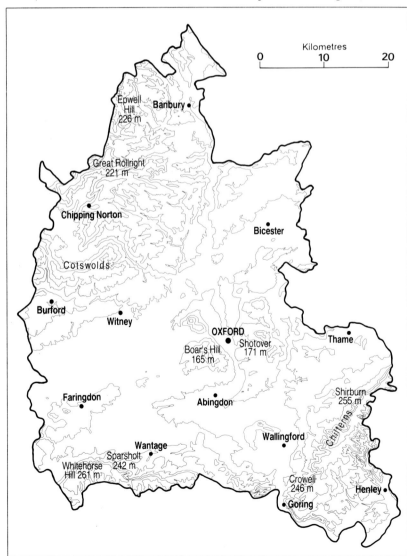

more than 330 m in Gloucestershire, do not rise above 226 m in Oxfordshire, at Epwell Hill west of Banbury, and 221 m at Great Rollright. The county's minor scarps between the Cotswolds and the Chilterns nowhere exceed Shotover's 171 m.

The Thames, sometimes still called the Isis above its junction with the Thame at Dorchester, is the county's major river. It rises in the Gloucestershire Cotswolds and from Goring to Henley still forms the county boundary with Berkshire. On its north bank it collects three smaller rivers also draining from the Cotswolds, the Windrush at Newbridge, the Evenlode at Cassington which has itself received the Glyme below Blenheim, and in Oxford the Cherwell, which has received the Ray at Islip. The Thame, its only other north-bank tributary, drains the lower end of the Vale of Aylesbury. On its south bank the Thames has only two major tributaries within Oxfordshire, the Cole at St John's Bridge in the extreme west, forming the boundary with Wiltshire, and the Ock, which joins at Abingdon after draining the Vale of White Horse. All these rivers drain highly calcareous geological formations, so the water of the main river is lime-rich throughout its course in the county.

GEOLOGY

The oldest rocks in Oxfordshire are the Jurassic Lias clays. These are found in some of the valley bottoms around Banbury and the upper Evenlode valley around Kingham. Next comes the Middle Lias, which produces rounded, and sometimes still gorsy, hilltops. It provides the ironstone that is mined in parts of north Oxfordshire, as well as the warm rufous brown building stone of many villages in that corner of the county. In a few places, as at Bruern, the Lias is overlain by some of our youngest deposits, slightly acid gravels laid down within the past million years or so.

The most important rock in Cotswold Oxfordshire is the Oolite limestone, which underlies most of the dipslope towards the Thames, trends north-eastwards through the Ardley area into Northamptonshire and outcrops in a few places in the scarplands further east, as at Charlton-on-Otmoor. It still has a few woods and patches of unimproved limestone grassland on the steeper slopes, which the Windrush and Evenlode have carved out, but nothing to compare with the Beechwoods and grassy downs which survive along its escarpment in Gloucestershire. This is the source of the honey-coloured building stone that has made Cotswold buildings world famous, and is, or has comparatively recently been, worked at such quarries as Ardley, Stratton Audley and Taynton. The well known Stonesfield 'slates', thinly bedded limestones from quarries at Stonesfield and Fawler, have been widely used for roofing Cotswold buildings. In a few places, such as North Leigh Heath and parts of

Wychwood Forest, there are slightly acid Plateau Drift deposits over the Oolite, laid down, like those on the Lias, within quite recent geological times.

South-east of the Oolite begin the series of first Jurassic and then Cretaceous deposits that create the minor scarps and vales which occupy the centre of the county. First comes the Forest Marble, named from Wychwood Forest. This was once used for polished 'marble' chimney-pieces. This is followed by the Cornbrash, a rather reddish and rubbly ('brashy') fertile arable soil. Then follow two fairly broad bands of calcareous clay sandwiching another limestone belt. The lower is the blue-grey Oxford Clay, stretching right across the county from the upper Thames valley through to Otmoor.

On top of the Oxford Clay comes the Corallian limestone or Coral Rag, which includes beds of rubbly coral rock, and forms the ridge stretching north-eastwards from Faringdon that outcrops conspicuously around Oxford, where it has been somewhat grandiloquently named the Oxford Heights. These low and partly wooded summits include Wytham (164 m), Boar's Hill (165 m), Cumnor Hill (159 m) and Shotover (171 m), now a country park. Wytham crowns the University's

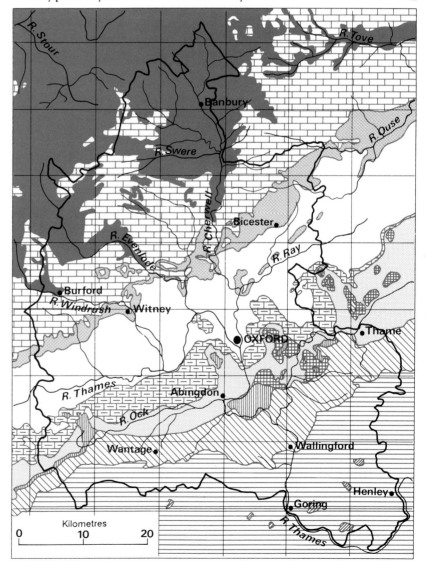

Figure 2.2.
Geological map of Oxfordshire.

Eocene	London Clay	
	Reading Beds	
Upper Cretaceous	Chalk	
	Upper Greensand	
	Gault	
Lower Cretaceous	Lower Greensand	
	Wealden	
Upper Jurassic	Purbeck and Portland Beds	
	Kimmeridge	
	Corallian	
	Oxford Clay	
Middle Jurassic	Cornbrash	
	Oolite	
Lower Jurassic	Lias	

research estate, where workers from the Edward Grey Institute of Field Ornithology, from David Lack onwards, have done so much seminal research on the birds. Several other well known woodlands south-west of Oxford, such as those at Tubney, together with the calcareous mires at Cothill and Dry Sandford, and Bullingdon Bog within the city limits, also lie on the Corallian. Its rock, much quarried at Headington and elsewhere to build Victorian Oxford, proved to wear badly so that it is now little used.

Above the Corallian, comes the Kimmeridge Clay, named from a village on the Dorset coast. It forms the northern strip of the Vale of White Horse, and underlies Bagley Wood south of Oxford. East and north-east of the city the Jurassic peters out in a complex mixture of Kimmeridge Clay and Portland Beds, which are limestone, with some of the hills, as at Shotover, capped by a tiny deposit of Lower Greensand.

The lowest layer of Cretaceous rocks, the Lower Greensand, which produces a slightly acid soil, is very infrequent in our area. Apart from the hilltop patches just mentioned, the only sizable outcrop is just north of Culham in the Thames valley east of Abingdon. So the Gault Clay often lies immediately on top of the Jurassic deposits in most parts of the Vale of White Horse and the low-lying farmlands east of Oxford, such as those around Drayton St Leonard. The Gault merges into the Upper Greensand, which produces a small scarp looking across to the Chilterns between Watlington and Aston Rowant, with its miniature summit at Adwell Cop (144 m).

All the way along the downland ridge from Whitehorse Hill above Uffington to Streatley on the Berkshire Downs, and across the Thames from Goring to Chinnor in the Chilterns, the Chalk escarpment looks out northwards across the clay vales and their associated scarps. South and south-east of the summits it is Chalk all the way to the county boundary. The tops of the Chilterns are covered with Clay-with-Flints, the result of millions of years of weathering of the Chalk, and sufficiently acid to enable heather and even rhododendrons to grow in a few places. This clay soil leads to the main difference between our two chalk ranges: the Chilterns are largely wooded, usually with Beech, but the Berkshire Downs are mainly bare and cultivated. Both still have some chalk grassland on the steeper slopes of the escarpment. The Chilterns also have a few scattered deposits from the later Eocene age, for instance near Nettlebed and Woodcote; they produce slightly acid soils.

The youngest of our geological deposits are the river gravels of the Thames valley, mainly deposited within the last million years. Near Dorchester and around Standlake and Stanton Harcourt, the commercial exploitation of these gravels has produced many freshwater pools that have had an important impact on the birdlife of the county. In some ways they are a substitute for the annual winter floods that have been largely eliminated by modern drainage.

HABITAT CHANGE

As indicated above, by far the largest area of habitat available for birds in Oxfordshire, 68.5% of the county area, consists of farmland, made up of 46.8% arable and 21.7% grassland. The next largest habitat grouping is urban land with 18.3%, followed by 8.2% of various kinds of woodland. Unimproved grassland plus parkland follow with 5.2%. Fresh water, heathland, fen and other semi-natural habitats each occupy less than 1% of the county area (Steel and Varley 1991). Consequently birds which have failed to adapt to man's domination of the countryside are comparatively scarce in Oxfordshire, and becoming scarcer, as semi-natural habitats continue to diminish.

Wildlife habitat can be changed in two main ways, directly by changes in land use, such as conversion to arable farmland, afforestation and building development, and indirectly as a result of various kinds of pollution. Of the direct means of change, farming and forestry are both means of exploiting the soil, the basic renewable natural resource of the countryside, for human benefit. On the other hand, the building of houses, shops, offices, factories and industrial plant does not exploit the soil as such, but may actually cover it up or physically remove it along with the vegetation, wildlife and other renewable resources. Mining and quarrying of minerals exploits non-renewable resources, but in so doing is liable to damage the renewable resource of the soil, either by removing the topsoil or by covering it over with its spoilheaps.

The past 100 years has seen several major trends in habitat change in Britain. Throughout the period much of southern and midland England, including Oxfordshire, especially around towns and larger villages, has been steadily urbanised, with extensive conversion of farmland, to both industrial sites and domestic building. The great national traumas of the two world wars led to two spasms, in the third and fifth decades of the century, of conversion of grassland to arable, and of replanting broadleaved woodland with conifers. This was followed by a period in which governments and latterly also the European Commission distorted the agricultural and timber markets by heavy subsidies, resulting in both overproduction on the farms and destruction of much semi-natural habitat on which farming and forestry would otherwise have been uneconomic. Throughout the century farmland and semi-natural habitat have been steadily built on for housing and industry, and in the Thames valley and north Oxfordshire respectively, gravel and ironstone have been extensively and destructively exploited. As a result, since the Second World War, the Oxfordshire countryside has undergone one of those 'seismic' changes comparable only to the original neolithic farming revolution and the aftermath of the enclosure movements of the sixteenth and early nineteenth centuries. Indeed during the past 40 years England as a whole has lost no less than 95% of its hay meadows, 90% of its lowland ponds, four-fifths of its chalk and limestone grasslands, half its ancient woodlands and well over 100,000 miles of hedges (Lean 1989). The latest BBONT survey shows that there are no longer any bogs left in Oxfordshire, only 2.5 ha of heathland, 27 ha of fens and 345 ha of lowland grassland, while only 2% of the county's woodlands are undamaged ancient woodlands (BBONT 1990).

Along with this direct destruction of wildlife habitat and the concomitant and often equally important changes in agricultural practice has been a more insidious form of change: pollution. This has resulted both from industrialisation and from intensive agriculture with, for instance, toxic discharges into streams by inadequately monitored industrial plants and farms, acid rain emanating from power stations, and high levels of pesticides and fertilizers remaining in the soil and leached off farmland by heavy rain.

Habitat Change due to Farming

Ever since farming began in Britain some 4,000–5,000 years ago, wildlife has had to adapt itself to the increasing proportion of the land surface occupied by farmland. However, during the past century, more and more animals and plants have been failing to adapt themselves to the increasingly intensive practices of modern farmers, notably the ploughing of permanent grasslands, heaths and former woodlands, the cessation of grazing on heaths and rough grasslands, and the drainage of wetlands. Such 'reclamation' by ploughing has always been the most dramatic impact of agriculture on natural habitats, involving as it does not only the total destruction of the existing vegetation, but often also a substantial loss of the soil itself. The most notable example of this in Oxfordshire was the grubbing up of the greater part of Wychwood Forest during the nineteenth century, to make the arable farmland that now surrounds Leafield.

The official ploughing-up campaign in the First World War, which stimulated the Hon. Charles Rothschild to produce Britain's first list of wildlife sites in need of protection, was relatively short-lived in its acute effects. The collapse in prices that followed the repeal of the Corn Production Act in 1920 soon restored much of the new arable land to grass, though not without substantial damage to its flora and invertebrate fauna. The extensive ploughing of long-established grasslands during the Second World War, however, had a much more lasting effect, because under the Agriculture Act 1947, and later the European Common Agricultural Policy, the post-war governments maintained and even enhanced the subsidies on food production that made arable farming so profitable. Thus some four-fifths of the southern chalk downland and the limestone grassland of the Cotswolds, have been lost to arable or 'improved' grassland (leys) as a result of this policy (NCC 1984).

Indeed chalk and limestone turf has tended to survive only on slopes too steep to plough, and until the recent cancellation of land reclamation grants farmers were starting to use their crawler tractors to plough even these last redoubts of the native calcareous fauna and flora (Ratcliffe 1984). Moreover, some surviving and supposedly safe stretches of chalk turf, as at Pitstone Hill, Buckinghamshire, have been 'improved' by adding fertilizers, while elsewhere the vegetation has been changed by intensively grazing cattle, which produce much richer manure than the droppings of the sheep whose extensive grazing originally created the classic short turf of the unenclosed downs. The bird most adapted to arable farming is the Lapwing, which needs access to the soil both to feed and breed (Nicholson 1951). It is, however, adversely affected by the modern tendency towards more autumn tillage and earlier spring tillage, while modern crops and their improved husbandry have reduced the number of bare patches on which they like to breed, and larger and faster tractors and wider hoes have increased losses of nests and chicks. Indeed, recent changes in Lapwing populations in southern England seem to be largely due to fluctuations in the proportion of spring tillage (Shrubb 1988). Stone Curlews too have suffered from the ploughing of the chalk downland (Batten et al. 1989). So it is not surprising that both Stone Curlews and Wheatears have almost ceased to breed on the Oxfordshire Chilterns and Berkshire Downs, where there is almost no original chalk turf away from the escarpment (Moore 1962) and none that is not too steep for the Stone Curlew.

The neutral grasslands of lowland Britain have decreased even more than the chalk and limestone ones, 95% of them now lacking any significant wildlife interest and another 2% being in some way harmed by intensive agriculture (NCC 1984). These are the grasslands whose soil is neither very acid, as on many southern heaths, nor very alkaline, as on the chalk downs and limestone wolds. The twin perils of ploughing and fertilizers have reduced herb-rich hay meadows, with their characteristic and often colourful flora that includes Fritillary and Green-winged Orchid, to being probably the least common type of semi-natural grassland remaining in Britain. One reason for this is that many farmers now feed silage rather than hay to their livestock, and this is usually cut from sown grass/clover leys before they flower. As a result, many hay meadow species only survive on streamsides, road verges and rough grassland.

The bird which has been most affected by the loss of traditional hay meadows is the Corncrake. A hundred years ago, the rasping call of this bird was a familiar sound to Warde Fowler in the Evenlode valley near Kingham. In the British Isles today it is almost confined to the western fringes of Scotland and to Ireland. Whether the hay meadows are ploughed, converted to permanent pasture or allowed to revert to rough grazings makes little difference; although its tastes are more catholic in Europe, in Britain and Ireland the Corncrake will only breed in traditionally harvested hay meadows, where farmers continue to mow their hay both late in the season and from the centre outwards (Batten *et al.* 1989).

Conversion of the acidic grasslands and heaths of southern England to heavily fertilized arable has also decimated the native fauna and flora of these habitats, which suffer as well from such diverse threats as fire, afforestation, natural invasion by trees, building development and military and recreational pressures. Six of the main heathland areas in southern and eastern England lost some two-fifths of their heaths between 1950 and 1984 (Ratcliffe 1984). The Stonechat, once a common Oxfordshire bird, is one of the heathland species which Norman Moore showed did not survive when heathland was ploughed and fertilized (Moore 1962). The Woodlark is another heathland bird whose available habitat has severely shrunk. Neither Stonechat nor Woodlark any longer breed in Oxfordshire.

One of the most striking developments, especially since 1950, has been the loss of hedges, those lines of scrub and woodland so characteristic of the English countryside, grubbed out to make larger fields, now that fewer of them are needed as stock-proof barriers. As a result, some parts of eastern and midland England now look barer and more open than at any time since the open-field farming of the Middle Ages. In 1950 there may have been around half a million miles of hedgerow in England and Wales, more than one-fifth of which have since been grubbed up. Between 1947 and 1969 hedges were being lost at the rate of 2,600 miles a year, accelerating to 2,900 miles in the 1970s and to an astonishing 4,000 miles a year during the early 1980s (Joyce *et al.* 1988). This has naturally had a devastating effect on the birds and other wildlife that inhabit hedges, especially since a recent survey has shown that 16% of the hedges in west Oxfordshire were lost between 1946 and 1986 (Joyce *et al.* 1988), and more than half the survivors are low, 'gappy' and in poor condition to attract nesting birds (Williams 1987). At the same time a quarter of the drystone walls in Cotswold Oxfordshire were also destroyed, though these are much less important as bird habitat (Joyce *et al.* 1988).

The impact on wildlife of the arable crops themselves, both old and new, as distinct from the fertilizers and pesticides used to enhance their productivity, is less spectacular. The increase in the plantings of brassicas, including Oilseed Rape, whose bright yellow flowers many people resent for their intrusion into the traditionally green English countryside, is probably at least partly responsible for the great increase in the number of Woodpigeons, for which they provide an admirable winter feed.

How much of the appearance of our countryside depends on the grazing of cattle and sheep soon becomes evident when that grazing stops. This was most strikingly illustrated during the collapse in the early 1920s of the subsidised agriculture of the First World War. When traditional extensive sheep grazing, so well described for Wiltshire by W. H. Hudson in *A Shepherd's Life* (1910), became uneconomic, many of the chalk downs and limestone wolds began first to grow taller grasses, and then to scrub up. The early stages of scrub invasion are well shown in photographs taken in the 1920s of two steep Chiltern escarpment slopes at Chinnor Hill (Tansley 1939) and nearby Crowell Hill (Massingham 1940). Today both these slopes are seral Ashwoods. This scrubbing up destroys the chalk turf with its plants and insects just as effectively as ploughing it, and brings in not only a different association of plants and insects but warblers, Blackbirds, Chaffinches and many other birds that cannot nest in open grassland. The longer grass also deters Stone Curlews, which like to nest on almost bare ground.

On heaths, whose very existence depends on normal succession to scrub and woodland being prevented by periodic burning in order to provide fresh forage for stock, the end of grazing can quickly lead to the final destruction of the habitat, with a rapid reversion to scrub unless rabbits continue some grazing pressure (Perry 1987).

Drainage operations for agriculture have had a marked impact both on lowland rivers and streams and on the fens, mires, bogs and wet grazing marshes in their valleys, in Oxfordshire most especially on Otmoor.

Habitat Change due to Forestry

By 1900 there was very little left of the forests that had covered about half the land area of Britain some 5,000 years earlier, and few if any of the surviving woods remained untouched by man since then. Moreover, much of the recent planting, especially of conifers, was of species not native to the area, so when we talk of 'ancient woods' today, we perforce refer, largely to Oakwoods or Beechwoods that have been managed by man for many years, and which hopefully do not contain many non-native trees.

Fellings during the two world wars made a serious impact on British woodlands, both the ancient and the more recently planted, so that by 1924 the post-glacial tree cover of 50% had been reduced to 5.4% (Tubbs 1986). In 1919 the Forestry Commission was created to promote tree-planting and its success in afforestation, especially with conifers, had nearly doubled the tree cover, to 9.4%, by the early 1980s (Ratcliffe 1984). However, many of these plantations merely replaced existing broadleaved woods; in the past 50 years two-fifths of the ancient semi-natural woods in 23 counties have been lost to conifers. Overall losses of ancient woods have been even greater. At first, European Larch and its hybrid with Japanese Larch were favoured on the more fertile lowland soils, with European conifers such as Scots Pine and Norway Spruce on the poorer upland soils. Soon, however, Sitka Spruce, which was adapted to the cool wet climate of western North America, was found to do best in the similar climate of western Britain, so that this species now comprises more than 95% of all conifers being planted in Britain. In drier areas other alien conifers, such as the North American Lodgepole Pine and Corsican Pine are better suited.

Such afforestation of ancient woodlands has of course completely changed their ecology, bringing radical changes to their fauna and flora, often with a considerable reduction in the number of species. At first, when the original habitat has been drained and ploughed, grazing stock fenced out and saplings planted, the ground flora and low shrubs on the site both grow and flower vigorously. At this stage the tussocks of grass and other tall vegetation create ideal conditions both for breeding warblers like the Whitethroat, Grasshopper and Willow Warblers and Tree Pipit, and for the Short-tailed Vole and other small rodents on which many raptors prey. In some parts of the country, this often results in a temporary increase in the number of predators such as Short-eared Owl or Montagu's Harrier although this has not been observed in Oxfordshire. Within a dozen years, however, the young trees grow tall enough to form a canopy and gradually shade out the original vegetation, which survives only along rides and other edges, together with its associated invertebrates and the mammals and birds which came in to take advantage of the temporary conditions of the early years. The shade is deepest in plantations where thinning and the cutting of lower branches have been largely abandoned to avoid the risk of windthrow (Ratcliffe 1984).

New plantations lack the abundance of dead and decaying wood on which so many beetle and other invertebrate larvae and their woodpecker predators feed. Fortunately they do also have some positive advantages to wildlife. Crossbills, Siskins, Coal Tits and Goldcrests are all adapted to live among conifers, and have spread widely among some of the new coniferous plantations. Crossbills, for instance, have nested at the BBONT Warburg Reserve at Bix Bottom in the Chilterns.

A highly specialised form of forestry, the cultivation of osiers for making baskets and hurdles, has greatly decreased in recent years, and this seems to have been an important cause of the recent severe decline in the British breeding population of the Marsh Warbler. This, always very local bird, used to breed in osier beds at Kingham in the Evenlode valley. However, the sale and destruction of these beds brought an end to Warde Fowler's detailed observations on their nesting between 1893 and 1904 (Warde Fowler 1913). It now seems about to go extinct even in its last stronghold in the Avon valley in Worcestershire.

Habitat Change due to Mineral Working

Unlike farming and forestry, which exploit the soil as a renewable natural resource, so retaining the possibility that the original habitat can be restored, the exploitation of such unrenewable resources as ironstone and gravel often actually destroys the topsoil as well as the subsoil. Strip-mining for ironstone and gravel-digging, both practised in Oxfordshire, remove the topsoil, but this can be stored and brought back, so that the possibility of re-creating farmland remains. Gravel is usually dug in areas with a high water table, resulting in flooded freshwater pits of widely varying depths, as at Dorchester and Stanton Harcourt, that have enormously increased the available waterfowl habitat in the county, both for breeding and in winter. There are 30–40 flooded pits in the Standlake area alone. Reservoirs constructed to supply water to towns, such as Farmoor south-west of Oxford, also provide valuable winter habitat, but if they have concrete banks they are of little use to breeding birds.

The Little Ringed Plover is a characteristic bird of working gravel pits in Britain, and its spread throughout the lowlands, including Oxfordshire, and increase to over 600 pairs (Parrinder 1987) since it first bred on the shore of one of the temporarily half-empty Tring Reservoirs in 1938, has been largely aided by the large number of active gravel workings.

Quarrying chalk for cement or limestone for building stone can scar the landscape even more than gravel diggings, but when abandoned, such quarries, especially the smaller ones, can revert to valuable wildlife habitat. The natural colonisation of abandoned chalk and limestone pits and quarries by lime-loving plants provides admirable habitat for their associated invertebrates. The vertical sides and steeper slopes will always resemble a natural chalk or limestone cliff or scree, but the flatter surfaces can fairly soon become species-rich calcareous grassland. The quarry tailings on the steep slopes of a Cotswold limestone quarry, abandoned only at the beginning of the century, were found in the late 1950s to be still in the fairly early stages of colonisation, with boulders protruding through loose screes, and the lime-loving plants present were still mainly those of bare ground (Hanson 1960).

The darker side of chalk and limestone quarrying lies in the very large areas now being completely quarried away for the cement industry, for instance for chalk at Chinnor on the edge of the Chilterns and for limestone at Shipton-on-Cherwell on the edge of the Cotswolds. The Berkshire Downs have mercifully been spared this conspicuous form of exploitation.

TERRESTRIAL HABITATS

Farmland, which covers more than two-thirds of the county area, is clearly the most important single bird habitat in Oxfordshire. Some 70% of this farmland is arable, mainly under wheat and barley, with an almost even split between the two crops, and the rest is grassland. Curiously enough, due to the way the BTOs Register of Ornithological Sites was designed, neither this substantial block of bird habitat, nor the next largest bird habitat type, urban land, merits a separate chapter in the standard survey of British bird habitats (Fuller 1982).

Until recent changes in agricultural practice speeded up the harvesting-to-sowing process, you could stand on the crest one of Oxfordshire's escarpments on any autumn day and look out across the plain to perceive all too clearly the domination of the countryside by the tractor and the farm subsidy. The bare brown soil of the freshly ploughed cornfields, tinged reddish in parts of the Cotswolds, stretched away to the horizon, interspersed with the bright green of the grass fields and the darker green of scattered coniferous plantations. The hedgerows and deciduous woodlands stood out as yellowish strips and patches, turning brown from mid-November until April.

These winter arable fields attract large flocks of birds which feed on soil invertebrates, especially Rooks and Jackdaws, Lapwings, Skylarks and Black-headed and other gulls, with smaller numbers of Pheasants and Partridges. There are also large flocks of Woodpigeons, often with a few Stock Doves, which feed especially on the leaves of plants, such as rape, other brassica crops and the new shoots of winter cereals.

As the winter wheat and barley sprouts, most of the countryside turns green again, varied only by the brown of the leafless hedges and deciduous woodlands, until in late April and May the garish yellow of the rape fields brings a strong contrast. As the vegetation grows taller in spring, arable fields become unsuitable feeding habitat for most ground feeders, and few of them, except for Partridges, Lapwings, Corn Buntings (especially in barley fields), and sometimes also Reed Buntings and Yellow Wagtails, stay to breed. Lapwings, in particular, prefer to nest in spring cereal fields rather than grass leys.

From July to September the arable fields once more stand out from the rest of the landscape as the wheat and barley ripens and is harvested, leaving a now often rather short-lived stubble. At this time they once more become good bird feeding habitat, as flocks of House Sparrows go there to feed, first on the ripe grain and then, with Chaffinches, Greenfinches, Yellowhammers and other small seed-eaters on the weed seeds and tailings after harvesting. Woodpigeons feed on the rape seed and, with Turtle Doves, also on weed seeds in the autumn stubbles. Most of the winter feeding birds begin to return once the fields are stubble again — now mostly a fairly short-lived phase in the arable year since it has usually been burned in recent years.

Of the 30% of the county's farmland which is under grass, just under two-thirds is 'improved', i.e. rendered artificially uniform by chemical fertilization and the sowing of grass cultivars, and the rest 'semi-improved' or semi-natural. Grassland can also be classified in two other ways; by its soil acidity and by its farming use. Natural grassland can be either acid, neutral or calcareous. There is very little acid grassland in Oxfordshire, but the neutral grassland tends to be damper and is mainly found in the valleys, while the calcareous grassland is dry and on the

Plate 2.1.
Didcot Power Station viewed from the Berkshire Downs showing extensive arable cultivation.
Farmland makes up two-thirds of the area of Oxfordshire and some 70% of this is arable. It is the most important single habitat for birds in the county.
Photo: J.W. Brucker.

Plate 2.2.
Marshy grassland on Otmoor.
This valuable habitat provides breeding sites
for lowland waders such as Snipe, Redshank
and Curlew, but sadly its extent in the county
has declined considerably during the
twentieth century due to drainage schemes
for intensive agriculture.
Photo: J.W. Brucker.

hills. Farmed grassland can be either a ley, a sown crop, or semi-natural grassland more or less changed by fertilizers. Both kinds can be either pasture, grazed by livestock, usually cattle or sheep, or meadow, harvested for hay and then often grazed. In the north and west of Britain many pastures are rough grazings on the edge of moorland, but scarcely 2% of the grassland in Oxfordshire is rough grazing. The classic contrast between pasture and meadow near Oxford is between Port Meadow, which is grazed, now mainly by the citizens' horses, and Oxey, Pixey and Yarnton Meads, which are still governed by a medieval strip system and mown for hay every summer.

As with the arable fields, the bird biomass of grasslands is much greater in the winter half of the year. Large flocks of Rooks, Woodpigeons, Lapwings, Golden Plovers, Starlings, Fieldfares and Redwings feed on farmed grassland in Oxfordshire, with smaller numbers of Carrion Crows, Jackdaws and Blackbirds. Golden Plovers especially favour the drier valley grasslands of the Cherwell, Ock, Thame and upper Thames. The grass in pastures is kept short by the grazing animals in late spring and early summer, and so provides better breeding habitat for ground-nesters, while in hayfields the grass is allowed to grow tall as May advances. In Oxfordshire Skylarks breed in drier farmed grasslands and Lapwings in damper ones. The Kestrel also prefers to nest close to grassy farmland.

Very little unimproved (not recently ploughed or fertilized) grassland remains in Oxfordshire, only 3.5% of the county area, compared with 21.7% improved or semi-improved. Of this remnant, three-fifths is neutral and the rest calcareous. Only 113 ha of unimproved acid grassland remain in Oxfordshire, and the almost equally negligible 345 ha of marshy grassland is best dealt with under freshwater habitats. There is thus little scope for unimproved grasslands as such to make any distinctive contribution to the county's breeding avifauna. In winter their feeding birds differ little from those of the farmed grasslands. Where neutral grasslands adjoin water bodies they may provide feeding and breeding grounds for species more appropriately dealt with under freshwater habitats. The remnant chalk and limestone grasslands on the Chilterns, Cotswolds and Berkshire Downs have long lost the Wheatear and almost lost the Stone Curlew, the two most distinctive open downland breeding species, although they still have some Meadow Pipits and share Lapwings and Skylarks with the farmed grassland. Short-eared Owls and sometimes also Hen Harriers resort to the remaining open grasslands of the downs when vole numbers are high. The rapidly scrubbing up semi-natural grasslands of the county are today more noted for their scrub birds.

Parkland is a specialised form of grassland (sometimes nowadays arable), still with more than 4,000 ha in Oxfordshire, especially in such great Cotswold parks as Blenheim, Cornbury and Heythrop. Its scattered and often very old trees attract such hole-nesters as Jackdaw, Stock Dove, Tawny Owl and both Green and Great Spotted Woodpeckers. Parkland around Oxford is one of the main breeding areas of the Lesser Spotted Woodpecker in the county. The Sahelian drought is probably mainly responsible for the loss of the Redstart from its former stronghold in the old Oaks of Blenheim Park.

Farmland does not consist only of fields, but also of the hedges which mark their boundaries. These strips of scrub and woodland bring with them the birds of these habitats. This is why many of the most characteristic birds of farmland, such as Blackbird, Wren and Blue Tit, are primarily scrub and woodland birds. Moreover, woodpeckers, as well as predators such as Kestrel, Hobby, Barn and Little Owls, Magpie and Carrion Crow, often nest both in isolated trees on farms and in the trees that grew up in the hedgerows before the machines that trim modern hedges began to slice off all their potential successors. Hedges, as noted above, are decreasing in Oxfordshire, but are still responsible for the great majority of the county's farmland breeding birds, both in numbers and in species. In winter, hedgerows, especially large overgrown ones whose hawthorns have been allowed to flower and fruit, are much favoured by Fieldfares and Redwings.

Two birds that were common in Oxfordshire hedgerows 30 years ago are less so today: the Whitethroat largely because of the Sahelian drought, the Yellowhammer probably due to the same pesticide-linked causes which have resulted in a decrease in seed-eaters generally. For the Yellowhammer, farmland rather than scrub can be described as optimal habitat because clutch-sizes are larger in farmland (O'Connor 1980). The Wren, on the other hand, only spreads out into farmland hedges when its favoured woodland habitat becomes saturated (Williamson 1969).

The second largest habitat type in Oxfordshire is urban land. This covers almost one-fifth (18.3%) of what is usually regarded as one of England's more rural counties. This consists of houses and gardens in towns, suburbs and villages; commercial and industrial buildings such as factories, offices and power stations; streets and town parks; and building sites and various other kinds of waste ground. Another 300 ha in the county consists of the artificial grasslands devoted to playing fields, mainly in and around towns and villages, and golf courses, mainly in the countryside. This rich mixture of habitats, woodland and scrub in parks and gardens, grassland in parks, playing fields and waste ground, and cliff-like nesting places on buildings, is equivalent to a wooded gorge with nesting sites for both tree- and cliff-nesters and grassland on the tops for them to feed on. Lawns and playing fields are closely mown and so of great value to thrushes and other birds foraging for soil animals.

Not surprisingly therefore, urban land provides good habitat for woodland and scrub birds, but only if they can adapt themselves to the proximity to man. This might be why buntings, for instance, which are notably shy of man, do not normally visit gardens in either towns or villages. The typical garden birds — Blackbird, Song Thrush, Robin, Dunnock, Wren, Chaffinch, Greenfinch, Great and Blue Tits — are all birds of woodland and scrub. The Coal Tit also feeds and breeds in gardens where conifers have been planted. Some birds, like the Blackbird and the two tits, feed and breed in quite small gardens in town centres, where they meet with such typical cliff-nesters as the Starling and the Feral Pigeon (a descendant of the wild Rock Dove). A comparatively recent development has been the occurrence of Magpies in the centre of Oxford.

The House Sparrow and Collared Dove are special cases, highly adapted to be commensals with man and so at least as common in town centres as in villages and around farmsteads, where they are attracted especially by spilt grain. The Carrion Crow is a tree- or ledge-nester, which usually nests in trees in town parks rather than on buildings, whereas the Jackdaw nests in holes and crevices in buildings and is frequent in Oxford. Starlings also nest in holes in both trees and buildings. The Spotted Flycatcher is very much a garden bird, breeding also in parks, churchyards and cemeteries, while Pied Wagtails

Plate 2.3.
Chalk grassland and Juniper scrub on the BBONT nature reserve at Aston Upthorpe. Traditionally, the chalk downlands provided suitable breeding sites for birds such as the Stone Curlew. Today, due largely to changes in agricultural practice, such species are rare. The best examples of chalk downland are conserved in reserves managed by BBONT, the National Trust and English Nature.
Photo: P.C. Creed.

Plate 2.4.
A view of Oxford from the tower of St Mary's church looking east.
The urban environment, with its diverse mosaic of gardens and parks, provides a home for a wide range of species. For example, some 207 species have been recorded in the city of Oxford since 1900, of which 88 species have bred.
Photo: P.C. Creed.

and Greenfinches are both much attracted to the mixture of habitats found in and near towns and villages. Swallows, House Martins and Swifts all nest on or in buildings, in towns, suburbs, villages and isolated farms. A famous colony of Swifts at the University Museum in Oxford was the subject of David Lack's book *Swifts in a Tower* (1956). The drier waste ground in and around gravel pits, cement works and other industrial or development sites often becomes very overgrown with weeds, such as Mugwort, thistles and various members of the cabbage family. These sites develop a distinctive bird community of weed-seed feeders, which may include Red-legged Partridge, Turtle Dove, and, on thistles and Teasels, also Goldfinch.

Woodland occupies a relatively small part of Oxfordshire, no more than 6%, of which 54% is broadleaved , 33% mixed broadleaved and coniferous and the rest pure conifer plantations. Most of the broadleaved woodland is Oak, with the slightly acid soils of Bagley and Tubney Woods giving rise to patches of Oak-Birch woodland, where Goldfinches, Redpolls and Siskins may be seen feeding on the Birches in winter (Woodell 1985). In the Chilterns, Oak woodland is uncommon, most of the woods being Beech plantations, originally for the High Wycombe furniture trade; with little shrub undergrowth, they are relatively birdless at all times of year. In good mast years, however, flocks of Bramblings appear and feed on the fallen nuts. Ashwoods occur mainly in the Cotswolds and especially on the steeper sides of the Evenlode valley, with a few also along the escarpment of the Berkshire Downs and one or two patches of seral Ashwood in the Chilterns, as on Chinnor and Crowell Hills. There are no extensive Alderwoods, but Alder carr has developed on the edges of Cothill and other fens, and Alder trees line the Cherwell in

Oxford city and many other rivers and streams throughout the county. Like Birches, Alders provide winter feeding for Redpolls and other small finches.

Because they spill over into farmland and urban land, the commonest woodland birds are also among the commonest species in the whole county. Fuller (1982) has shown that the most numerous breeding birds in British woodlands as a whole are Wren, Blue Tit, Blackbird, Woodpigeon, Willow Warbler and Robin, followed by a second group consisting of Great Tit, Starling, Dunnock, Chaffinch and Song Thrush. All these are common birds of both farmland and Oak woodland in Oxfordshire, and all except Woodpigeon and Willow Warbler are also common garden birds.

The regular breeding birds of the well wooded Wytham estate may be taken as typical of broadleaved Oxfordshire woodlands (Gosler 1990). Apart from the 11 widespread and common birds just mentioned, they can be grouped by whether they nest on the ground (Woodcock), in tall herbs and shrubs (Turtle Dove, Cuckoo, Long-tailed Tit, Blackcap, Garden Warbler, Lesser Whitethroat, Greenfinch, Bullfinch), in the tree canopy (Sparrowhawk, Carrion Crow, Jay, Magpie, Mistle Thrush, Hawfinch), or in tree-holes (Stock Dove, Tawny Owl, three woodpeckers, Jackdaw, Coal Tit, Marsh Tit, Willow Tit, Nuthatch, Treecreeper, Spotted Flycatcher).

Coppicing, where Hazel or Ash is cut on a regular rotation and Oaks are left to form a canopy, used to be a more frequent form of woodland management than it is today (Rackham 1986). A recent study of a coppiced wood, Brasenose Wood (18 ha) on the eastern outskirts of Oxford, shows that the breeding birds are very similar to those at nearby Wytham (Fuller and Steel 1990, Gosler 1990). The two most numerous species were Great and Blue Tit, while Wren, Robin, Blackbird, Song Thrush, Garden Warbler, Blackcap, Chiffchaff and Willow Warbler all had half a dozen or more pairs, with 4–5 pairs of Dunnock, Long-tailed Tit, Chaffinch and Bullfinch.

Some Oakwood specialities have disappeared in recent years, thanks to a complex combination of factors including the Sahelian drought. Thus the Redstart now rarely breeds in Wychwood Forest or Wytham Wood, or indeed any of its former traditional sites in the county; the Nightingale is now largely confined to the woodlands and scrub around Otmoor; and the Turtle Dove is increasingly scarce.

Coniferous woodlands have their specialised bird fauna, including Coal Tit, Goldcrest and Crossbill. These woodlands are all planted in Oxfordshire, except for the Yew wood on Watlington Hill in the Chilterns, which, like the Beechwoods has no shrub understory and very few breeding birds. Coal Tits and Goldcrests feed and breed in many coniferous plantations in the county, including those at Wytham, as well as in patches of conifers in otherwise broadleaved woodland and in isolated planted conifers, including Yews, in parks and gardens. Crossbills are also attracted to quite isolated patches of conifers during their irruptions, for instance, regularly to a small mature Larch plantation at Chinnor Hill in the Chilterns. They have bred in the Banbury area in some recent years. Redpolls also often feed on Larches. The Sparrowhawk favours conifer plantations for its nests, but hunts widely outside them.

Scrub is the archetypal succession habitat, being always a stage between open grassland or heathland and woodland. It can vary from a few scattered bushes in open grassland to a dense canopy with tree saplings emerging from it and eliminating ground flora by shutting out the light. When it eventually develops into woodland, a belt of scrub usually still separates it from the open grassland. This is the woodland edge habitat favoured by so many warblers and other birds. In Oxfordshire, scrub other than small patches, occupies less than 1% of the county area, most of which is steadily replacing the 1.4% of remaining chalk and limestone grassland. Ornamental shrubs planted in town parks, larger gardens and groups of adjacent smaller gardens often make excellent breeding and feeding habitat for scrub-loving birds.

Once scrub is more than a foot or two high, it begins to attract birds which need song posts in their breeding territory – only the Corn Bunting is prepared to sing from a clod of earth. These include the Tree Pipit, now very rare in the county, the Woodlark, extinct here as a breeding bird, for more than 20 years, and many warblers. The Willow Warbler will breed in scrub of almost any height, but most other warblers, such as Blackcap, Garden Warbler and Lesser Whitethroat, together with the Nightingale, are typical of the woodland edge and like an elevated song post. The Chiffchaff in particular likes a song post at least 15 m high in its nesting territory.

In scrub in the Buckinghamshire Chilterns, Fuller (1982) found that most of the breeding birds were common woodland/farmland/garden species: Willow Warbler and Dunnock bred in all kinds of scrub, but Blackbird and Chaffinch preferred denser scrub. Two non-garden species, the Linnet and Yellowhammer colonised young scrub with an open canopy but disappeared again as it became denser. In a year-round study of feeding niches in grassland with thick scrub on a Surrey common, the late Geoffrey Beven found that the birds that fed most in the shrubs were the thrushes (except the ground-feeding Song Thrush), the tits, especially

Plate 2.5.

Oak woodland near Bruern, west Oxfordshire. 'Coppice-with-standards' is the traditional management practice for the ancient semi-natural woodlands of the county. Many bird species are associated with this habitat or breed most successfully here. One such woodland estate, at Wytham near Oxford, has been studied in greater detail by ecologists than any other woodland in Britain.
Photo: J.W. Brucker.

Plate 2.6.
Farmoor II Reservoir viewed from the
south-east.
Large numbers of waterfowl from Europe,
such as the Tufted Duck, Pochard and Coot
shown here, use these reservoirs and the
nearby lower Windrush Gravel Pits to feed
and rest in winter. However, the bird are easily
disturbed by sailing so that when this occurs,
it is essential that they have alternative sites to
occupy. In recent years attempts have been
made to leave part of the Farmoor I Reservoir
free from such activities so that the birds can
settle there.
Photo: J.W. Brucker.

Long-tailed Tit, Wren, Bullfinch, Greenfinch,
Whitethroat, Chiffchaff and Willow Warbler
(Bevan 1964).

In Oxfordshire, as in most of southern
Britain, scrub is largely composed of Hawthorn,
wild roses and brambles. On the chalk, it is
intermixed with Dogwood, Privet, Wayfaring-
tree and Spindle, while in the clay vales,
Blackthorn is also a major scrub species. Birds
eat the fruits of all these shrubs, but it is the
haws of the Hawthorn that bring so many
Redwings, Fieldfares and Blackbirds to feed in
scrub in autumn and winter. These thrushes,
and also Greenfinches, will also eat the hips of
wild roses, especially in cold weather, but fewer
birds are attracted to the fruits of Blackthorn
(sloes) or other shrubs.

The only other major terrestrial habitat is
heathland. There was never much heathland in
Oxfordshire, but today, with only 2.5 ha, it is
virtually extinct and so makes a negligible
contribution to the habitat available to birds in
the county.

FRESHWATER HABITATS

Some 1,350 ha or 0.5% of Oxfordshire is
covered by open water. This may seem
insignificant compared with the 99.5% of
terrestrial habitat, but as bird habitat its
importance is quite disproportionate to its extent.
Freshwater habitats with still water include
lakes, ponds, reservoirs, canals and the winter
floods from rivers, which merge into the wetter
marshes and grasslands. The flowing water of
rivers and streams with its high oxygen content
provides a quite distinct habitat for both fishes
and invertebrates, the prey of many birds.
Together these bring into the county avifauna a
group of birds not found in any other habitat.

Still water in the shape of farm and village
ponds and ornamental lakes in parkland is
dotted all over the clay vales, but is less frequent
on the uplands. The largest of these waters is the
lake in Blenheim Park, created nearly 300 years
ago by damming the River Glyme, but many are
just small ponds, which unfortunately are steadily
being filled in as they are no longer needed for
watering livestock. Flooded gravel pits are
numerous in the Thames valley around Stanton
Harcourt and Standlake (the lower Windrush
complex) above Oxford and Dorchester and
Sonning Eye below the city. The two large
adjacent reservoirs constructed at Farmoor
around 1975 are the county's largest areas of
open water and together with Grimsbury
reservoir near Banbury, are its only concrete-
banked reservoirs. Clattercote, north of Banbury,
as a canal reservoir, has vegetated banks. The
Oxford Canal, which runs alongside the
Cherwell for many miles, is a linear still water.

Moorhen, Coot, Mallard and Little Grebe
are the most frequent breeding waterfowl of the
smaller ornamental lakes and ponds, where
even Tufted Duck may sometimes nest. The
larger ones without concrete banks, such as
Blenheim, Clattercote and the major gravel
pits, attract, in addition, breeding Mute Swan,
Canada Goose, Mallard, Gadwall, Tufted Duck,
Great Crested Grebe and Redshank. Sand
Martins still nest in the banks of some of the
larger gravel pits, as at Stanton Harcourt, but
the constant changes in their management
means that the colonies are more than usually
impermanent. Kingfishers too may both feed
and breed at gravel pits. The large cement
works, such as those at Chinnor at the foot of
the Chiltern scarp and Shipton in the Cherwell
valley, form another distinct artificial wetland
habitat. In the breeding season their deep pools
may attract Mallard and Canada Geese, and the

shallower ones both Ringed and Little Ringed Plovers.

In winter, most of the waterfowl resort to the larger waters, including Farmoor, and are joined by many more species, the regulars including Teal, Wigeon, Pochard, Goosander and Goldeneye, the last two preferring deeper waters. A flock of up to 100 Cormorants feeds and roosts in winter between Farmoor Reservoir and the large gravel pits a little further west. There is another roost at Sonning Eye gravel pit. Farmoor and the larger pits, such as Dorchester and Stanton Harcourt, hold large winter gull roosts, mainly of Black-headed, Herring and Lesser Black-backed Gulls. These roosts last from late summer to April, with some non-breeders staying into the summer. Gulls use these sites for resting rather than feeding although a few have bred in recent years at Stanton Harcourt.

On spring and autumn migration many waders come to feed along the banks of the larger still waters, especially the gravel pits. These include not only the more local Lapwings, Redshanks and Snipe, but also migrant Common and Green Sandpipers, Ringed Plover and Dunlin. The winter visitor Jack Snipe likes shallow pools with emergent vegetation. Grey Herons also feed by all kinds of fresh water and in nearby wet meadows. Swallows, martins and Swifts, often in quite large flocks, feed over the open waters of the county during both spring and autumn migration.

The Thames is by far the major river of the county, and its breeding waterfowl include most of those which breed on the lakes and ponds, notably Mute Swan, Canada Goose, Mallard, Great Crested and Little Grebes, Moorhen and Coot. In addition, Kingfishers are more frequent on rivers than on still water, and Sand Martins still nest in many of the Thames banks below

Oxford. All these except the Sand Martin are present during the winter. Most are also to be found along the larger Thames tributaries, such as the Windrush, Evenlode, Cherwell and Thame, and some also on the Oxford Canal. Mute Swans, for instance, will nest along stretches as narrow as the River Thame below Thame town, and the Little Grebe is commoner on the tributaries than on the main river. The Moorhen and Mallard are the main water birds likely to breed along the many small streams of the county, such as Bayswater Brook outside Oxford or the Cuttle Brook above Thame although Water Rail may also occur.

In winter many Oxfordshire rivers flood, for instance the Thames at Port Meadow, the Cherwell above Somerton, the Ray at Otmoor, the Windrush above Burford and the Thame at Thame. These winter floods attract large flocks of waterfowl, especially Canada Goose, Mallard, Wigeon and Teal, together with gulls and Lapwings. Among the more noteworthy rarer visitors is the small flock of Whooper Swans which has wintered in the Clifton area of the Cherwell valley for many years past.

Bridges and weirs across rivers and the pollard willows along the banks of streams provide nesting places for ledge and hole-nesters respectively. The ledge-nesters include the Grey Wagtail and, on the uppermost reaches of at least one Cotswold stream, the Dipper. House Martins nest under Swinford Bridge on the Thames near Eynsham, while a few still frequent the site of what used to be one of the largest House Martin colonies in Britain, Clifton Hampden Bridge on the Thames. Some of the more interesting hole-nesters in pollard willows are now either all but extinct in the county, like the Redstart, or less common in them than they once were, like the Little Owl.

In the breeding season the marshy meadows

Plate 2.7.

The river Thame at Ickford.
With their lush bankside vegetation, the slow-flowing rivers which drain the county of Oxfordshire epiomise the English countryside itself. This important habitat is home to many species such as Grey Heron, Little Grebe and Kingfisher, and in the bankside reedbeds, also Reed Warblers and occasionally a Water Rail.
Photo: J.W. Brucker.

Plate 2.8.
Port Meadow, Oxford in January.
Winter flood meadows such as this on the
Thames provide resting and feeding
opportunities for a wide variety of waterfowl,
such as Wigeon and Shoveler, and waders
such as Snipe and Lapwing which may occur
in large numbers in some winters. Birds such
as Ruff and Dunlin also regularly use the
meadows on passage. Birdwatching in such
sites can often produce unexpected results
such as the occasional spring Garganey.
Photo: P.C. Creed.

which so readily flood in winter together with the reedbeds and other tall herb vegetation along the rivers and in the valleys attract both waders, such as Lapwing, Redshank, Curlew and Snipe, and a small group of passerines: Reed Bunting, Reed Warbler, Sedge Warbler and formerly also the Marsh Warbler, which has not bred since 1960. The Reed Warbler, one of the few Oxfordshire birds largely associated with a single plant, the Common Reed *Phragmites australis*, to whose stems it attaches its nest, will, however, also nest in other tall waterside plants, such as the Great Willowherb *Epiloblum hirsutum* Many Oxfordshire Cuckoos parasitise Reed Warblers, while a few favour Sedge Warblers. Both Grasshopper Warbler and Snipe still breed on the large expanse of marshy meadows on Otmoor, and the Redshank returned to breed there after the tall grasses which had dominated the wetter areas were once more cut for hay. There are no very extensive reedbeds in Oxfordshire, but the larger ones provide a breeding habitat for the Water Rail.

CHAPTER THREE
The Climate of Oxfordshire

Situated off Europe's western seaboard, influenced by prevailing west or south-west airstreams and the North Atlantic Drift, the British Isles as a whole enjoy a relatively moist, equable climate. Oxfordshire's land-locked position in the English south midlands is in turn responsible for its mildly continental climatic regime, at least in comparison with coastal counties of Britain. This is manifest in a relatively large diurnal and annual temperature range (see Table 3.1), and annual rainfall figures which, together with the seasonal distribution, are similar to the drier parts of eastern Britain. For example, in July, Oxford's mean daily maximum temperature (21.5°C) is higher than many other parts of the UK [cf. Birmingham, 20.5°C; Plymouth, 19.0°C; Edinburgh, 18.5°C]. Wallingford's mean annual rainfall of 570 mm is similar to that of Cambridge (550 mm), considerably drier than other parts of the south [cf. Bristol (790 mm), Southampton (803 mm)]. Distance from the sea, and the shelter from westerly maritime influence afforded by the Welsh mountains and the Cotswolds, are the two main reasons for these characteristics.

The Radcliffe Observatory in Oxford has one of the longest, most reliable and best-maintained meteorological records in the world, with continuous daily records of temperature and precipitation since 1814. Table 3.1, derived from the Observatory's records, summarises those climatic elements which are of greatest importance to bird populations. The following paragraphs discuss more fully their temporal and spatial variations within the county.

Relief is perhaps the most important factor governing local climatic variation in Britain. With the highest ground in the Chilterns and Cotswolds not rising more than 300 m above sea level, local differences of climate in Oxfordshire are rather small. Nevertheless, the distribution of precipitation closely reflects topography (mostly due to orographic uplift of moist air masses increasing rainfall over higher ground) and the highest values in the region, 800+ mm per year, occur on the high ground of the Cotswolds, Chilterns and Berkshire Downs. The lowest values, down to around 570 mm per year, occur on the low ground of the Thames valley. There is no evidence of a decrease in rainfall from west to east across the county.

As indicated by Table 3.1, seasonal variation in rainfall in Oxfordshire is relatively small. On average, spring is the driest period (the three months February–April account for less than 20% of annual rainfall) with autumn/early winter the wettest (October–December account for almost 30% of the annual total). This seasonal distribution is similar throughout the region.

In southern England, snow is an extremely variable component of climate: in Oxford the mean number of days when sleet or snow falls is 18.5 (1815-1978) but with a range of 4-51. Within the county, altitude is again important in determining the distribution of snow, controlling both when precipitation will turn to sleet or snow, and also the persistence of snow

Table 3.1.
Summary of Long Period Observations, Radcliffe Meteorological Station, Oxford.
Altitude: 63.4 m
Latitude: 51°46'N
Longitude: 01°16'W

	Year	Jan	Feb	Mar	Apr	May	Jun	Jul	Aug	Sep	Oct	Nov	Dec
Mean monthly air temperature, 1815-1989, (°C)	9.5	3.6	4.1	5.6	8.2	11.5	14.8	16.5	16.0	13.6	10.0	6.3	4.6
Monthly mean daily maximum temperatures, 1881-1989,(°C)	13.8	6.6	7.2	9.9	13.0	16.7	19.7	21.5	21.0	18.5	14.1	9.7	7.4
Monthly mean daily minimum temperatures, 1881-1989, (°C)	6.0	1.2	1.2	2.2	4.1	7.0	10.1	12.1	11.8	9.8	6.6	3.7	2.1
Absolute maximum temperature, 1815-1989, (°C)	35.1	14.7	17.7	22.1	27.1	30.6	34.3	33.9	35.1	33.5	27.3	19.0	15.2
Absolute minimum temperature, 1815-1989,(°C)	-16.6	-16.6	-16.2	-10.9	-4.9	-1.8	1.3	4.4	3.5	-0.6	-5.1	-8.8	-16.1
Mean monthly precipitation, 1767-1989 (mm)	641.8	51.8	40.6	41.3	42.9	50.9	54.0	60.4	58.6	60.3	64.6	61.1	55.2
Precipitation range, driest/wettest months, 1767-1989 (mm)	353.4	5.3	0.0	1.5	0.5	1.5	1.8	0.8	2.0	2.5	4.3	4.8	1.7
	1034.7	138.7	119.6	133.6	112.5	143.1	193.0	183.4	133.2	206.7	188.2	186.4	143.3
Mean number of days with sleet/snow, 1881-1989	17.9	4.5	4.4	3.8	1.4	0.1	0.01	0.01	0.0	0.0	0.1	0.9	2.7
Mean number of days of snow cover, 1926-1989	11.1	4.4	3.5	1.1	0.1	0.0	0.0	0.0	0.0	0.0	0.0	0.2	1.9
Mean number of air frosts, 1881-1989, (days)	48.4	10.9	10.2	8.1	3.0	0.4	0.0	0.0	0.0	0.02	1.5	5.5	8.8
Mean number of ground frosts, 1881-1989, (days)	18.0	17.0	16.5	10.7	3.7	0.3	0.0	0.03	1.4	6.7	12.5	16.9	103.7

cover. As a result, the average number of days per year when sleet or snow falls rises from 25 on the Oxford clay vale to 35-40 on the high ground of the Downs and Cotswolds. Snow in Oxfordshire is normally confined to the period late November to early April.

The statistics of seasonal variation in temperature are given in Table 3.1. The mean annual temperature of 9.5°C varies little across the region. Observations indicate that higher and more exposed parts of the Cotswolds and Chilterns may be up to 1°C cooler each month, on average, than the Central Vale. In winter, there may be more variation in temperature within the region, as local topography, exposure and soil-type all affect minimum temperatures. Sheltered, low-lying areas such as valley bottoms, experiencing a drain of cold air which stagnates during winter nights, have a greater frequency of frost than open, well-ventilated sites on higher ground. The influence of urban areas on the radiation budget, and the type of ground surface involved, also means that cities will have fewer days of frost than rural areas at the same altitude. Oxford records a mean of 42 days with air frost each year; the average in Abingdon is 52 days. Throughout the county there are normally between 40 and 60 days of air frost per year. Usually, only the months of July and August are completely frost-free.

Annual sunshine totals for the county are around 1,400-1,500 hours, usually slightly more in the east than in the cloudier west. At Wallingford in the Thames valley in the south-east of the county, for instance, it has averaged 1,416 hours over 10-15 recent years. Naturally there is much less sunshine in the winter half of the year, at Wallingford only 32.5 hours in December, compared with 209 hours in June. Since the smoke abatement legislation of the 1950s there is no longer much smoke pollution to bring denser fogs and so lower sunshine totals in town centres. However, natural fogs do still occur, sometimes in the form of low clouds hanging over the Chilterns and other hilltops, sometimes in the form of ground fogs that blot out the sun from the vales while the hilltops are bathed in bright winter sunshine.

The predominant wind direction across Oxfordshire is south-west to west, with occasional periods of persistent north-east winds, typically in spring. On the whole, the county is sheltered: a mean of 2-3 days per year when gale-force winds occur (i.e. with mean speeds in excess of 33 knots), compares with about 30 days in south-west England. Topography, and smaller obstructions such as towns and woods, locally affect both wind speed and direction. Over hills, mean wind speeds are generally higher than low ground. For example, Abingdon experiences wind speeds in excess of Beaufort force 6 for 0.7% of the year; for Little Rissington in the Cotswolds, 226 m above sea level, the equivalent figure is 3.0%.

In terms of long-term trends in Oxfordshire's climate, Smith (1980) warned of the inherent dangers of forecasting on the evidence of apparent trends "... many trends have only been identified at the very moment they have been reversed". Tracing the records of the Radcliffe Observatory back to 1814 and beyond, the precipitation data show a fluctuation between wetter and drier periods at Oxford. The wettest 10-year period on record is that of 1874-83 (mean annual precipitation 729 mm), the driest 1893-1902 (m.a.p. 563 mm). However there is no progressive trend one way or the other, and no evidence of a regular cyclical pattern. Similarly, there is little evidence of a real change in temperature from available data. Since 1920 there has been a slight warming during the spring and autumn seasons, countered by winters which have been, in general, colder than the long-term average (see Smith 1980, fig. 9). At the time of writing it is tempting to correlate recent warm summers and mild winters with the much-publicised greenhouse effect. For example, the winters 1987-88, 1988-89 and 1989-90 have seen mean air temperatures for the months of December, January and February of 5.6, 6.8 and 7.1°C respectively, well above the long term winter mean of 4.0°C. This relationship is by no means proven, but if warming does occur, there is likely to be a significant impact on bird populations.

Human impact on climate is more fully understood on a smaller scale. The 'urban heat island' is a well-documented phenomenon of large towns and cities (e.g. Oke 1975, 1976). A heat island is the occurrence of warmer air in the urban canopy than the surrounding countryside, resulting from a complex interaction of changes in the aerodynamic, radiative, thermal and moisture regimes of the city. A study of Oxford's heat island (Riddington 1988) revealed differences in night-time air temperatures between the city centre and the rural environs of up to 3.7°C. This illustrates the potential advantages to birds of the urban climate. The large roost of Pied Wagtails at the John Radcliffe hospital in Headington is a case in point.

CHAPTER FOUR
The Atlas of Breeding Birds in Oxfordshire

In the late 1970s, members of the Oxford Ornithological Society decided that it was time to publish an updated county avifauna. In the years since the publication of Dr. Mary Radford's book, *The Birds of Berkshire and Oxfordshire* in 1966, many changes had taken place. Land-use in the county was altering very rapidly with the result that the status of many bird species had altered (see Chapter 2). Some of these changes were beneficial to the overall diversity and number of bird species, some detrimental. The shape of Oxfordshire itself had altered; the Boundary Commission's changes of 1974 increased the size of the county overnight by 30%. The effect was that the traditionally county-based ornithological societies had to alter their boundaries accordingly. For the OOS, this resulted in having to cover a much larger area.

The 1970s also saw an upsurge in the number of people with an interest in natural history generally, and birds in particular. This meant that whilst more people were able to contribute to the understanding of the county's birds, more people were wanting information about those birds. Hence, following much discussion and fund-raising, writing began. However, it soon became apparent that whilst our knowledge of certain species had improved dramatically, two factors made it impossible to complete the work, and as a result the project was shelved.

Those two weaknesses were to become prime motivating forces for the eventual undertaking of the Atlas of Breeding Birds in Oxfordshire, and were first, the inability to describe the status of all species accurately. This was particularly true of the commoner ones which are normally taken for granted by the average birdwatcher. Secondly, the inability to provide an accurate picture for the entire county, rather than for just the well-populated Oxford district.

As well as wishing to provide this information for largely academic purposes, there was a genuine and rapidly developing need to provide sound answers to questions raised regarding aspects of bird conservation in the county. Members of the OOS were, on a number of occasions, asked to provide answers to specific problems relating to a species or group of species over the entire county, or regarding the birdlife of a particular area. At the time, these questions could, for the most part, be answered only as 'guess-timates' and the need to rectify this situation became vital.

It was felt therefore, that the best way to address all of these problems and to provide the information that so many birdwatchers in the county required was to produce a complete set of distribution maps for all species breeding in the county. In doing so we would also be compiling a set of data against which any future changes in the county's bird populations could be measured.

The distribution of breeding birds is far from static and there are many factors which can bring about changes in status: long and short-term climatic change, changes in land-use and a host of other direct or indirect factors caused by a rapidly increasing human population. All have immense effects on our wildlife and, as naturalists, these changes are of great interest, as too are the precise reasons for them. Distribution maps, if compiled from data collected systematically, have enormous value for conservation, since it is man's activities in particular that are responsible for the most rapid and damaging environmental changes, often with disastrous consequences for our birdlife. Hence, if bird populations are to be assured of a future, conservation measures need to be implemented, and this cannot be done without accurate information, obtained objectively.

In 1984, coinciding with a further increase in interest in systematic ornithological fieldwork locally, as manifested by the effort put into the BTO's *Atlas of Wintering Birds*, a meeting was held within the OOS to discuss fieldwork. From this meeting came the resolve to embark upon a countywide atlas project. To enable it to be countywide, the help of the BOS, no strangers to organised fieldwork, was enlisted in order to cover the north of the county. Following a series of meetings, a protocol for the study was assembled and a system of organisation headed by the County Bird Recorder (JWB) and a project coordinator (ARH) was put into place. There then followed several months of intensive publicity in the media and to the various local natural history interest groups in the area to gain a sufficient number of fieldworkers to make the project viable. It was also necessary to ensure that all potential observers were well informed of the methods to be used and also directed to those parts of the county where their efforts would be most beneficial.

The key to success lay in the creation of an observer network, with groups of observers headed by an experienced local fieldworker. One such leader was appointed for each 10 km square and, as well as organising and assisting observers, they assembled and vetted records from their particular patch. This allowed us to ensure that a high standard of accuracy and consistency was maintained in the data recording as well as keeping themselves well informed of which areas needed most attention so as to most profitably direct future fieldwork.

Observers for the project fell into two categories. First, there were those experienced birdwatchers able to commit themselves to systematically covering a defined area and recording those species found there. Such data were submitted on cards provided by the county Biological Recording Scheme based at the county museum. Secondly, in an attempt to encourage as many people as possible to contribute, a system for casual recording was also devised. This meant that individuals with less time to spare could still contribute records to the survey from around their local patches or whilst making occasional visits to other parts of the county.

After the results had been checked by the 10 km square leaders, records were then passed on to the project coordinator for further checks and for the extraction of sensitive, confidential records. The bulk of the data was then passed on to be input onto computer and a database from which the maps could be produced and other statistics calculated. Also, input alongside that database, was a set of data relating to some aspects of the distribution of habitats and land-use in the county. Extracted from the Ordnance Survey's 1:25,000 series maps, this has proved useful in assessing the Atlas results in relation to a range of physical features.

Since the fieldwork for the project was to span four seasons, it was necessary to maintain interest in the work and to ensure that fieldworkers were directed to those parts of Oxfordshire most lacking in records. To this end, progress reports incorporating results and also advice regarding the timing of visits, etc. were published at the end of each season. Further information was sent to the local media and to the local natural history societies in order to attract yet more observers (see Appendix 6).

As previously noted, a good deal of time was spent in the early stages of the project in establishing sound and standardised methods based on the tried and tested procedures used by other groups. Advice was taken from as many sources as possible including those groups who had organised similar projects in other areas and from the BTO. Whilst with hindsight one or two aspects of this protocol might have been modified, it is felt that by keeping our overall aims very much to the fore, our system proved to be most satisfactory.

FIELDWORK METHODS

The project aimed to record the distribution of all breeding bird species in the whole county. One could argue that, in an ideal world, one would like to record every single bird breeding in Oxfordshire but this would be logistically impossible. Thus in order to rationalise this situation, the area to be covered needed to be divided into plots of equal size with the squares formed by the Ordnance Survey national grid offering the ideal system. Three possibilities existed:

a) The 10 km square. Although this was used in national atlas projects it was felt to be too large to give sufficiently high resolution at the county scale. This was true also of a 5 km square.

b) The 1 km square. Although this unit has been used to good effect by the BOS for projects in their area, countywide such a scale created too many units for us to ensure accuracy and adequate coverage over a relatively short time span.

c) The 2 km square or tetrad. This unit was accepted as the most realistic proposition and was adopted as the standard plot size.

However, the county boundary is not based on these squares. Hence, if we only used the civil boundary, many squares would be smaller than 2 km x 2 km. This would make it difficult to compare directly those areas at the edge of the county with others. Thus, to ensure that the entire county was covered evenly it was decided that where such a tetrad did not lie totally within Oxfordshire, the entire tetrad would be surveyed. Whilst this increased the area to be covered by 5%, it had the important advantage that we would have comparable and standardised areas.

The object therefore was to note on a simple presence or absence basis, all the species in each of the 753 tetrads which make up the county of Oxfordshire. Once breeding by a species in a tetrad had been confirmed, there was no further need to obtain further evidence for that species. However, proving that breeding has occurred is not as simple a proposition as one might imagine and presents all kinds of problems for the field ornithologist, particularly since we were anxious to ensure the welfare and success of the birds nesting. Thus breeding status can be classified into one of three grades, listed in Table 4.1, each of which can be defined by evidence obtained from observations fulfilling

Table 4.1.
Criteria recorded for each species in each tetrad as evidence of breeding.

Grade	Code	Evidence
Possible Breeding	✓	Birds recorded in breeding season in possible nesting habitat but no other indication of breeding noted.
Probable Breeding	S	Singing male present (or breeding calls heard) on more than one date.
	T	Bird (or pair) apparently holding territory.
	D	Courtship and display or agitated behaviour or anxiety calls from adults suggesting likely presence of nest or young nearby of brood patch on trapped female.
	N	Visiting probable nest site.
	B	Nest building (including excavation of nesting hole).
Confirmed Breeding	DD	Distraction display or injury feigning.
	UN	Used nest found.
	FL	Recently fledged young.
	FS	Adult carrying faecal sac.
	FY	Adult with food for young.
	ON	Adult entering or leaving nest site in circumstances indicating occupied nest.
	NE	Nest containing eggs or bird 'sitting tight'.
	NY	Nest with young seen or heard, or downy young of ducks, gamebirds, etc.

one of 14 criteria, from the least good to the best evidence.

Observers were asked to enter the appropriate code onto the recording card, thus attempting to ensure a standardised interpretation of breeding behaviour. Only the highest level of evidence obtained need be entered for each species in each tetrad. Fieldworkers were asked to bear in mind the following points:

a) Under evidence for possible breeding, the underlined portion (see Table 4.1) is important and is intended to rule out those birds using an area solely for feeding. Grey Herons, Swifts and hirundines in particular should be carefully considered in this respect.

b) FL The young of some species may move considerable distances from the nest soon after fledging but continue to be fed by adult birds.

c) FY Food may be carried considerable distances to nests and often cross into neighbouring tetrads.

d) NY Downy young leave the nest soon after hatching and may move some distance, potentially crossing tetrad boundaries.

Observers were asked to maximise their efforts in a particular tetrad by visiting at different times of day, at all times of the breeding season bearing in mind the differences between species groups and to visit all habitats present within each tetrad.

RESULTS

A total of 35,815 records of 127 species were submitted during the course of the Oxfordshire

Table 4.2.
The full list of 127 species recorded during the four years of fieldwork for the Atlas of Breeding Birds in Oxfordshire project 1985-1988. The species are listed in order of occurrence across tetrads in the county from the commonest to the scarcest. For each species, the number of tetrads in which breeding was suspected (possible and probable) and confirmed are given, together with sub-totals and the % of tetrads in which the species was recorded.

		Poss	Prob	Conf	Prob +Conf	Poss +Prob +Conf	%			Poss	Prob	Conf	Prob +Conf	Poss +Prob +Conf	%
1	Blackbird	2	168	581	749	751	99.7	65	Kingfisher	75	47	48	95	170	22.6
2	Chaffinch	7	274	467	741	748	99.3	66	Willow Tit	34	69	51	120	154	20.5
3	Woodpigeon	50	267	430	697	747	99.2	67	Tufted Duck	62	29	54	83	145	19.3
4	Blue Tit	26	148	567	715	741	98.4	68	Little Grebe	22	40	79	119	141	18.7
5	Wren	8	375	355	730	738	98.0	69	Feral Pigeon	60	30	38	68	128	17.0
6	Starling	49	39	648	687	736	97.7	70	Meadow Pipit	51	30	30	60	111	14.7
7	Robin	12	290	432	722	734	97.5	71	Lesser Spotted Woodpecker	28	52	21	73	101	13.4
8	Great Tit	29	222	482	704	733	97.3	72	Grey Heron	75	6	14	20	95	12.6
9	Yellowhammer	17	377	339	716	733	97.3	73	Grey Wagtail	43	14	35	49	92	12.2
10	Dunnock	26	357	341	698	724	96.1	74	Hobby	70	11	8	19	89	11.8
11	Willow Warbler	9	449	257	706	715	95.0	75	Curlew	29	32	27	59	88	11.7
12	Carrion Crow	153	74	485	559	712	94.6	76	Reed Warbler	5	44	37	81	86	11.4
13	House Sparrow	52	90	570	660	712	94.6	77	Grasshopper Warbler	13	56	5	61	74	9.8
14	Magpie	156	121	432	553	709	94.2	78	Barn Owl	32	23	19	42	74	9.8
15	Skylark	8	547	147	694	702	93.2	79	Great Crested Grebe	11	11	51	62	73	9.7
16	Pheasant	94	283	322	605	699	92.8	80	Woodcock	27	37	8	45	72	9.6
17	Greenfinch	55	371	262	633	688	91.4	81	Tree Pipit	7	47	11	58	65	8.6
18	Swallow	147	114	422	536	683	90.7	82	Snipe	26	27	10	37	63	8.4
19	Collared Dove	87	303	279	582	669	88.8	83	Redshank	14	28	10	38	52	6.9
20	Song Thrush	33	256	376	632	665	88.3	84	Nightingale	8	36	7	43	51	6.8
21	Jackdaw	161	111	386	497	658	87.4	85	Sand Martin	16	4	19	23	39	5.2
22	Blackcap	22	422	192	614	636	84.5	86	Quail	3	35	1	36	39	5.2
23	Stock Dove	186	195	239	434	620	82.3	87	Hawfinch	13	10	7	17	30	4.0
24	Cuckoo	68	500	45	545	613	81.4	88	Wood Warbler	11	16	2	18	29	3.9
25	Mistle Thrush	95	152	360	512	607	80.6	89	Water Rail	10	9	2	11	21	2.8
26	House Martin	125	58	408	466	591	78.5	90	Pochard	15	3	0	3	18	2.4
27	Rook	132	28	424	452	584	77.6	91	Buzzard	9	4	2	6	15	2.0
28	Whitethroat	22	346	214	560	582	77.3	92	Redpoll	8	7	0	7	15	2.0
29	Chiffchaff	15	445	114	559	574	76.2	93	Wheatear	10	2	1	3	13	1.7
30	Red-legged Partridge	176	234	161	395	571	75.8	94	Little Ringed Plover	2	2	9	11	13	1.7
31	Linnet	120	270	174	444	564	74.9	95	Whinchat	8	3	1	4	12	1.6
32	Goldfinch	122	244	196	440	562	74.6	96	Greylag Goose	8	2	2	4	12	1.6
33	Moorhen	65	79	385	464	529	70.3	97	Redstart	5	5	1	6	11	1.5
34	Mallard	124	83	317	400	524	69.6	98	Common Crossbill	6	1	2	3	9	1.2
35	Swift	274	66	176	242	516	68.5	99	Ruddy Duck	3	2	2	4	7	0.9
36	Bullfinch	124	235	157	392	516	68.5	100	Ringed Plover	3	1	3	4	7	0.9
37	Kestrel	262	119	110	229	491	65.2	101	Firecrest	3	0	3	3	6	0.8
38	Lapwing	89	178	210	388	477	63.3	102	Common Tern	1	1	4	5	6	0.8
39	Great Spotted Woodpecker	107	180	186	366	473	62.8	103	Teal	6	0	0	0	6	0.8
40	Pied Wagtail	173	70	218	288	461	61.2	104	Long-eared Owl	3	1	2	3	6	0.8
41	Long-tailed Tit	93	98	265	363	456	60.6	105	Gadwall	0	5	1	6	6	0.8
42	Spotted Flycatcher	74	122	244	366	440	58.4	106	Siskin	3	2	0	2	5	0.7
43	Grey Partridge	170	159	104	263	433	57.5	107	Black-headed Gull	3	0	2	2	5	0.7
44	Lesser Whitethroat	32	281	105	386	418	55.5	108	Mandarin	3	1	1	2	5	0.7
45	Corn Bunting	23	294	83	377	400	53.1	109	Montagu's Harrier	4	0	1	1	5	0.7
46	Treecreeper	104	151	142	293	397	52.7	110	Stone Curlew	2	0	3	3	5	0.7
47	Jay	153	138	98	236	389	51.7	111	Goshawk	5	0	0	0	5	0.7
48	Green Woodpecker	96	186	107	293	389	51.7	112	Common Sandpiper	2	0	1	1	3	0.4
49	Turtle Dove	92	243	47	290	382	50.7	113	Dipper	1	1	1	2	3	0.4
50	Garden Warbler	35	252	88	340	375	49.8	114	Ring-necked Parakeet	2	1	0	1	3	0.4
51	Little Owl	113	129	110	239	352	46.7	115	Cormorant	2	0	0	0	2	0.3
52	Tawny Owl	74	171	107	278	352	46.7	116	Egyptian Goose	0	0	2	2	2	0.3
53	Sparrowhawk	185	74	92	166	351	46.6	117	Wood Duck	1	0	1	1	2	0.3
54	Goldcrest	48	201	91	292	340	45.2	118	Shoveler	2	0	0	0	2	0.3
55	Reed Bunting	39	185	109	294	333	44.2	119	Short-eared Owl	2	0	0	0	2	0.3
56	Yellow Wagtail	80	98	133	231	311	41.3	120	Nightjar	0	2	0	2	2	0.3
57	Coal Tit	54	136	117	253	307	40.8	121	Black Redstart	1	1	0	1	2	0.3
58	Marsh Tit	45	132	101	233	278	36.9	122	Green Sandpiper	2	0	0	0	2	0.3
59	Coot	44	24	187	211	255	33.9	123	Serin	1	1	0	1	2	0.3
60	Tree Sparrow	77	56	111	167	244	32.4	124	Snow Goose	0	0	1	1	1	0.1
61	Nuthatch	52	96	89	185	237	31.5	125	Pied Flycatcher	1	0	0	0	1	0.1
62	Sedge Warbler	19	115	73	188	207	27.5	126	Cirl Bunting	1	0	0	0	1	0.1
63	Canada Goose	59	26	112	138	197	26.2	127	Herring Gull	1	0	0	0	1	0.1
64	Mute Swan	50	17	112	129	179	23.8		TOTAL	6,167	13,319	16,329	29,648	35,815	

Atlas giving a breakdown of grades as follows:

Confirmed breeding   109
Probable breeding   9
Possible breeding   9

The prime aim of this study was to document the status of the breeding birds in Oxfordshire for a particular period. This has been achieved with some success and the distribution maps and a discussion of those results are given in the appropriate species accounts. From these, it has been possible to assess the relative distributional abundances (not necessarily the same as actual numerical abundance) for the species recorded and these are given in Table 4.2.

By combining and comparing those results we have also been able to identify the areas of the county which have the greatest number of breeding species and this is of considerable value in bird conservation (Figure 4.1). The highest count for a single tetrad was 83 species in SU5296 which, as one might expect has a great diversity of habitat including river, gravel-pits and woodland. In addition, 14 tetrads were found to hold more than 70 species, and again these tetrads offered a great diversity of habitat types.

There was a considerable range in the number of species present in a tetrad from 14–83. This range is however not as great as that found in some other county atlas projects and this reflects the fact that there are no extremes of habitat, particularly in relation to altitude, that are low in species diversity. The lowest counts are from squares of little habitat diversity and where the

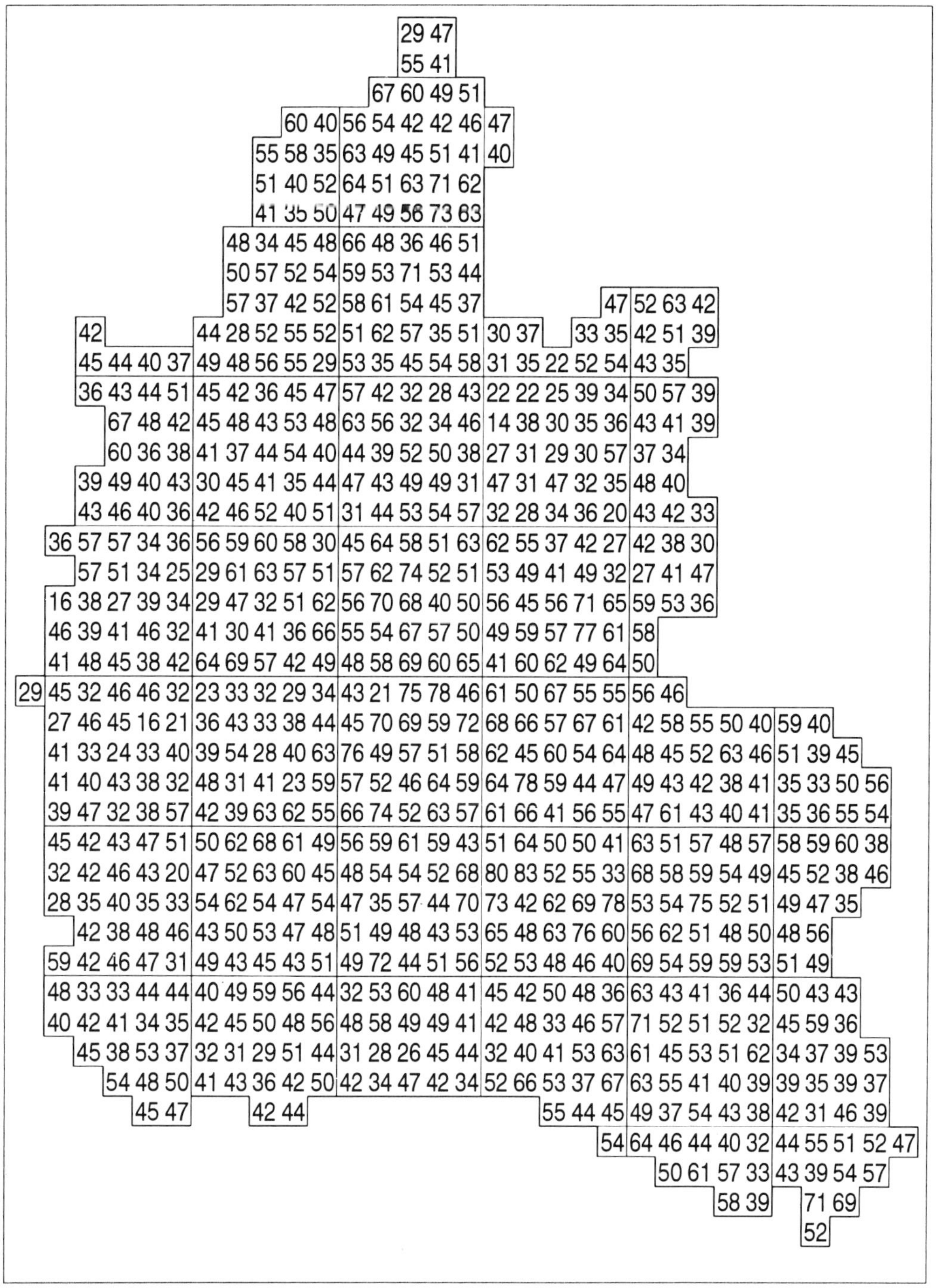

Figure 4.1.
Map of Oxfordshire showing the number of breeding species recorded in each tetrad during the four years of the Atlas project, 1985-1988.

Table 4.3.

The distribution of tetrads by species diversity. Each range shows the number of tetrads with a species count in the prescribed band class.

No. of Species	Class Midpoint	No. of Tetrads
13-17	15	3
18-22	20	7
23-27	25	12
28-32	30	51
33-37	35	74
38-42	40	117
43-47	45	125
48-52	50	132
53-57	55	103
58-62	60	71
63-67	65	36
68-72	70	14
73-77	75	7
78-82	80	1

Table 4.4.

Development of the database over the four years of the survey in terms of the number of records and the quality of data received.

Year of survey	% tetrads with records	Av. No species/ covered tetrad	Total No. records	Av.level of recording
1	53	31	12,500	2.2
2	80	38	22,600	2.18
3	95	42	30,500	2.25
4	100	47	35,815	2.29

land-use is mostly intensive agriculture. Table 4.3 shows the distribution of tetrads by species diversity bands grouped in classes of five.

Despite Oxfordshire being predominantly an agricultural area, over the county as a whole most tetrads offered a species total in the range of 30–65 species. This is not really a true indication of the species diversity sustained by an arable landscape but more a reflection of the sample size (i.e. the tetrad) used, since there are few rural squares without a small copse or a village sufficient to provide nesting opportunities for a range of species. If the project had been undertaken using the 1 km square as the basic recording unit, a much wider variation in the counts per square would have become apparent. For example, in one tetrad on the Cotswolds, one observer (ARH) carefully scoured a tetrad and recorded almost 50 breeding species. Yet within that tetrad, two of the 1 km squares, elevated, without habitation and mostly dominated by cereal fields, were found to have fewer than ten species. The other 1 km squares included a river, woodland and a number of mature gardens.

COMPARISONS WITH OTHER STUDIES

It is interesting to make direct comparisons of the Oxfordshire Atlas with those similar studies undertaken in other counties or regions in the south of England such as Hertfordshire (Mead and Smith 1982), Greater London (Montier 1977), Kent (Taylor et al. 1982), Devon (Sitters 1988) and Norfolk (Kelly 1986). However in attempting such a comparison one must bear in mind that those studies were not undertaken during the same period, nor were they carried out over the same length of time as the Oxfordshire project. However some interesting general points can be made. As might be expected, Oxfordshire fares well for a range species typical of open countryside such as Chaffinch, Yellowhammer, Stock Dove, Lesser Whitethroat, Whitethroat and Yellow Wagtail. Pigeon and crow species are well represented as too are the gamebirds. Waterways birds also feature, with Little Grebe, Mute Swan, Tufted Duck, Coot and Kingfisher being found in a relatively high number of tetrads when compared with other regions of the country. Indeed the county has the highest percentage of tetrads with breeding Canada Geese. The recovery of the Sparrowhawk following the pesticide problem puts that species high on the list and the rate at which observers encountered Hobby is higher than for other surveys.

On the other hand, breeding waders such as Snipe and Redshank are very poorly represented as too are Tree Pipit and Nightingale. Furthermore, Oxfordshire has the lowest incidence for Barn Owl, Sand Martin and Redstart.

As previously noted, not too much should be read into these comparisons. We know that species such as Redstart and Nightingale have been in decline and that Stock Dove and Canada Goose have increased. These points do however serve to demonstrate these population changes and may help to give some direction to further studies or conservation initiatives.

VALIDITY OF THE OXFORDSHIRE ATLAS

It is all very well to present the mass of data gathered during the Oxfordshire Atlas, but how does one know it to be correct? To be honest, one cannot make any guarantees but we can make informed statements about the confidence that we can have in the data with regard to particular species. Some species are, by their very nature, difficult to locate let alone show to be breeding, whilst some, through nocturnal or crepuscular habits, will be missed if there are insufficient local observers. Mistakes can be made; incorrect identification, incorrect interpretation of behaviour and the accidental misassigning of tetrads may have occurred. However, the use of the network of 10 km square leaders each with a good local knowledge and close liaison with the fieldworkers, has helped to reduce mistakes and these checks were further supported by checks made by the Atlas coordinator. In this respect, it is interesting that the number of species recorded in a tetrad is correlated with that in its neighbouring tetrad and that this reflects regional differences which are unlikely to have arisen by observer differences or bias (see Appendix 5).

We are sure that some records will have been missed but it was felt that by extending the project for a further season or more, would not have yielded a significantly greater amount of data and probably only have devalued the results for other species. After all, the study period used has to take account of the fact that the results must reflect the situation in an environment which is changing very rapidly.

Nevertheless, it is possible that an extended survey period could have elevated the category of breeding evidence for a number of records and perhaps improved the overall quality of individual records. An assessment of the quality of recording can be gained by assigning one point for a 'Possible' record, two for a 'Probable' and three for 'Confirmed' record in each tetrad. If these values are then summed and divided by the number of species recorded, an average value for the level of recording is obtained which gives an indication of how well a square has been covered. These values are given in Table 4.4. Overall, the average score for the Oxfordshire project is 2.25, which is slightly lower than a number of other county atlas projects. At first glance, this gave the organising committee some concern. However, two points need to be borne in mind. Firstly, our survey had a very high number of possible records for species such as Grey Heron and Swift which were clearly not breeding but were included due to some ambiguity in the instructions. In the final analysis these have been retained which has resulted in a slightly lower score. Secondly, for most species a 'Probable' record is as good as a 'Confirmed' record (and accepted as such in the new BTO Atlas). Indeed one could argue whether there is a case for scoring over all three categories of recording. Table 4.4 also shows the development of the database over the four years of the survey in terms of the number of records and the quality of data received.

At the completion of the four years of atlas fieldwork, the organising committee felt that the survey had been completed to a most satisfactory level. Due to some of the points mentioned above, there was some pressure to continue for a fifth season. However, on balance it was decided that a relatively large amount of effort would have to be expended for very little reward. The survey was then closed and efforts channelled into the interpretation of the overall

results, their publication and to begin to put the data to good use. Importantly, in the context of this latter point, the collected information was to be used to formulate a strategy for future ornithological fieldwork in Oxfordshire. If future fieldwork can be carried out with the same enthusiasm, dedication and interest as the 1985–88 Oxfordshire Atlas, then there is some hope for the bird-life of Oxfordshire.

The maps which follow this chapter show the results of the atlas project. The size of dot shows the highest grade of recording achieved for a given species in a given tetrad. Note that since the survey shows the results for four years' work, some scarce species may be over-represented if the observed distribution changed between years during the survey. However, on the whole this will not have occurred in many cases. Note also that for the security of those species involved, maps have not been included for locally rare or vulnerable species. The species maps are preceded by tetrad maps showing five of the principle habitats of the county.

Map 4.1.
Canals and rivers.

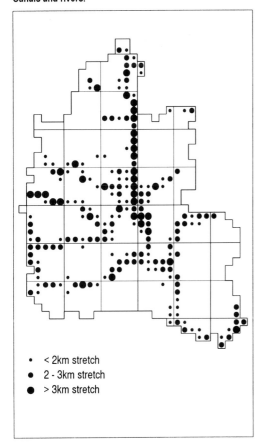

- • < 2km stretch
- ● 2 - 3km stretch
- ⬤ > 3km stretch

Map 4.2.
Reservoirs and gravel pits.

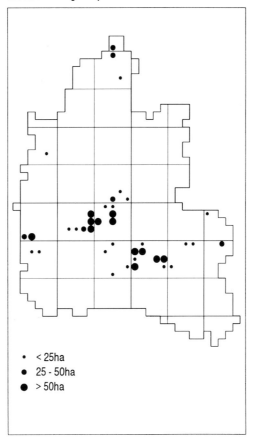

- • < 25ha
- ● 25 - 50ha
- ⬤ > 50ha

Map 4.3.
Coniferous woodland.

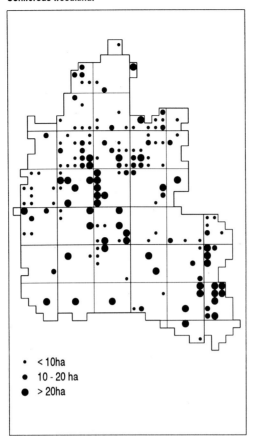

- •   < 10ha
- ●   10 - 20 ha
- ⬤   > 20ha

Map 4.4.
Broadleaved woodland.

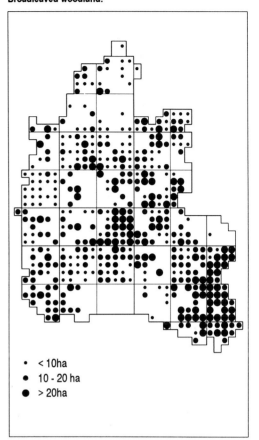

- •   < 10ha
- ●   10 - 20 ha
- ⬤   > 20ha

Map 4.5.
City and towns.

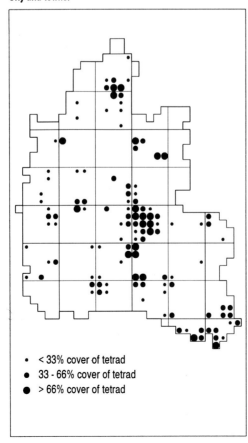

- •   < 33% cover of tetrad
- ●   33 - 66% cover of tetrad
- ⬤   > 66% cover of tetrad

Map 4.6.
Little Grebe. (Page 65)

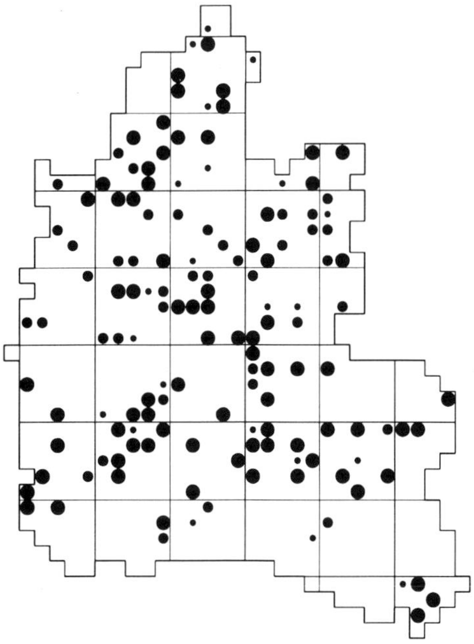

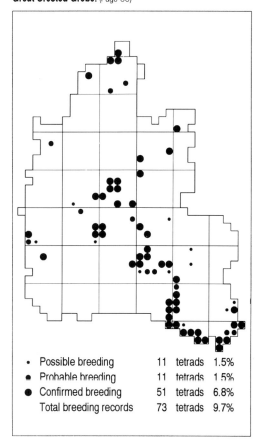

	Possible breeding	22	tetrads	2.9%
•	Probable breeding	40	tetrads	5.3%
●	Confirmed breeding	79	tetrads	10.5%
	Total breeding records	141	tetrads	18.7%

Map 4.7.
Great Crested Grebe. (Page 66)

	Possible breeding	11	tetrads	1.5%
•	Probable breeding	11	tetrads	1.5%
●	Confirmed breeding	51	tetrads	6.8%
	Total breeding records	73	tetrads	9.7%

Map 4.8.
Grey Heron. (Page 76)

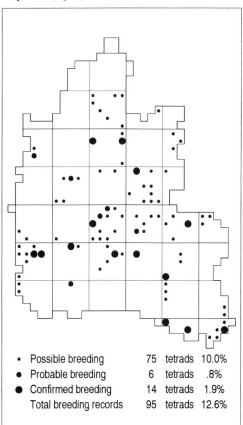

	Possible breeding	75	tetrads	10.0%
•	Probable breeding	6	tetrads	.8%
●	Confirmed breeding	14	tetrads	1.9%
	Total breeding records	95	tetrads	12.6%

Map 4.9.
Mute Swan. (Page 80)

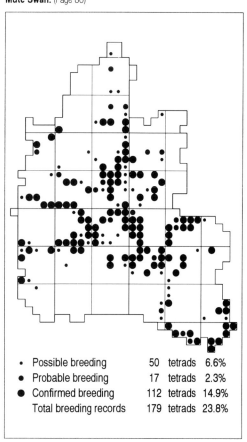

	Possible breeding	50	tetrads	6.6%
•	Probable breeding	17	tetrads	2.3%
●	Confirmed breeding	112	tetrads	14.9%
	Total breeding records	179	tetrads	23.8%

Map 4.10.
Canada Goose. (Page 83)

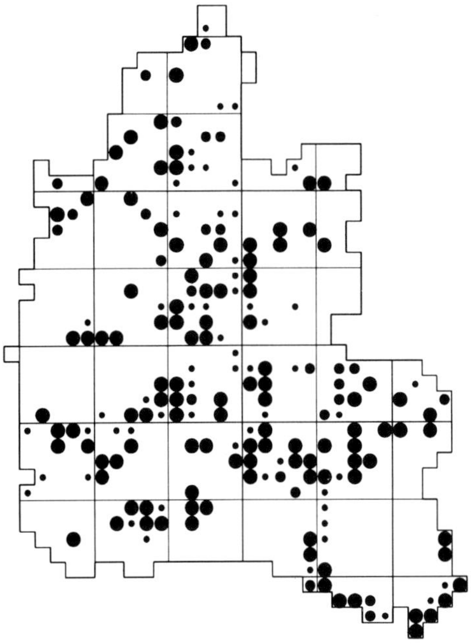

•	Possible breeding	59 tetrads	7.8%
•	Probable breeding	26 tetrads	3.5%
●	Confirmed breeding	112 tetrads	14.9%
	Total breeding records	197 tetrads	26.2%

Map 4.11.
Mallard. (Page 87)

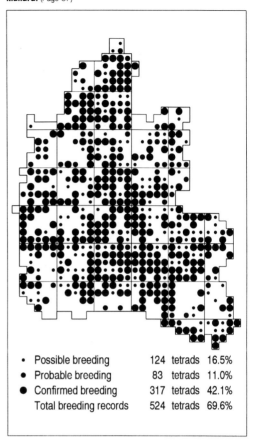

•	Possible breeding	124 tetrads	16.5%
•	Probable breeding	83 tetrads	11.0%
●	Confirmed breeding	317 tetrads	42.1%
	Total breeding records	524 tetrads	69.6%

Map 4.12.
Pochard. (Page 90)

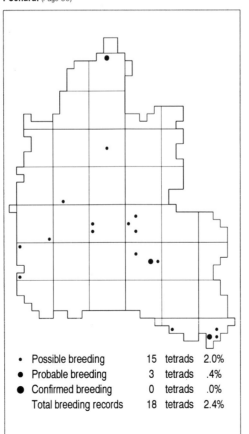

•	Possible breeding	15 tetrads	2.0%
•	Probable breeding	3 tetrads	.4%
●	Confirmed breeding	0 tetrads	.0%
	Total breeding records	18 tetrads	2.4%

Map 4.13.
Tufted Duck. (Page 91)

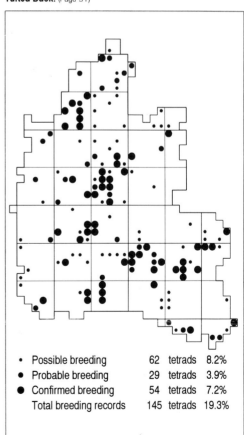

•	Possible breeding	62 tetrads	8.2%
•	Probable breeding	29 tetrads	3.9%
●	Confirmed breeding	54 tetrads	7.2%
	Total breeding records	145 tetrads	19.3%

Map 4.14.
Sparrowhawk. (Page 99)

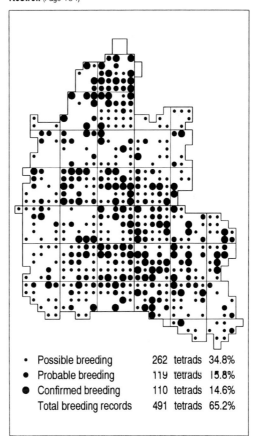

	Possible breeding	185	tetrads	24.6%
•	Probable breeding	74	tetrads	9.8%
●	Confirmed breeding	92	tetrads	12.2%
	Total breeding records	351	tetrads	46.6%

Map 4.15.
Kestrel. (Page 104)

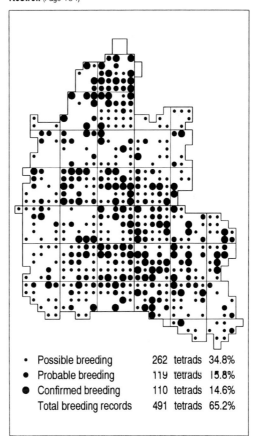

	Possible breeding	262	tetrads	34.8%
•	Probable breeding	119	tetrads	15.8%
●	Confirmed breeding	110	tetrads	14.6%
	Total breeding records	491	tetrads	65.2%

Map 4.16.
Red-legged Partridge. (Page 108)

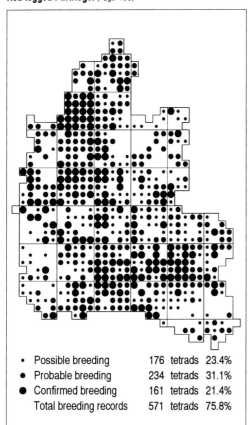

	Possible breeding	176	tetrads	23.4%
•	Probable breeding	234	tetrads	31.1%
●	Confirmed breeding	161	tetrads	21.4%
	Total breeding records	571	tetrads	75.8%

Map 4.17.
Grey Partridge. (Page 109)

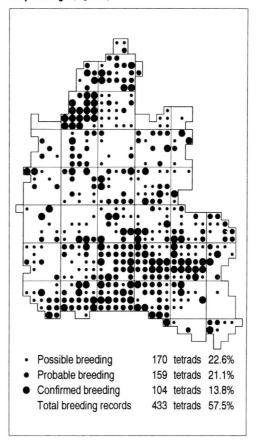

	Possible breeding	170	tetrads	22.6%
•	Probable breeding	159	tetrads	21.1%
●	Confirmed breeding	104	tetrads	13.8%
	Total breeding records	433	tetrads	57.5%

Map 4.18.
Pheasant. (Page 111)

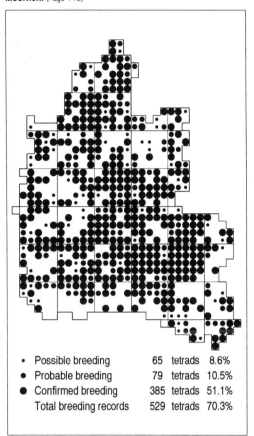

- Possible breeding   94   tetrads   12.5%
- Probable breeding   283   tetrads   37.6%
- Confirmed breeding   322   tetrads   42.8%
    Total breeding records   699   tetrads   92.8%

Map 4.19.
Moorhen. (Page 113)

- Possible breeding   65   tetrads   8.6%
- Probable breeding   79   tetrads   10.5%
- Confirmed breeding   385   tetrads   51.1%
    Total breeding records   529   tetrads   70.3%

Map 4.20.
Coot. (Page 114)

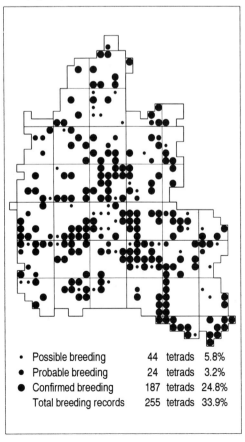

- Possible breeding   44   tetrads   5.8%
- Probable breeding   24   tetrads   3.2%
- Confirmed breeding   187   tetrads   24.8%
    Total breeding records   255   tetrads   33.9%

Map 4.21.
Lapwing. (Page 123)

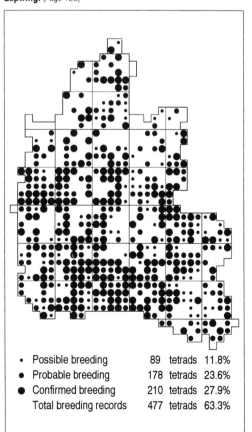

- Possible breeding   89   tetrads   11.8%
- Probable breeding   178   tetrads   23.6%
- Confirmed breeding   210   tetrads   27.9%
    Total breeding records   477   tetrads   63.3%

Map 4.22.
Snipe. (Page 128)

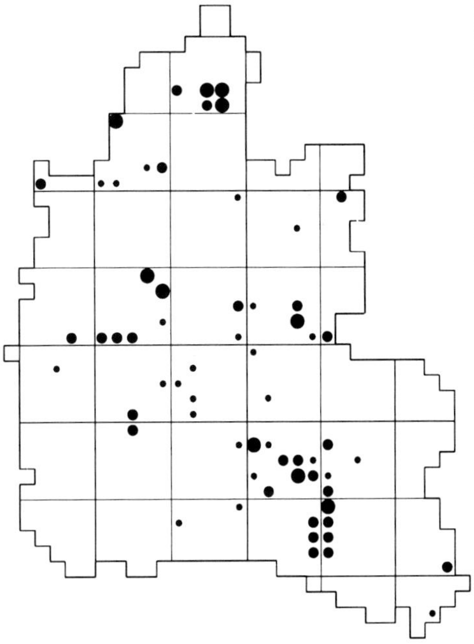

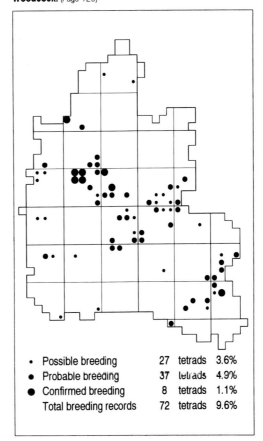

•	Possible breeding	26	tetrads	3.5%
●	Probable breeding	27	tetrads	3.6%
●	Confirmed breeding	10	tetrads	1.3%
	Total breeding records	63	tetrads	8.4%

Map 4.23.
Woodcock. (Page 129)

•	Possible breeding	27	tetrads	3.6%
●	Probable breeding	37	tetrads	4.9%
●	Confirmed breeding	8	tetrads	1.1%
	Total breeding records	72	tetrads	9.6%

Map 4.24.
Curlew. (Page 131)

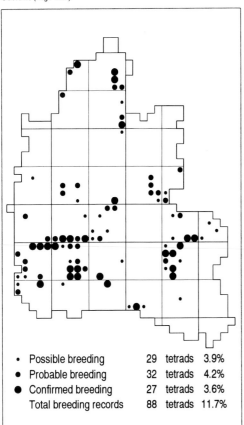

•	Possible breeding	29	tetrads	3.9%
●	Probable breeding	32	tetrads	4.2%
●	Confirmed breeding	27	tetrads	3.6%
	Total breeding records	88	tetrads	11.7%

Map 4.25.
Redshank. (Page 133)

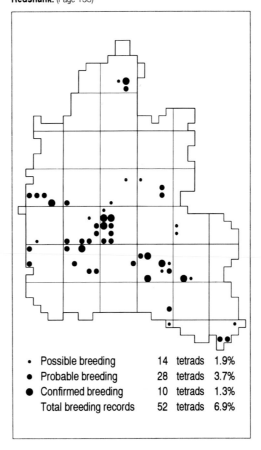

•	Possible breeding	14	tetrads	1.9%
●	Probable breeding	28	tetrads	3.7%
●	Confirmed breeding	10	tetrads	1.3%
	Total breeding records	52	tetrads	6.9%

Map 4.26.
Feral Pigeon. (Page 149)

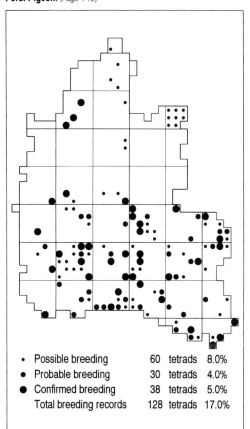

•	Possible breeding	60 tetrads	8.0%
•	Probable breeding	30 tetrads	4.0%
●	Confirmed breeding	38 tetrads	5.0%
	Total breeding records	128 tetrads	17.0%

Map 4.27.
Stock Dove. (Page 149)

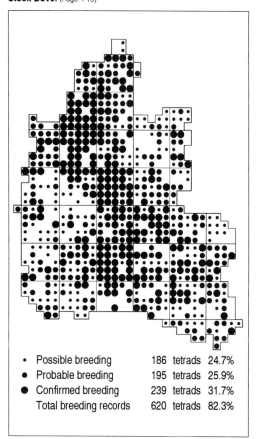

•	Possible breeding	186 tetrads	24.7%
•	Probable breeding	195 tetrads	25.9%
●	Confirmed breeding	239 tetrads	31.7%
	Total breeding records	620 tetrads	82.3%

Map 4.28.
Woodpigeon. (Page 150)

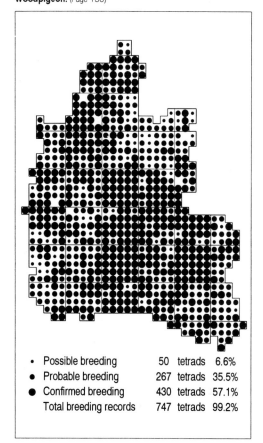

•	Possible breeding	50 tetrads	6.6%
•	Probable breeding	267 tetrads	35.5%
●	Confirmed breeding	430 tetrads	57.1%
	Total breeding records	747 tetrads	99.2%

Map 4.29.
Collared Dove. (Page 151)

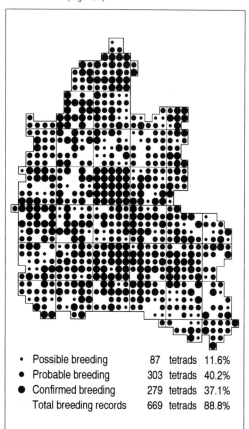

•	Possible breeding	87 tetrads	11.6%
•	Probable breeding	303 tetrads	40.2%
●	Confirmed breeding	279 tetrads	37.1%
	Total breeding records	669 tetrads	88.8%

Map 4.30.
Turtle Dove. (Page 151)

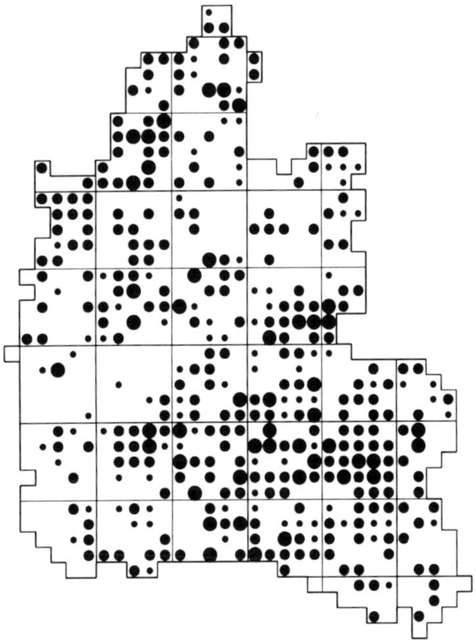

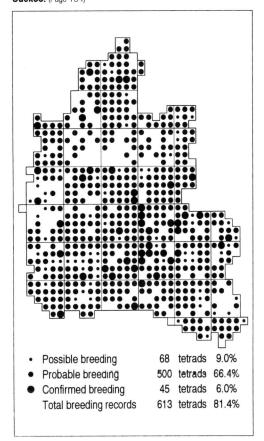

·	Possible breeding	92 tetrads	12.2%
•	Probable breeding	243 tetrads	32.3%
●	Confirmed breeding	47 tetrads	6.2%
	Total breeding records	382 tetrads	50.7%

Map 4.31.
Cuckoo. (Page 154)

·	Possible breeding	68 tetrads	9.0%
•	Probable breeding	500 tetrads	66.4%
●	Confirmed breeding	45 tetrads	6.0%
	Total breeding records	613 tetrads	81.4%

Map 4.32.
Little Owl. (Page 158)

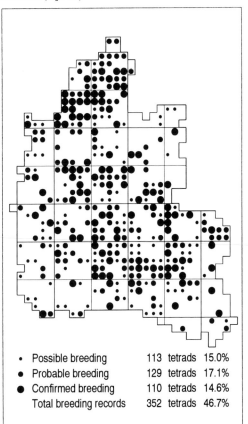

·	Possible breeding	113 tetrads	15.0%
•	Probable breeding	129 tetrads	17.1%
●	Confirmed breeding	110 tetrads	14.6%
	Total breeding records	352 tetrads	46.7%

Map 4.33.
Tawny Owl. (Page 159)

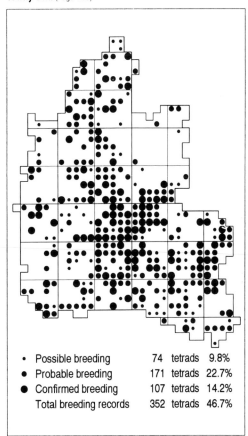

·	Possible breeding	74 tetrads	9.8%
•	Probable breeding	171 tetrads	22.7%
●	Confirmed breeding	107 tetrads	14.2%
	Total breeding records	352 tetrads	46.7%

Map 4.34.
Swift. (Page 164)

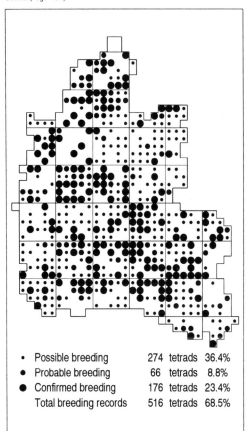

	Possible breeding	274	tetrads	36.4%
•	Probable breeding	66	tetrads	8.8%
●	Confirmed breeding	176	tetrads	23.4%
	Total breeding records	516	tetrads	68.5%

Map 4.35.
Kingfisher. (Page 166)

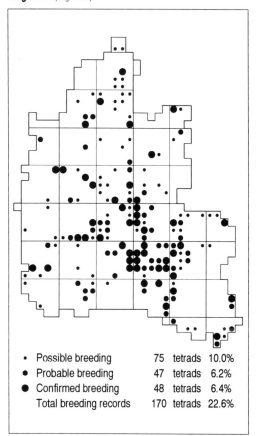

	Possible breeding	75	tetrads	10.0%
•	Probable breeding	47	tetrads	6.2%
●	Confirmed breeding	48	tetrads	6.4%
	Total breeding records	170	tetrads	22.6%

Map 4.36.
Green Woodpecker. (Page 171)

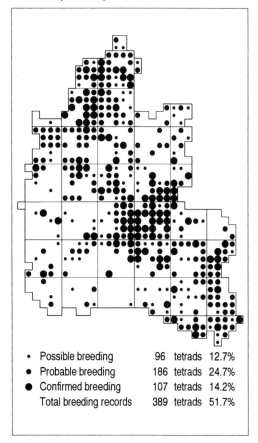

	Possible breeding	96	tetrads	12.7%
•	Probable breeding	186	tetrads	24.7%
●	Confirmed breeding	107	tetrads	14.2%
	Total breeding records	389	tetrads	51.7%

Map 4.37.
Great Spotted Woodpecker. (Page 172)

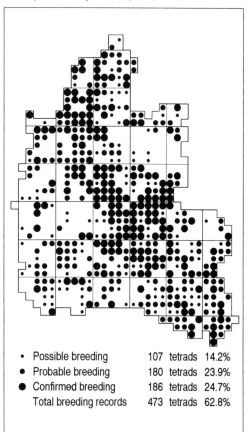

	Possible breeding	107	tetrads	14.2%
•	Probable breeding	180	tetrads	23.9%
●	Confirmed breeding	186	tetrads	24.7%
	Total breeding records	473	tetrads	62.8%

Map 4.38.
Lesser Spotted Woodpecker. (Page 173)

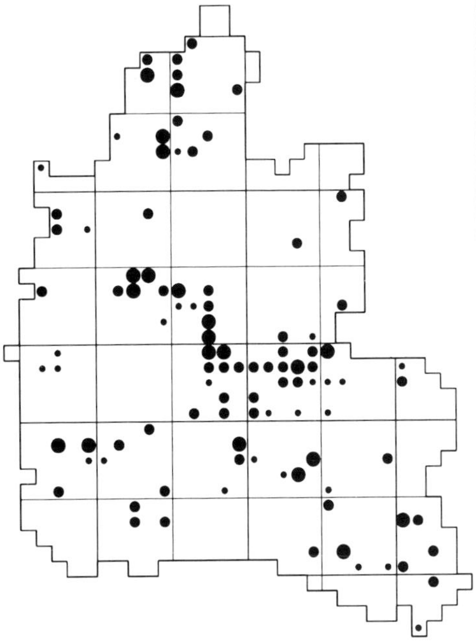

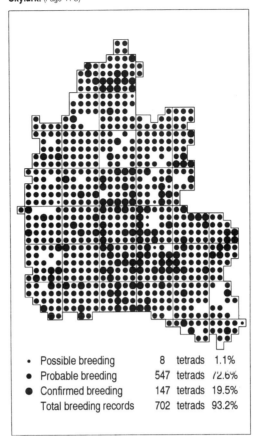

- ·   Possible brooding   28   tetrads   3.7%
- ●   Probable breeding   52   tetrads   6.9%
- ●   Confirmed breeding   21   tetrads   2.8%
-      Total breeding records   101   tetrads   13.4%

Map 4.39.
Skylark. (Page 175)

- ·   Possible breeding   8   tetrads   1.1%
- ●   Probable breeding   547   tetrads   72.6%
- ●   Confirmed breeding   147   tetrads   19.5%
-      Total breeding records   702   tetrads   93.2%

Map 4.40.
Sand Martin. (Page 177)

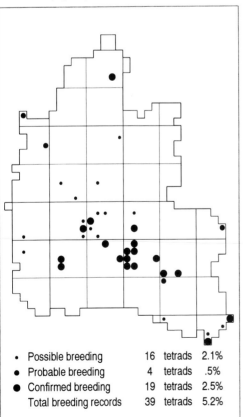

- ·   Possible breeding   16   tetrads   2.1%
- ●   Probable breeding   4   tetrads   .5%
- ●   Confirmed breeding   19   tetrads   2.5%
-      Total breeding records   39   tetrads   5.2%

Map 4.41.
Swallow. (Page 178)

- ·   Possible breeding   147   tetrads   19.5%
- ●   Probable breeding   114   tetrads   15.1%
- ●   Confirmed breeding   422   tetrads   56.0%
-      Total breeding records   683   tetrads   90.7%

Map 4.42.
House Martin. (Page 179)

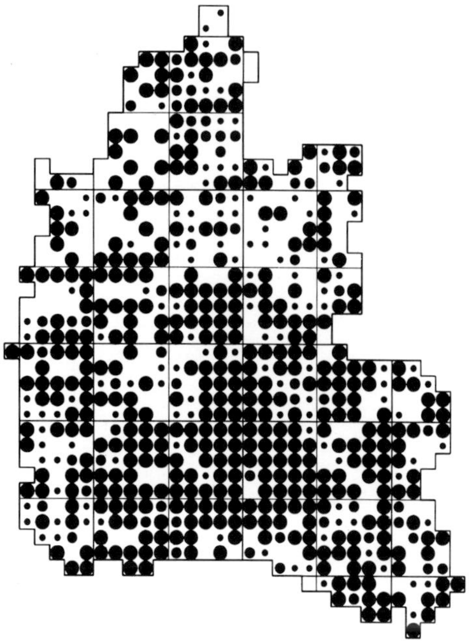

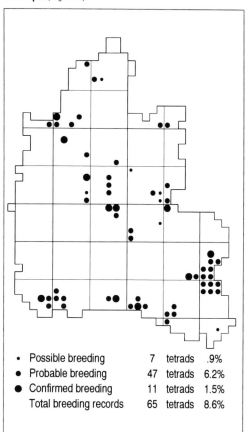

•	Possible breeding	125	tetrads	16.6%
•	Probable breeding	58	tetrads	7.7%
●	Confirmed breeding	408	tetrads	54.2%
	Total breeding records	591	tetrads	78.5%

Map 4.43.
Tree Pipit. (Page 181)

•	Possible breeding	7	tetrads	.9%
•	Probable breeding	47	tetrads	6.2%
●	Confirmed breeding	11	tetrads	1.5%
	Total breeding records	65	tetrads	8.6%

Map 4.44.
Meadow Pipit. (Page 182)

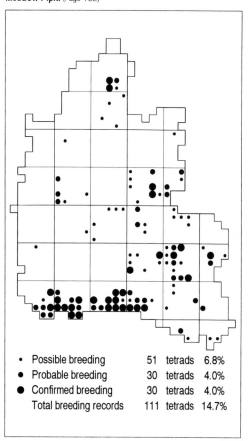

•	Possible breeding	51	tetrads	6.8%
•	Probable breeding	30	tetrads	4.0%
●	Confirmed breeding	30	tetrads	4.0%
	Total breeding records	111	tetrads	14.7%

Map 4.45.
Yellow Wagtail. (Page 183)

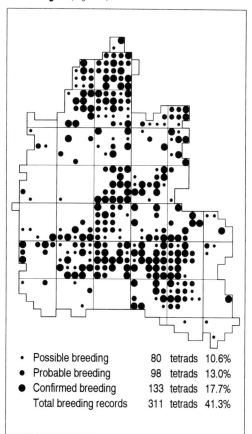

•	Possible breeding	80	tetrads	10.6%
•	Probable breeding	98	tetrads	13.0%
●	Confirmed breeding	133	tetrads	17.7%
	Total breeding records	311	tetrads	41.3%

Map 4.46.
Grey Wagtail. (Page 184)

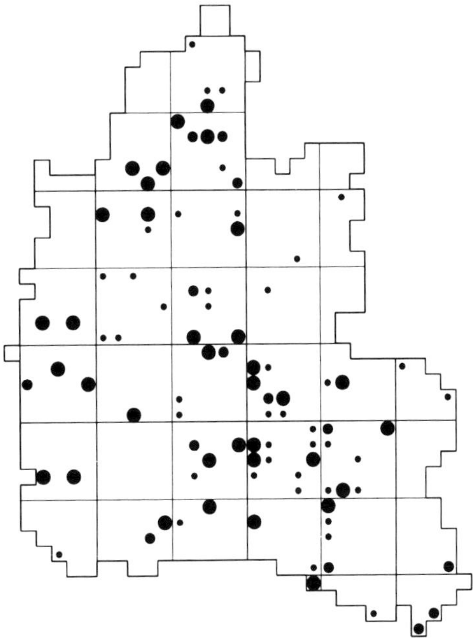

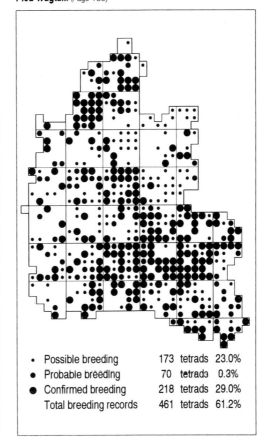

• Possible breeding	43	tetrads	5.7%
• Probable breeding	14	tetrads	1.9%
● Confirmed breeding	35	tetrads	4.6%
Total breeding records	92	tetrads	12.2%

Map 4.47.
Pied Wagtail. (Page 185)

• Possible breeding	173	tetrads	23.0%
• Probable breeding	70	tetrads	0.3%
● Confirmed breeding	218	tetrads	29.0%
Total breeding records	461	tetrads	61.2%

Map 4.48.
Wren. (Page 189)

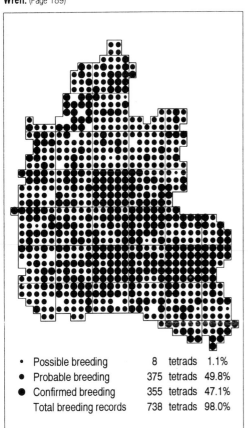

• Possible breeding	8	tetrads	1.1%
• Probable breeding	375	tetrads	49.8%
● Confirmed breeding	355	tetrads	47.1%
Total breeding records	738	tetrads	98.0%

Map 4.49.
Dunnock. (Page 190)

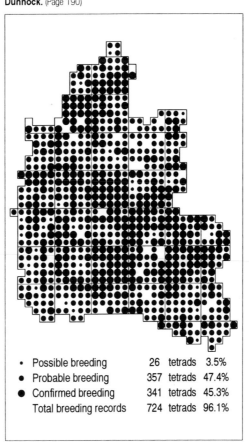

• Possible breeding	26	tetrads	3.5%
• Probable breeding	357	tetrads	47.4%
● Confirmed breeding	341	tetrads	45.3%
Total breeding records	724	tetrads	96.1%

Map 4.50.
Robin. (Page 191)

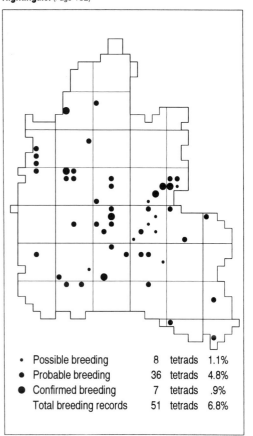

• Possible breeding	12 tetrads	1.6%
• Probable breeding	290 tetrads	38.5%
● Confirmed breeding	432 tetrads	57.4%
Total breeding records	734 tetrads	97.5%

Map 4.51.
Nightingale. (Page 192)

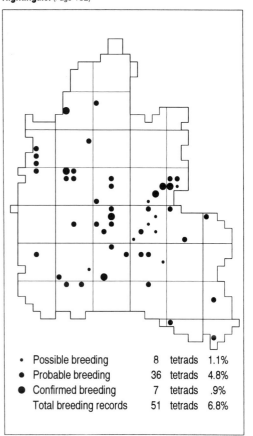

• Possible breeding	8 tetrads	1.1%
• Probable breeding	36 tetrads	4.8%
● Confirmed breeding	7 tetrads	.9%
Total breeding records	51 tetrads	6.8%

Map 4.52.
Blackbird. (Page 196)

• Possible breeding	2 tetrads	.3%
• Probable breeding	168 tetrads	22.3%
● Confirmed breeding	581 tetrads	77.2%
Total breeding records	751 tetrads	99.7%

Map 4.53.
Song Thrush. (Page 198)

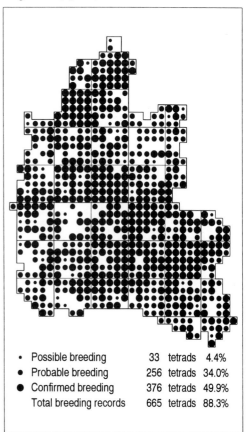

• Possible breeding	33 tetrads	4.4%
• Probable breeding	256 tetrads	34.0%
● Confirmed breeding	376 tetrads	49.9%
Total breeding records	665 tetrads	88.3%

Map 4.54.
Mistle Thrush. (Page 200)

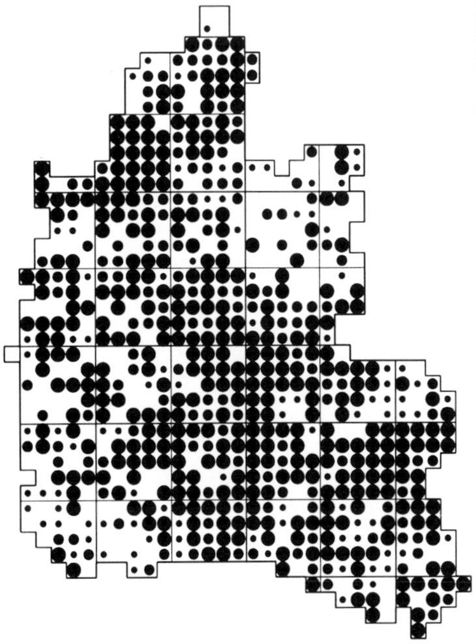

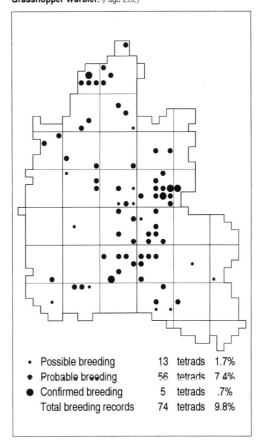

•	Possible breeding	95	tetrads	12.6%
•	Probable breeding	152	tetrads	20.2%
●	Confirmed breeding	360	tetrads	47.8%
	Total breeding records	607	tetrads	80.6%

Map 4.55.
Grasshopper Warbler. (Page 202)

•	Possible breeding	13	tetrads	1.7%
•	Probable breeding	56	tetrads	7.4%
●	Confirmed breeding	5	tetrads	.7%
	Total breeding records	74	tetrads	9.8%

Map 4.56.
Sedge Warbler. (Page 203)

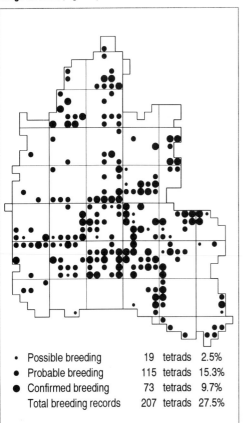

•	Possible breeding	19	tetrads	2.5%
•	Probable breeding	115	tetrads	15.3%
●	Confirmed breeding	73	tetrads	9.7%
	Total breeding records	207	tetrads	27.5%

Map 4.57.
Reed Warbler. (Page 204)

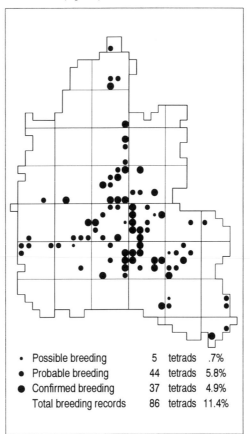

•	Possible breeding	5	tetrads	.7%
•	Probable breeding	44	tetrads	5.8%
●	Confirmed breeding	37	tetrads	4.9%
	Total breeding records	86	tetrads	11.4%

Map 4.58.
Lesser Whitethroat. (Page 206)

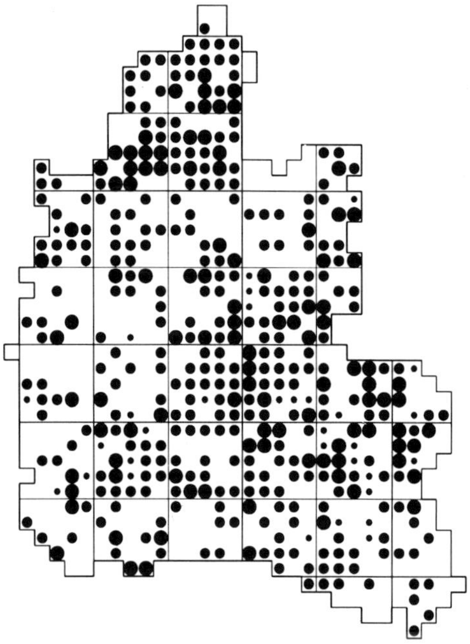

•	Possible breeding	32 tetrads	4.2%
●	Probable breeding	281 tetrads	37.3%
⬤	Confirmed breeding	105 tetrads	13.9%
	Total breeding records	418 tetrads	55.5%

Map 4.59.
Whitethroat. (Page 207)

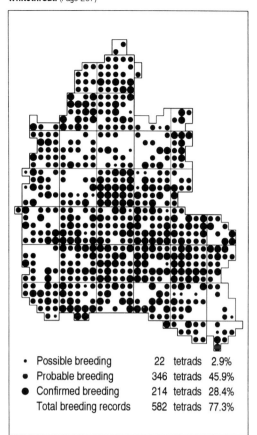

•	Possible breeding	22 tetrads	2.9%
●	Probable breeding	346 tetrads	45.9%
⬤	Confirmed breeding	214 tetrads	28.4%
	Total breeding records	582 tetrads	77.3%

Map 4.60.
Garden Warbler. (Page 207)

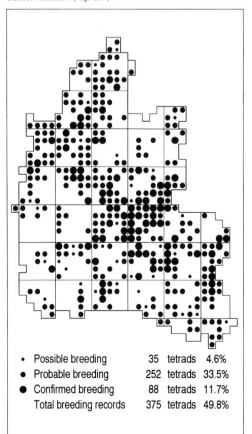

•	Possible breeding	35 tetrads	4.6%
●	Probable breeding	252 tetrads	33.5%
⬤	Confirmed breeding	88 tetrads	11.7%
	Total breeding records	375 tetrads	49.8%

Map 4.61.
Blackcap. (Page 208)

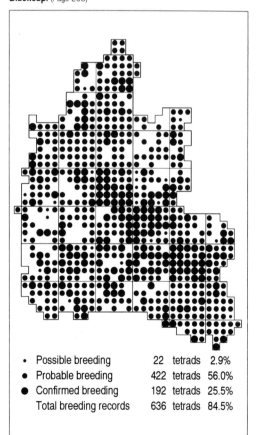

•	Possible breeding	22 tetrads	2.9%
●	Probable breeding	422 tetrads	56.0%
⬤	Confirmed breeding	192 tetrads	25.5%
	Total breeding records	636 tetrads	84.5%

Map 4.62.
Wood Warbler. (Page 209)

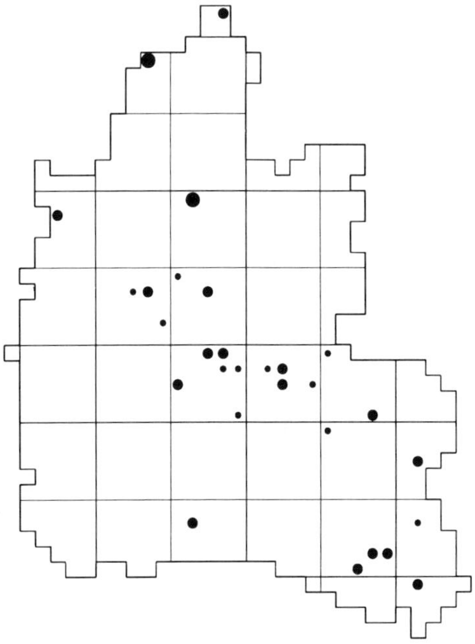

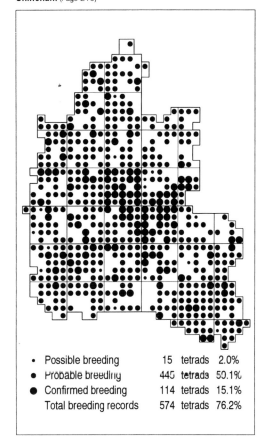

	Possible breeding	11	tetrads	1.5%
•	Possible breeding	11	tetrads	1.5%
•	Probable breeding	16	tetrads	2.1%
●	Confirmed breeding	2	tetrads	.3%
	Total breeding records	29	tetrads	3.9%

Map 4.63.
Chiffchaff. (Page 210)

•	Possible breeding	15	tetrads	2.0%
•	Probable breeding	445	tetrads	50.1%
●	Confirmed breeding	114	tetrads	15.1%
	Total breeding records	574	tetrads	76.2%

Map 4.64.
Willow Warbler. (Page 211)

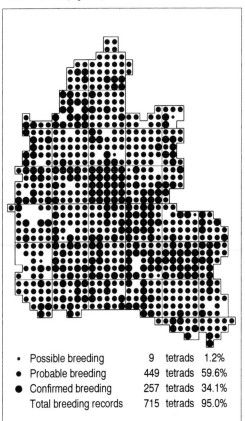

•	Possible breeding	9	tetrads	1.2%
•	Probable breeding	449	tetrads	59.6%
●	Confirmed breeding	257	tetrads	34.1%
	Total breeding records	715	tetrads	95.0%

Map 4.65.
Goldcrest. (Page 211)

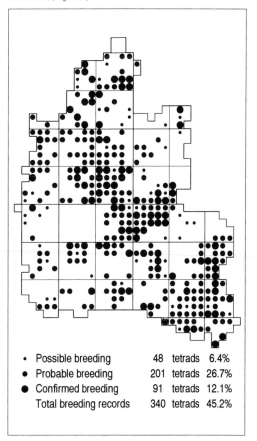

•	Possible breeding	48	tetrads	6.4%
•	Probable breeding	201	tetrads	26.7%
●	Confirmed breeding	91	tetrads	12.1%
	Total breeding records	340	tetrads	45.2%

Map 4.66.
Spotted Flycatcher. (Page 214)

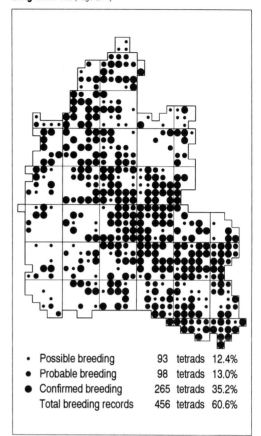

•	Possible breeding	74 tetrads	9.8%
•	Probable breeding	122 tetrads	16.2%
●	Confirmed breeding	244 tetrads	32.4%
	Total breeding records	440 tetrads	58.4%

Map 4.67.
Long-tailed Tit. (Page 217)

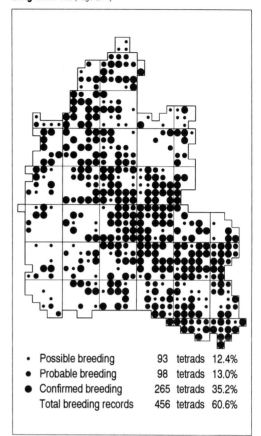

•	Possible breeding	93 tetrads	12.4%
•	Probable breeding	98 tetrads	13.0%
●	Confirmed breeding	265 tetrads	35.2%
	Total breeding records	456 tetrads	60.6%

Map 4.68.
Marsh Tit. (Page 219)

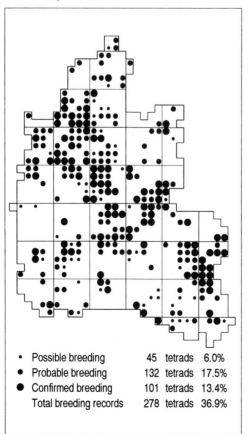

•	Possible breeding	45 tetrads	6.0%
•	Probable breeding	132 tetrads	17.5%
●	Confirmed breeding	101 tetrads	13.4%
	Total breeding records	278 tetrads	36.9%

Map 4.69.
Willow Tit. (Page 220)

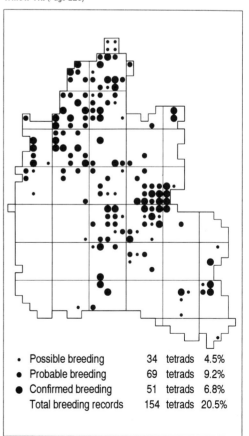

•	Possible breeding	34 tetrads	4.5%
•	Probable breeding	69 tetrads	9.2%
●	Confirmed breeding	51 tetrads	6.8%
	Total breeding records	154 tetrads	20.5%

Map 4.70.
Coal Tit. (Page 221)

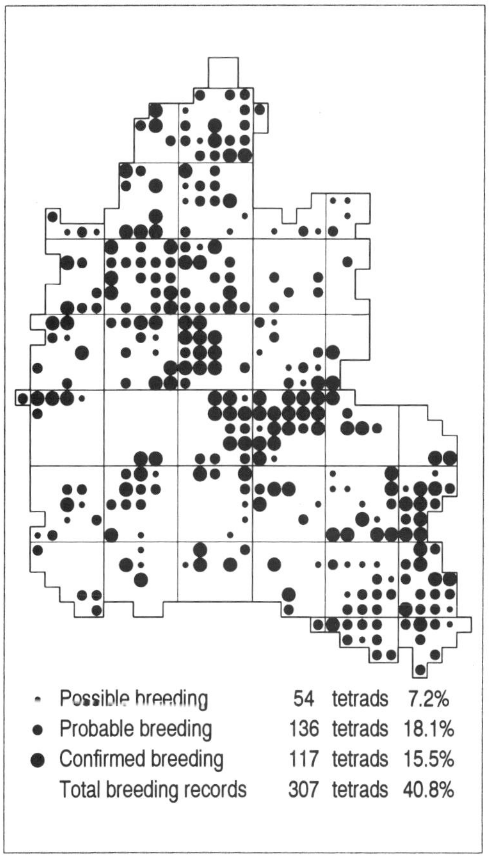

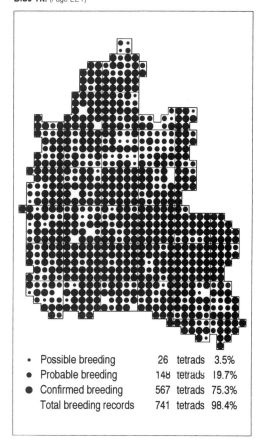

· Possible breeding	54	tetrads	7.2%
● Probable breeding	136	tetrads	18.1%
● Confirmed breeding	117	tetrads	15.5%
Total breeding records	307	tetrads	40.8%

Map 4.71.
Blue Tit. (Page 221)

· Possible breeding	26	tetrads	3.5%
● Probable breeding	148	tetrads	19.7%
● Confirmed breeding	567	tetrads	75.3%
Total breeding records	741	tetrads	98.4%

Map 4.72.
Great Tit. (Page 222)

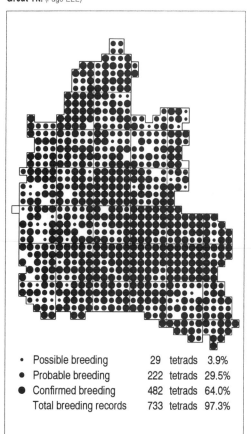

· Possible breeding	29	tetrads	3.9%
● Probable breeding	222	tetrads	29.5%
● Confirmed breeding	482	tetrads	64.0%
Total breeding records	733	tetrads	97.3%

Map 4.73.
Nuthatch. (Page 224)

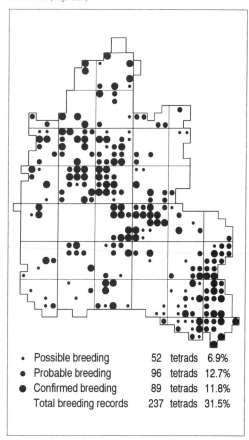

· Possible breeding	52	tetrads	6.9%
● Probable breeding	96	tetrads	12.7%
● Confirmed breeding	89	tetrads	11.8%
Total breeding records	237	tetrads	31.5%

Map 4.74.
Treecreeper. (Page 226)

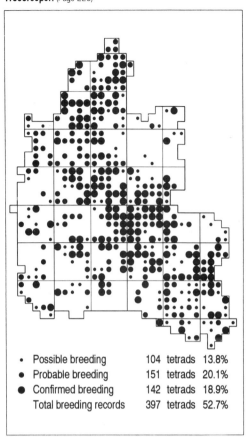

•	Possible breeding	104	tetrads	13.8%
•	Probable breeding	151	tetrads	20.1%
●	Confirmed breeding	142	tetrads	18.9%
	Total breeding records	397	tetrads	52.7%

Map 4.75.
Jay. (Page 230)

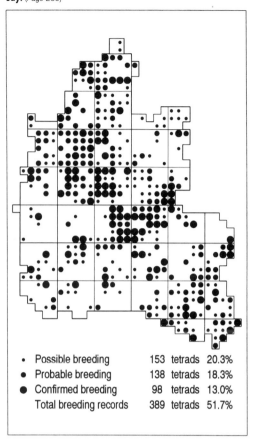

•	Possible breeding	153	tetrads	20.3%
•	Probable breeding	138	tetrads	18.3%
●	Confirmed breeding	98	tetrads	13.0%
	Total breeding records	389	tetrads	51.7%

Map 4.76.
Magpie. (Page 231)

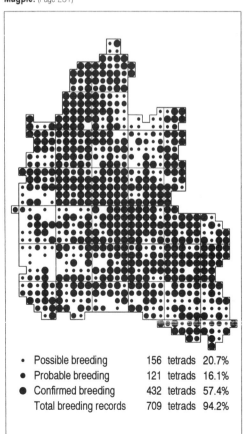

•	Possible breeding	156	tetrads	20.7%
•	Probable breeding	121	tetrads	16.1%
●	Confirmed breeding	432	tetrads	57.4%
	Total breeding records	709	tetrads	94.2%

Map 4.77.
Jackdaw. (Page 232)

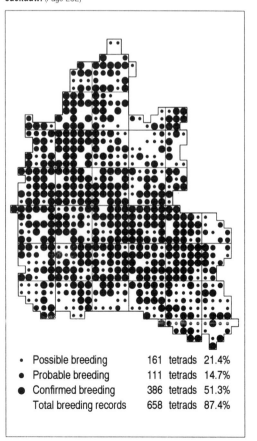

•	Possible breeding	161	tetrads	21.4%
•	Probable breeding	111	tetrads	14.7%
●	Confirmed breeding	386	tetrads	51.3%
	Total breeding records	658	tetrads	87.4%

Map 4.78.
Rook. (Page 232)

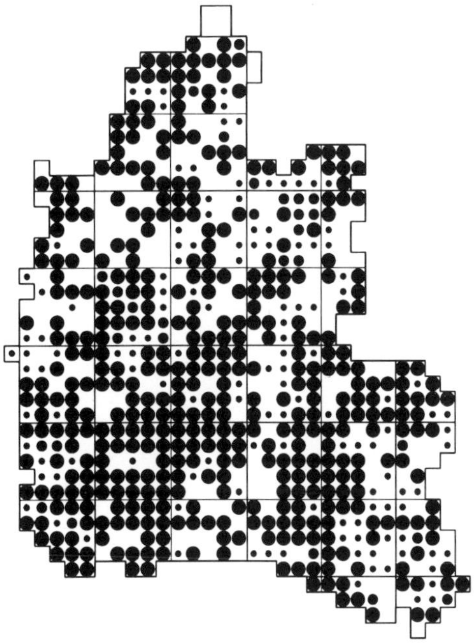

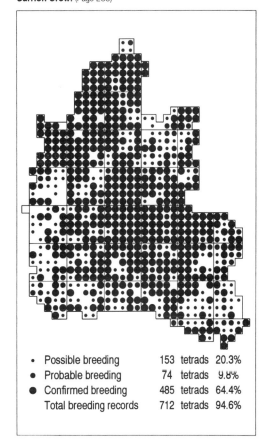

•	Possible breeding	132	tetrads	17.5%
•	Probable breeding	28	tetrads	3.7%
●	Confirmed breeding	424	tetrads	56.3%
	Total breeding records	584	tetrads	77.6%

Map 4.79.
Carrion Crow. (Page 233)

•	Possible breeding	153	tetrads	20.3%
•	Probable breeding	74	tetrads	9.8%
●	Confirmed breeding	485	tetrads	64.4%
	Total breeding records	712	tetrads	94.6%

Map 4.80.
Starling. (Page 235)

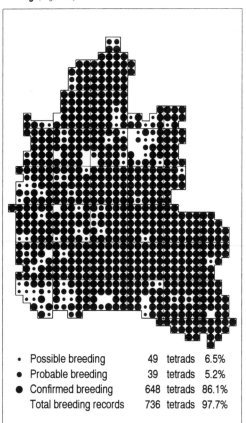

•	Possible breeding	49	tetrads	6.5%
•	Probable breeding	39	tetrads	5.2%
●	Confirmed breeding	648	tetrads	86.1%
	Total breeding records	736	tetrads	97.7%

Map 4.81.
House Sparrow. (Page 237)

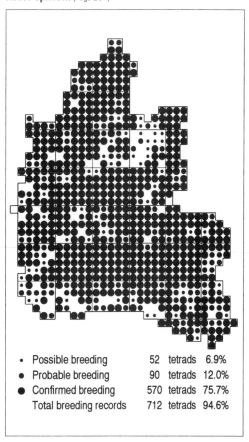

•	Possible breeding	52	tetrads	6.9%
•	Probable breeding	90	tetrads	12.0%
●	Confirmed breeding	570	tetrads	75.7%
	Total breeding records	712	tetrads	94.6%

Map 4.82.
Tree Sparrow. (Page 238)

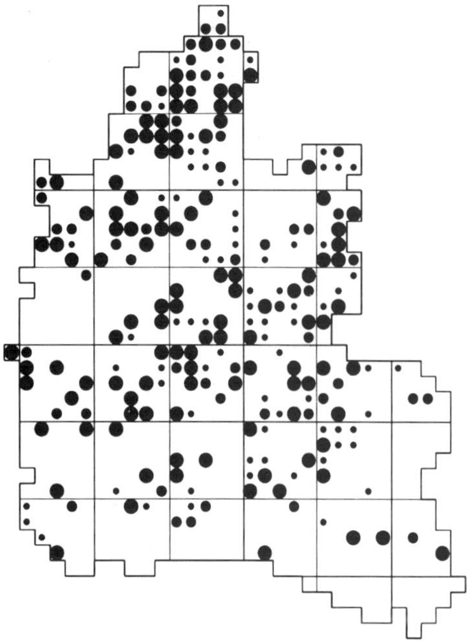

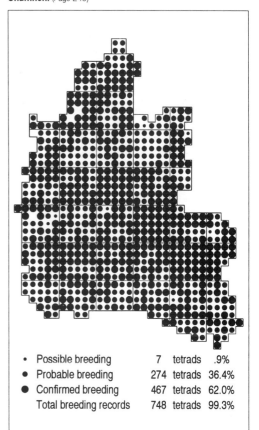

	Possible breeding	77	tetrads	10.2%
	Probable breeding	56	tetrads	7.4%
	Confirmed breeding	111	tetrads	14.7%
	Total breeding records	244	tetrads	32.4%

Map 4.83.
Chaffinch. (Page 240)

	Possible breeding	7	tetrads	.9%
	Probable breeding	274	tetrads	36.4%
	Confirmed breeding	467	tetrads	62.0%
	Total breeding records	748	tetrads	99.3%

Map 4.84.
Greenfinch. (Page 242)

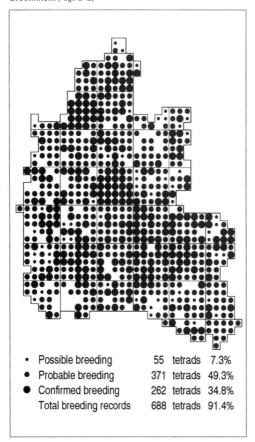

	Possible breeding	55	tetrads	7.3%
	Probable breeding	371	tetrads	49.3%
	Confirmed breeding	262	tetrads	34.8%
	Total breeding records	688	tetrads	91.4%

Map 4.85.
Goldfinch. (Page 242)

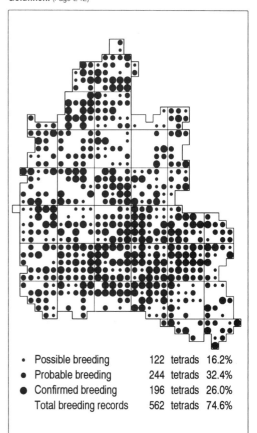

	Possible breeding	122	tetrads	16.2%
	Probable breeding	244	tetrads	32.4%
	Confirmed breeding	196	tetrads	26.0%
	Total breeding records	562	tetrads	74.6%

Map 4.86.
Linnet. (Page 245)

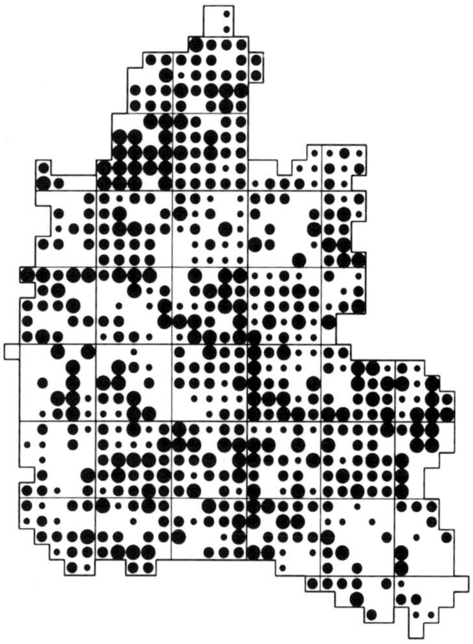

•	Possible breeding	120	tetrads	15.9%
•	Probable breeding	270	tetrads	35.9%
●	Confirmed breeding	174	tetrads	23.1%
	Total breeding records	564	tetrads	74.9%

Map 4.87.
Bullfinch. (Page 247)

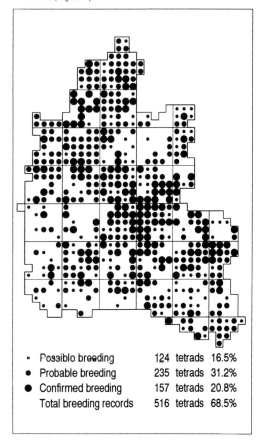

˙	Possible breeding	124	tetrads	16.5%
•	Probable breeding	235	tetrads	31.2%
●	Confirmed breeding	157	tetrads	20.8%
	Total breeding records	516	tetrads	68.5%

Map 4.88.
Hawfinch. (Page 248)

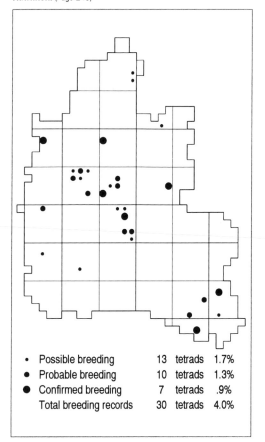

•	Possible breeding	13	tetrads	1.7%
•	Probable breeding	10	tetrads	1.3%
●	Confirmed breeding	7	tetrads	.9%
	Total breeding records	30	tetrads	4.0%

Map 4.89.
Yellowhammer. (Page 250)

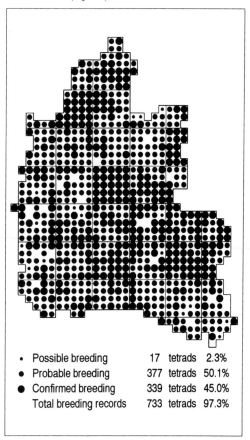

•	Possible breeding	17	tetrads	2.3%
•	Probable breeding	377	tetrads	50.1%
●	Confirmed breeding	339	tetrads	45.0%
	Total breeding records	733	tetrads	97.3%

Map 4.90.
Reed Bunting. (Page 252)

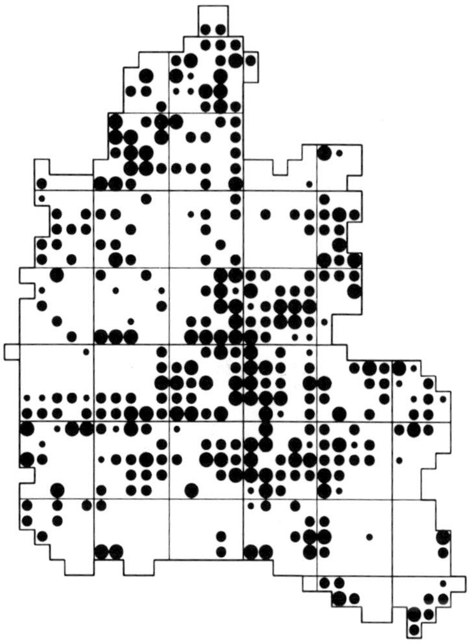

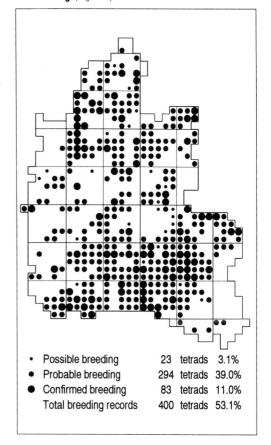

•	Possible breeding	39 tetrads	5.2%
●	Probable breeding	185 tetrads	24.6%
⬤	Confirmed breeding	109 tetrads	14.5%
	Total breeding records	333 tetrads	44.2%

Map 4.91.
Corn Bunting. (Page 253)

•	Possible breeding	23 tetrads	3.1%
●	Probable breeding	294 tetrads	39.0%
⬤	Confirmed breeding	83 tetrads	11.0%
	Total breeding records	400 tetrads	53.1%

CHAPTER FIVE
The Species Accounts

This section details the extent of our knowledge of each of the bird species that have occurred in Oxfordshire between 1900 and the end of 1989. In a very few cases, exceptional records have been included from 1990 and even 1991.

Species order

The systematic list closely follows the sequence and scientific nomenclature proposed by Voous (1977). (A small number of species fall outside of the precise regimen of this sequence to facilitate design and layout considerations. However, the complete check-list of the birds of Oxfordshire given in Appendix 1 does follow this system.)

References

The information given here has come from a wealth of sources, and we have attempted to credit the source of the information where possible. For these, a list of references is given. However, much of the work is based on records submitted to the county bird recorder and the archivists of the various ornithological and natural history societies in Oxfordshire who would then have passed details on to the county recorder. These may be casual records sent in on an annual or monthly basis, or as a result of a survey organised by the societies and summarised in their respective annual reports. Where no reference is cited, the reader can assume that the record has come from the county bird report for the year concerned. However, a prerequisite for inclusion is that the record had first been accepted and published by the county bird recorder.

In the interests of space and avoiding repetition, where a reference to *The Handbook of Birds of Europe, the Middle East and North Africa. The Birds of the Western Palearctic Vols I–VI* (Cramp or Cramp and Simmons eds) is cited this is given as BWP. Also, where reference is given to *The Atlas of Wintering Birds in Britain and Ireland*, the citation is to Lack 1986 rather than to the authors of individual accounts that appear within that book.

Names

To avoid cluttering the text too much and hence detract from easy reading, scientific names of plants, other bird species and animals are not included in the scripts, apart from the heading to each species in the systematic list. A list of scientific names of species mentioned in the text is given in Appendix 3.

For vernacular names of bird species we have used the one most commonly known rather than those more recently suggested by the BOU which are not in common use amongst birdwatchers.

Arrival and departure dates

Dates of arrival and departure of migrant species are given. These are based on the period 1974–1989. Prior to this, records for Oxfordshire and Berkshire were reported together and it is difficult to extract appropriate figures for all species in all years.

The Banbury Ornithological Society

The BOS is renowned for the high quality of their fieldwork, much of which is presented in this book. It must be noted that their study area covers parts of Warwickshire and Northamptonshire as well as Oxfordshire and in interpreting the results of fieldwork it has not always been possible to extract the data pertinent to Oxfordshire alone. However, it is felt that generally speaking there is not a significant difference in the landscape features as pertaining to birds and these results can be interpreted as being applicable to this county.

BOS Random Square Survey

This on-going survey by members of the BOS, is a winter fieldwork exercise which aims to visit over a period of time, each of the 1,200 1 km squares in their fieldwork area and to obtain a more complete picture of the distribution of birds for the records.

Common Bird Census (CBC)

This national scheme organised by the BTO provides an annual measure of abundance of breeding bird species in woodland and farmland habitats. By censussing the same sample plots over a long period and using basic field techniques, population changes can be expressed as an index of relative abundance.

Nest Record Card

This important long-term project, again organised by the BTO, aims to collect data on breeding biology and success by careful observation of birds' nests throughout a season. Information is entered on to a standardised card and the information collected by many observers across the country is then pooled.

Stanton Harcourt Gravel Pits

In the vicinity of Stanton Harcourt, Standlake and Hardwick to the west of Oxford, is a large complex of gravel pits. These are referred to either as the 'Stanton Harcourt' or 'lower Windrush' Gravel Pits.

Waterways Bird Survey

This national scheme is also organised by the BTO and uses similar fieldwork techniques to the CBC. However, the plot is essentially a linear one and the aim is to monitor bird populations annually along rivers, streams and canals.

Winter Wildfowl Counts

Many of the wildfowl accounts in this text include tables or figures showing the numbers of those species present in the county in particular years or months. These data are drawn from counts made for the national wildfowl counts organised by the Wildfowl and Wetlands Trust. The counts aim to look at patterns of movement of the different species as well as to provide estimates of numbers.

In Oxfordshire all of the major waters are counted including reservoirs, gravel pits, lakes and certain flood-meadows. Where results of these wildfowl counts are given the figures are derived from the mid-Oxfordshire sites only and exclude birds on the gravel pits in the Henley/Reading area and from the north of the county. They are also made on one pre-determined day in each month. That is, the middle weekend of the month from September to March. Hence although counts are synchronised and the figures are comparable between months and years, they cannot indicate the absolute maximum number of birds in the county in a given month which may be higher than the national counts indicate.

Family: Gaviidae
Divers

Divers are winter visitors to Oxfordshire from more northerly breeding grounds. Three species have occurred in the county and while one is extremely rare here, the others have been occurring with greater frequency and regularity in recent years. This partly reflects the increase in the availability of open water due to gravel extraction.

RED-THROATED DIVER
Gavia stellata

The Red-throated Diver is an occasional winter visitor to Oxfordshire. All observations are of single birds, except at Farmoor Reservoir on 16 January 1985 when there were two. Most visits are in mid-winter (Figure 5.1). Red-throated Divers in Oxfordshire are considered accidental since visits are usually brief. Most records are from the larger lakes, gravel pits and reservoirs.

There were seven records in the period 1900-1963, compared with 25 from 1964-1989 which appears to indicate an increase, but this could equally reflect the rise in the number of observers. The latter figure is also inflated by the inclusion of nine records from the period of February to April 1979 when unusually cold conditions forced exceptional numbers inland of several species which normally winter at sea.

The county bird reports contain three records of oiled birds, and two of sick birds which died after a few days. One found alive on a road near Faringdon in November 1967, which may have mistaken the road at night for a waterway, was given an assisted passage to the sea.

BLACK-THROATED DIVER
Gavia arctica

This rare winter visitor is the scarcest of the divers in Oxfordshire, with only six records this century. All are of single birds. One which

spent a week on the Thames at Port Meadow in February 1929 met the fate of many rarities in those days when it was shot by a local man who, as Tucker records in the OOS annual report, "unfortunately was not prosecuted". One found on the A40 road near Wheatley on 12 April 1956 was released on the River Cherwell at the Botanic Gardens where it remained until 23 June. Other records were at Bloxham, 23 January 1905; Blenheim, 6–9 December 1935; Stanton Harcourt Gravel Pit, 20 November 1975; and Farmoor Reservoir, 25-28 December 1976.

GREAT NORTHERN DIVER
Gavia immer

Although historically considered a rare winter visitor to Oxfordshire, recent records of overwintering suggest a gradual change in status to being a regular winter visitor in small numbers. Neighbouring inland counties have seen similar changes.

From the beginning of the century until 1984 the Great Northern Diver was unquestionably a rare winter visitor with only eight records of single birds (in 1937, 1944, 1955, 1957, 1962, 1966, 1970 and 1978). All were noted in mid-winter between 8 November and 9 February. Unlike other divers, they showed a tendency to stay for a while in the area. For example, one of the above birds stayed for 16 days and four for seven days.

From 1984 there were not only more records,

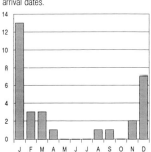

Figure 5.1. Red-throated Diver.
Monthly distribution of records based on arrival dates.

but some individuals remained for several weeks. In that year, two flew in to Farmoor Reservoir on 25 November. One of these stayed until 11 February 1985 when it was joined again by a second from 13–26 January. Then in 1988 Great Northern Divers took up winter residence once more when one was at Dorchester from 24 November until 11 December, and two stayed together at Farmoor Reservoir from 28 December until 16 April 1989. This behaviour was repeated a third time in the following winter when individuals were again at Farmoor Reservoir from 5 November 1989 until 15 January 1991, and at Dorchester Gravel Pit from 16 December 1989 until the end of March 1990. Plumage differences suggest that different birds were involved in these long visits.

The presence of large waters well stocked with fish presumably has encouraged this development. A succession of mild winters may also have contributed. One over-wintering first-year bird in 1990/91 showed its inexperience when most waters froze over in February 1991, since it was trapped in a small ice-free patch where it eventually died.

Family: Podicipedidae
Grebes

Like divers, grebes have benefited from the creation of extensive stretches of open water resulting from gravel extraction during the last 30 years. Unlike the divers though, two species of grebe breed in good numbers in Oxfordshire while the other three British species occur in winter with increasing frequency.

LITTLE GREBE
Tachybaptus ruficollis

The Little Grebe has remained a fairly numerous resident during the last hundred years though numbers have fluctuated. It nests most commonly along quieter stretches of the narrow, reedy tributaries of the Thames, with a few pairs on the Thames itself. Some breed on ornamental lakes in parks, and others on well-vegetated gravel pit waters.

The Oxfordshire Atlas map shows that the Little Grebe was found in 10.5% of tetrads, compared with the Great Crested Grebe which, requiring larger waters, was recorded in some 7% of tetrads. The BOS breeding survey in 1967 found that of 19 water bodies occupied by pairs of Little Grebes only three were large enough to accommodate Great Crested Grebes, whose minimum territory size was put at 1.8 ha. by B.W. Tucker (OOS Report 1933). After the breeding season and during the winter it also appears on open lakes, and more frequently on the Thames. At this time the population may be supplemented by wintering birds although there is no local proof apart from one ringing recovery. This concerns a bird ringed at Abberton (Essex) on 12 August 1982 which was recovered dead 156 km west at Standlake on 13 March 1983. Vinnicombe suggests that while some move in winter on to rivers and streams less susceptible to freezing, others may move to the south coast, or even to the Continent. The only local evidence of cold-weather movement is its appearance at such times on streams in the city of Oxford, where temperatures are higher.

The Little Grebe was especially numerous in the winters of the 1930s when 'rafts' of 30 to 40 birds were found frequently at Blenheim. In those days it also nested along the Thames, even at places like Port Meadow where there was a considerable amount of human activity. Fewer were seen after the severely cold winter of 1947, but by 1960 it seemed to have recovered its numbers for in January of that year winter flocks at Blenheim reached the best-ever total of 52. The prolonged cold weather of 1963, when virtually all waters were iced over continuously for three months, had a devastating effect. A photograph of a Little Grebe which had been frozen into the Oxford Canal was used to replace the Stone Curlew on the cover of the OOS annual report that year to reflect the way in which birds had suffered. This individual was fortunate, for after what was described as 'radiation therapy and diet treatment' at the Radcliffe Infirmary it was restored to health and released. Others were not so lucky, and fewer were to be seen in following years. A survey in the Banbury area in 1971 showed it to be virtually restricted to still waters, but by 1977 it was again breeding regularly on the rivers Cherwell and Evenlode with a minimum of five pairs between Somerton and Clifton (Easterbrook 1983). Since then winter 'rafts' have been noted occasionally, one of 22 at Dorchester in 1988 being the largest.

Maintenance of population levels must be assisted by its ability to continue nesting in fine

summers until late September as in Oxford in 1910, and at Cuttings in 1989.

Among the constraints on the Little Grebe are the clearance of waterside banks, and the progressive loss of ponds and other small water bodies. To some extent this has been balanced by the creation of many gravel pit lakes. The occupancy of these new places is on a lesser scale than might be expected, and competition from the thriving population of Great Crested Grebes for available cover could be a possible factor. Pollution may not pose such a problem locally – at least one pair has bred annually on a heavily polluted lake at Middleton Stoney where Mallard and Tufted Duck have failed to raise young. Few breed on the Thames today, for pressure from human activities seems to have increased to a degree which the secretive Little Grebe cannot accept. However, in 1990 the population was generally at a reasonably high level, and the immediate future of this adaptable little bird seems secure.

GREAT CRESTED GREBE
Podiceps cristatus

Radford (1966) described the dramatic improvement in the status of the Great Crested Grebe in the previous 160 years from that of a rare winter visitor to a locally common resident. This progress has continued, interrupted only by cold winters as in 1963. It is to be found now, both in winter and summer on most lakes and on the wider stretches of the River Thames.

The creation of many more potential nesting places, particularly at gravel pit lakes, provides opportunities which Great Crested Grebes accept readily. This can be illustrated by lists of sites at which breeding was recorded during BTO surveys. In 1931 only eight locations were named, mostly beside ornamental lakes in the grounds of large estates. The main centre of

population then was Blenheim Park (first colonised in 1908). In 1965 16 sites were recorded, and by 1975 the number had risen to 19. Breeding on the Thames is described below.

Overwintering has been encouraged by the presence of large areas of water which usually remain frost free, as at Farmoor Reservoir, Dix Pit at Stanton Harcourt, and Queenford Pit at Dorchester. The proportion of wintering birds which breed locally is unknown, but fluctuations in flock sizes suggest movements into and out of the county at this time.

The ending of human persecution in the early years of the twentieth century was the starting point for a population growth which continues today. The way in which numbers subsequently built up is demonstrated by breeding season counts organized by the BTO. Summarizing the findings for Oxfordshire, Campbell (1975) shows that there were 44–46 birds in 1931, 80–89 in 1965, and in 1975 a total of 138 birds, plus birds at Sonning Eye and Henley Road Gravel Pits. From the mid-1930s until the 1960s there were occasional breeding records from the River Thames. From the 1970s noticeably more bred there despite a substantial growth in river traffic. Most were in the wider stretches below Oxford, but at least four pairs inhabited the upper Thames.

By the 1980s the population appeared to have reached saturation point. Some pairs attempted to nest in places far from ideal. In 1990, for example, one pair built in an exposed position on the edge of an island totally devoid of vegetation in a gravel pit at Stanton Harcourt. Surprisingly they succeeded in rearing one young bird. In early spring there is intense competition for suitable sites. For example, at Wolvercote Gravel Pit in March 1991, seven pairs were displaying vigorously, and seeking nest sites on a lake which is only large enough to hold one pair. In summer, Farmoor Reservoir became a gathering place for non-breeding birds. Summaries of maximum counts per month there show the presence in some summers of considerable numbers (e.g. 1989 June maximum of 83) but fewer in others (e.g. 1987 June maximum of 11), which might reflect fluctuating population levels and breeding conditions from year to year. These birds spent most of their time resting in a close flock, with couples occasionally indulging in a little display.

Until the late 1960s most Great Crested Grebes left the area in the winter. Since then an increasing number have remained. This is shown by an analysis of local Wildfowl Count totals. The 63 counts made in the winters of 1971/72 to 1979/80 at all waters in the Oxford area between Dorchester, Stanton Harcourt and Blenheim produced an average count of 62 birds. The same number of counts in the winters of 1980/81 to 1988/90 produced an average of 103 birds. The main collection is usually at Farmoor Reservoir where Oxfordshire's highest single count of some 150 birds was made in January 1987.

Severe and prolonged cold in winter can still cause difficulties, and breeding success may be seriously affected by adverse weather conditions in spring. For example, after a cold, wet period from March to July 1987 a count made on major waters around Oxford on 21 July produced a total of 61 adults, but only 11 juveniles. However, such problems might often be compensated for by the length of the breeding season which extends from March until October. On one occasion a juvenile was still being fed by its parents in November.

Unless there is a reduction in available nesting sites the future of the Great Crested Grebe in Oxfordshire looks assured.

RED-NECKED GREBE
Podiceps grisegena

Formerly rare, the Red-necked Grebe (illustrated below left, Black-necked Grebe right) is now an occasional winter visitor to gravel pits and reservoirs in Oxfordshire. Although they have been noted in each month from September to April most appeared in the coldest months of January and February (Figure 5.2). Usually these were solitary birds, but up to four have appeared together on occasions.

There were three singles between 1915 and 1964, and seven between 1965 and 1978 (within the period 2 September to 5 April). Oxfordshire shared an exceptional influx into inland Britain following several days of strong easterly winds in the second half of February 1979. At least twelve different birds were scattered around the county at various sites, and singles appeared on several subsequent dates until 2 April.

In the 11 winters from 1979/80 to 1989/90 there were 14 sightings involving a total of 19 birds. On occasions some remained for several days: from 11–30 January 1987 there were between one and four at Farmoor Reservoir, and between 30 September and 28 October, one or two at Dorchester Gravel Pits. Possibly the presence of large areas of water at these sites encourages them to stay longer.

SLAVONIAN GREBE
Podiceps auritus

An occasional visitor making brief visits to gravel pits and reservoirs. It has been recorded in every month except May, June and July. The Slavonian Grebe was rarer in the nineteenth and first half of the twentieth century when there were few large expanses of water, and most were then reported on the River Thames. Nearly all records are of single birds, but there are two of individuals accompanying solitary Black-necked Grebes which allowed a helpful comparison for identification.

Of the three grebe species which are occasional visitors to the county the Slavonian Grebe is the most frequent, and has been noted increasingly since 1930. Between 1930 and 1959 there were just seven records involving eight birds. From 1960–1989 there were 50 records of 52 birds. Seven records in the early months of 1979 were exceptional. This was part of an influx into inland Britain following intensely cold conditions on the North Sea shores of Europe (Chandler 1981). As with several other species (see Red-necked Grebe), it was unusually numerous then.

The Slavonian Grebe is most likely to be found in November, and again in February and early March when birds are on passage to northern breeding grounds, probably in Iceland or Scandinavia (Figure 5.3)

BLACK-NECKED GREBE
Podiceps nigricollis

An occasional winter visitor and passage migrant. Most records are of solitary birds, but since 1981 there have been eight accounts of two or three together. They have been found at a random scatter of lakeland sites throughout the county.

Figure 5.4 shows that 57% of all records are in the period August to November. Some appear in December, January and February. Spring passage is noted from March to May, and has included individuals in attractive summer plumage. This passage is later than that of the Red-necked and Slavonian Grebes, presumably because of the later start to their breeding season (Pffor and Limbrunner 1981).

The Black-necked Grebe was considered very rare in the last century with only four Oxfordshire records (Aplin 1889). There was no improvement in the first half of the twentieth century. A single bird at Blenheim in November 1942 was the only sighting between 1900 and 1960. Since then there has been a steady increase

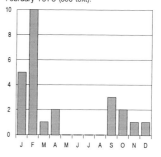

Figure 5.2. Red-necked Grebe.
Monthly distribution of records, based on dates of arrival, excluding January to February 1979 (see text).

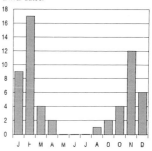

Figure 5.3. Slavonian Grebe.
Monthly distribution of records, based on arrival dates.

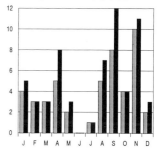

Figure 5.4. Black-necked Grebe.
Monthly distribution of records based on arrival dates, 1960-1989. Grey = number of records, black = number of birds.

Table 5.1. Black-necked Grebe.
Distribution of Oxfordshire records 1960-1989.

Period	No. of records	No. of birds
1960-69	8	9
1970-79	12	13
1980-89	27	38

N.B. Three instances when distinction between this and Slavonian Grebe were uncertain have not been included.

as shown by the summary of records for the next three decades (Table 5.1). Presumably the creation of several large waters during this period is an important factor.

The autumn of 1987 was exceptional with eight or nine records of some 13 birds between 15 September and 14 November. Some stayed several days. This may have been partly due to persistent easterly winds during the period. As though to illustrate the inconsistency of its occurrence, only one bird appeared in the following two years.

Family: Procellariidae
Petrels and Shearwaters

Of the five members of this family which occur with any regularity in British waters only two, the Fulmar and the Manx Shearwater have occurred as vagrants in Oxfordshire. Both species breed in large colonies around the British coast, but while the Manx Shearwater now occurs regularly in the county, the Fulmar is extremely rare here. Both are regarded as accidentals.

FULMAR
Fulmarus glacialis

A rare visitor. There were two early records in 1836 and 1839, then a long gap until one was seen on 8 June 1975 flying over Binsey. Other summer records since then are of single birds over Oxford on 18 June 1976, and over Farmoor Reservoir on 11 July 1981. The most unusual occurrence was of four individuals which reached different locations in mid-Oxfordshire after storms on 26 and 27 April 1981.

Although Fulmars have increased remarkably and now breed on almost all suitable cliffs around the coast of Britain, this is an entirely pelagic bird and its recent wandering inland must be accidental. Indeed, given the dramatic increase in the population during the twentieth century (Lloyd *et al.* 1991), it is perhaps surprising that more are not seen inland.

MANX SHEARWATER
Puffinus puffinus

Once rare, the Manx Shearwater is now an occasional autumn vagrant to Oxfordshire. The increase in reports may be partly due to improved observer cover but this seems unlikely to provide the whole answer. Recently Manx Shearwaters have appeared almost annually in the autumn (seven out of ten autumns in the 1980s). Most find it difficult to survive inland and are found dead or exhausted. Between 1920 and 1979 a total of eight were found dead or in a weak condition, all in the brief period 7–12 September. From 1980 to 1989 another 17 were found, all between 29 August and 11 October, although 13 were between 1 and 15 September. Two of these were found dead, and ten picked up exhausted and released on the coast. As might be expected, they have occurred at a wide scatter of sites.

The precise timing of these appearances might at first sight suggest something more than accidental, storm-driven wandering. The only hint of their origin comes from a ringing recovery mentioned in the OOS report for 1947 of an adult at Shrivenham on 7 September which had been ringed on Skokholm Island five days earlier. Two possible explanations of their occurrence have been proposed by local birdwatchers. First there could be a regular migratory movement over the centre of England at this time. This seems unlikely since one would expect more birds to be seen rather than merely the casualties and also this would not account for the increased frequency during the 1980s. Secondly, young birds leaving nests in the west of Britain may sometimes move off in the wrong direction. While it might seem difficult to understand how birds with such a highly developed sense of direction can apparently get lost, it is easy to believe that birds heading east along the south coast of Wales from the Welsh island colonies of Skomer and Skokholm might continue up the River Severn and keep going.

However, a third and rather simpler

explanation seems most plausable. This argues that the Manx Shearwaters which reach Oxfordshire are indeed recently fledged young from the Welsh islands, but that they have been blown eastwards through the Bristol Channel and River Severn in stormy weather rather than making an active decision to move eastwards. Certainly the timing of their appearances would strongly support any argument that these are recently fledged birds. It is unfortunate that none of the birds found here was aged.

Despite this debate, the main question concerning this species would seem to be why have they increased in occurrence so in the 1980s? The scatter of sites and nature of their discovery would suggest that it is not simply a reflection of increased observer coverage. An obvious suggestion is that the greater incidence in Oxfordshire reflects an increase in the population from which the birds come. However, although the Welsh colony populations may have increased during the last 30 years or so, the evidence is poor and any increase is likely to have been slight (Brooke 1990).

Family: Hydrobatidae
Storm Petrels

Both of the British breeding Storm Petrels have occurred as vagrants to Oxfordshire. Like the other tubenosed seabirds described above, these breed in large coastal colonies and are regarded as accidentals in the county. The little evidence that we have suggests that these originate on the west coast and wander or are storm-blown inland via the Bristol Channel. However, the relative abundance of the two species is surprising.

STORM PETREL
Hydrobates pelagicus

In the nineteenth and the first half of the twentieth century the Storm Petrel was described by Aplin (1889) as a "wanderer", by Jourdain (1925) as an "accidental visitor", and by Alexander (1947) as a "rare straggler". Alexander writes that it was "recorded nine times in the last sixty years in the months from October to January". Sometimes they were seen in small parties for Aplin reports groups of five (two of which were shot) and three, and Alexander one party of seven or eight birds.

The last record was after gales in December 1929 when several were driven inland and picked up in various parts of England, four of which were found in Oxfordshire. Since then, despite improved observer cover, there has not been a single record. It is difficult to explain the change, and the contrast with the increase in records of Leach's Petrel is striking.

LEACH'S PETREL
Oceanodroma leucorhoa

This is a rare visitor, usually driven inland by adverse weather conditions. Alexander (1947,

1952) cites six records prior to 1950 in the old Oxfordshire, and four or five in the old Berkshire (some of which may have been in the new Oxfordshire).

All recent occurrences have been in the autumn months from September to November, but interestingly, six instances mentioned by Aplin (1889) from the nineteenth century were in the winter from November to February.

In the second half of the twentieth century there were two major 'wrecks'. A series of gales in 1952 between 23 October and 7 November brought a total of nine, five of which were either dead or dying. Then on the morning of 3 September 1983 there were three separate records of individual birds, and two corpses found later in the month which probably relate to the same incident.

Other records, all of single birds, are from Henley Road Gravel Pit in November 1970, Dorchester in September 1977, Stanton Harcourt Gravel Pits in October 1981, Farmoor Reservoir in September 1988 and 1989. Also a petrel species, probably this, was noted at Farmoor in October 1986 and October 1989.

The increased incidence of this species in Oxfordshire contrasts strikingly with the Storm Petrel. This is yet more surprising given its more northerly distribution.

Family: Sulidae
Gannets

One species in this family breeds in Britain. Like the Tubenoses above, these form large breeding colonies of which the nearest is on the small island of Grassholm off the south coast of Wales. Those visiting Oxfordshire are generally storm-blown wanderers, probably blown inland through the Bristol Channel.

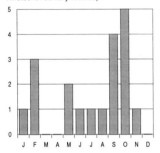

Figure 5.5. Gannet.
Monthly distribution of Oxfordshire records up to 1989 (excluding two undated nineteenth century records).

GANNET
Sula bassana

A rare visitor, usually at times of strong westerly winds. In the nineteenth century there were some six records of Gannets, but the first half of the twentieth century produced only one. Single birds were noted in 1952 and 1957, after which there was a gap of ten years until the period 1967–1972 when there were five records. Another absence followed until 1983–1988 when there were another seven records. There is no clear explanation for this uneven pattern. More than half of Oxfordshire's Gannets were found dead or in an exhausted state, but at least three were picked up, restored to health and transported to the coast. The only time they have appeared to be coping with life inland was on a stormy day in September 1970 when four adults spent about an hour plunge-diving for fish at Farmoor Reservoir shortly after trout had been introduced there. An indication that they might stray inland even in calm conditions was given in September 1985 when there were two accounts of juvenile Gannets (two and one) passing over in leisurely fashion at a time of clear skies and light winds. There have been no ring recoveries involving Oxfordshire. As one might expect, Oxfordshire records have occurred at a scattering of sites. Perhaps the strangest was one found asleep in Wytham Woods in 1970.

The months in which their autumn migration takes place produces the most sightings with 57% from August to November, but there are also winter and summer visits (Figure 5.5).

Family: Phalacrocoracidae
Cormorants and Shags

Both of the British breeding members of this family occur in Oxfordshire. However, while the Shag is a vagrant to the county, the Cormorant is now present throughout the year although they do not yet breed here. Like the Tubenoses, they most probably originate in the Welsh island colonies and wander inland via the Bristol Channel.

CORMORANT
Phalacrocorax carbo

A regular visitor from September until May, and also increasingly present during summer months with immatures remaining in the county. Nearly all sightings are from the main bases near roosts at Farmoor Reservoir, Stanton Harcourt Gravel Pits and Sonning Eye Gravel Pits, although they are being found with increasing frequency at other waters throughout the county.

Radford (1966) described it as "an occasional visitor" with small parties (maximum of six) seen from time to time, usually flying over, often after strong winds. By 1970 the creation of large stretches of water, well stocked with fish, enabled them to stay longer. In 1972, for example, there were 28 sightings spread through every month of the year except July. Numbers remained low with a maximum count of only five birds.

Regular wintering began when roosts were established in tall trees on islands at the Sonning Eye/Henley Road complex of gravel pits near Reading. Maximum counts here were 15 in 1978, 22 in 1979, 28 in 1982, 50 in 1983 and 82 in 1985. Meanwhile the Farmoor Reservoir flock gained strength, (Table 5.2) when two limnological inspection towers on the southern (Stage II) reservoir (completed in 1976) served as ideal roosting sites. With a ready supply of trout available in the immediate vicinity they were disinclined to move, and the attractions of this place became irresistible. By the winter of

1990–1991 counts in excess of 150 were regularly being made there.

Various devices were used to dissuade them from staying for not only were the fishermen concerned, but the steps on the towers became dangerously slippery as guano built up. The sequence of measures taken were as follows: lights and wire netting were fixed to the towers; recordings of alarm calls were played, villagers complained; a silhouette of a hawk was put on one of the towers; wire shields were fitted on the steps; electrified wires were fixed. None proved to be more than a temporary deterrent.

The pattern of frequency through the year at Farmoor Reservoir is shown in Figure 5.6.

Whilst there is a marked drop in numbers in the summer at Farmoor, increasing numbers of immature birds can be seen at the Stanton Harcourt Gravel Pits at this time each year. It would seem that the local population has yet to reach saturation point. Subsidiary roosts have been in use at Stanton Harcourt and Standlake Gravel Pits since 1987. The possibility of additional permanent roosting sites being found is suggested by the behaviour of parties of up to ten birds which spent much time perched in tall trees near the lake at Blenheim in 1990 and 1991.

When disturbed by boating activities at Farmoor and Sonning there is a local dispersal along the Thames valley. Sightings of colour-ringed individuals show that some of our Cormorants originate from the colony at St Margaret's Island, Tenby (Dyfed). There have

Table 5.2. Cormorant.
Maximum counts at Farmoor Reservoir, 1982-1990.

Year	Count
1982	47
1983	67
1984	78
1985	61
1986	89
1987	83
1988	101
1989	80
1990	167

Figure 5.6. Cormorant.
Monthly maximum counts at Farmoor Reservoir, 1989.

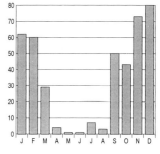

Figure 5.7. Shag.
Timing of visits, 1963-1989, based on
arrival dates.

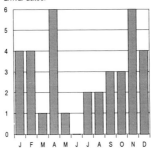

also been recoveries in Oxfordshire of birds ringed on Little Saltee, Ireland and on the Farnes, Northumberland. Some grey-headed birds have been noted in spring, and these could possibly be of Continental origin.

SHAG
Phalacrocorax aristotelis

The infrequent visits by Shags to Oxfordshire show little clear pattern in time, and although they are most likely to be seen in winter, they have occurred in every month except June (Figure 5.7). Nearly all records are of single birds.

Unlike Cormorants they seem unable to tolerate conditions inland. Often they have appeared in a sick or weakened condition after gales, and there are at least six accounts of Shags, usually immatures, lingering in the area before eventually dying. Another three were found dead on the A34 dual carriageway at Bagley Wood on 24 February 1988 and may have mistaken its shiny surface for a waterway on a wet night.

A quite exceptional occurrence was the eruptive movement in March 1962 which brought up to 35 to the Reading (Berkshire) area. Many of these stayed until late April, and two until July. As they spent much of their time on the River Thames they can be counted as Oxfordshire birds. The use of local gasometers for roosts may have been a key to their ability to remain here. Lack of cliff-like sites in our county where they can spend time drying their plumage may account for the difficulty they have here since the water-repellent qualities of their feathers is less than that of many other seabirds (Coulson 1961). Birds were also reported during this period from many places on the Thames such as Nuneham Railway Bridge (up to eight in April), Sutton Courtenay, Sandford and Oxford.

As with so many maritime species they have been noted more frequently during the last two decades. If the atypical events of 1962 are disregarded, there are 16 records prior to 1973, but 23 since then, with annual appearances apart from 1981, 1982, 1983 and 1987.

The only evidence of the origin of visiting Shags is of an immature found alive at Great Tew on 28 January 1984 which had been ringed on the Farne Islands in June the previous year (408 km), and another ringed as a nestling at Craigleith, North Berwick which was recovered at Benson the following October (506 km).

Family: Ardeidae
Herons

Of seven species which have occurred in Oxfordshire during the twentieth century, only the Grey Heron is common and breeds here. The others are all rare vagrants in varying numbers. Of the vagrants, most are of continental origin and occur during migration while the origin of the Bitterns which come here for the winter is unknown.

BITTERN
Botaurus stellaris

Single birds occur during most winters. The maximum number of records came from the winter of 1990/91 when ten sightings were reported. Oxfordshire possesses few extensive areas of the Bittern's favoured reedbed habitat. Typical sites in which wintering birds are found are the ditches and streams alongside the Thames where there is some cover, in the thickly vegetated stretch of the River Glyme at Blenheim near the cascade, beside pools in Wychwood Forest, and in the few existing reed-filled gravel pits as at Cassington.

Aplin (1889) believed the Bittern formerly bred "on Otmoor and in the low swampy country which at one time bordered the upper reaches of the Isis". He described it in the late nineteenth century as being reduced to the status of an occasional winter visitor. Jourdain (1925) hinted at signs of an increase describing the Bittern as, "not an uncommon visitor which should be rigidly protected now that it is re-establishing itself." He gave no local evidence to support this statement, and Radford (1966) could only find seven records of singles between 1900 and 1960, plus one of a pair in April and May 1907.

Recent years have seen an undoubted improvement. They were present in 16 of the 25 years from 1964–1989 with a total of 35 sightings. Nearly all were in the winter months of December, January and February. The exceptions were single records from the Cassington/Thames area on 30 October 1966 and 11 March 1991, and a surprising sighting of one there on 13 August 1970.

Sequences of records from successive years give the impression that individuals may return to the same site for several winters although this has not been proved. For example at Blenheim (seven winters including three successive years from 1981-1983); River Thames between Farmoor and King's Lock, or in the adjacent Cassington Gravel Pit (six winters between 1982 and 1991); River Thames between Cholsey and Goring (in five winters between 1976 and 1985); Wychwood Forest (in winters 1977/78, 1978/79, 1979/80).

Survival in this part of Britain in cold winters is not without hazard: three Bitterns were picked up dead (causes unknown) in the 1980s. There have been no ringing recoveries involving Oxfordshire.

LITTLE BITTERN
Ixobrychus minutus

A very rare visitor with four records in the nineteenth century and only two records during this century. One was picked up at Somerton in June 1909, and one was seen near the River Windrush at Beard Mill in May 1928.

NIGHT HERON
Nycticorax nycticorax

A very rare visitor with a total of four records. Singles at Burford in May 1891 (shot), Deddington, September 1934, Benson Weir, 22 May 1972, and Cassington Gravel Pit, 6- 29 July 1976.

SQUACCO HERON
Ardeola ralloides

A very rare visitor with just one record of a bird which stayed at Vicarage Pit, Stanton Harcourt 17-22 August 1975. It spent most of its time in the bushes on the island.

LITTLE EGRET
Egretta garzetta

A very rare vagrant with just one record. One seen briefly on Port Meadow at mid-day on 18 May 1988. There has been an increase in

Table 5.3. Grey Heron.
Monthly and geographical distribution of recoveries up to 1988 of birds ringed in Oxfordshire.

Month recovered Oxfordshire
J	F	M	A	M	J	J	A	S	O	N	D
6	6	5	4	7	0	1	1	0	7	5	10

Other 1 Total 53

Month recovered southern England
J	F	M	A	M	J	J	A	S	O	N	D
4	4	3	1	2	3	6	4	4	5	6	15

Other 2 Total 59

Month recovered northern England
J	F	M	A	M	J	J	A	S	O	N	D
0	0	1	1	0	0	0	0	0	0	0	1

Total 3

Month recovered Wales
J	F	M	A	M	J	J	A	S	O	N	D
0	0	0	1	3	0	0	0	1	0	3	0

Total 8

Month recovered Ireland
J	F	M	A	M	J	J	A	S	O	N	D
1	0	0	0	0	0	0	0	1	0	0	0

Total 2

Month recovered France
J	F	M	A	M	J	J	A	S	O	N	D
0	0	0	0	0	0	0	0	0	0	1	1

Total 2

Month recovered Spain
J	F	M	A	M	J	J	A	S	O	N	D
0	0	0	0	0	0	0	0	0	1	0	0

Total 1

Table 5.4. Grey Heron.
The distribution by distance of ringing recoveries involving Oxfordshire up to 1988.

| | Distance in km | | |
	0–9	10–99	100+
Number ringed in Oxfordshire	19	71	35
Number ringed elsewhere	19	41	20
Main period of recovery	May & Dec	Dec	Nov/Dec

sightings of this species in Britain in recent years and it is likely that more will occur in Oxfordshire if that trend continues.

GREY HERON
Ardea cinerea

A locally common resident inhabiting a variety of watery places from small ditches to large reservoirs throughout the Oxfordshire lowlands.

Although most frequently found near heronries in the breeding season, they sometimes travel several miles in foraging flights, and immature non-breeders may occur further afield at any time. In winter they wander considerably further.

Our understanding of their movements in Oxfordshire is based on a considerable amount of nestling ringing which was carried out from the 1930s to the 1960s. Table 5.3 shows that a total of 128 Oxfordshire-ringed birds were recovered, of which 53 (41%) were in Oxfordshire, and 59 (46%) in southern England. Table 5.4 shows the distribution of these recoveries by distance. Radford (1966) points out that the distribution of juvenile recoveries suggested a westward dispersal. Two birds which were ringed at Wytham were later found in the Deux-Sevres and Manche districts of France in January. A third of all recoveries were made in November and December. Since most recoveries are of birds found dead, this suggests that most mortality occurs at this time. Nevertheless, numbers in Oxfordshire appear to be stable through the winter, so the remaining local population is presumably supplemented by immigrants.

The breeding population can be assessed accurately because annual counts of all heronries have been made continuously since 1964 for the BTO (Table 5.5). Few are missed as all nests are in conspicuous tree top sites, and the

majority live at known colonies. There are few other species whose population changes can be monitored with such confidence. In earlier years the Torrington Diaries (1784) cited by Pickles (1960) described a heronry in Blenheim Park "where great numbers of herons are yearly bred". This has long since vanished.

In the nineteenth century and the first half of the twentieth century several other heronries disappeared. One at Tar Wood, Stanton Harcourt had about 26 nests from 1757–1887. The Otmoor heronry went extinct in about 1925. More recent losses were the North Aston heronry which existed from 1928–1963, and the one in Wytham Wood which had contained between six and 28 nests and had ten nests when it was abandoned in 1963 (Gosler 1990). Known causes for desertion of these various heronries include shooting and forestry work in the vicinity during the nesting season.

Three main heronries have contained most of the local breeding population in the upper Thames valley and central Oxfordshire in the second half of this century. The heronry at Buscot Park has survived at approximately the same level (16–28 nests) with the exception of 1965 when there were only five. About two miles away as the Heron flies another colony has existed intermittently at Buckland which at its peak contained 11 nests. This may function as an overflow site when Buscot numbers are at their peak. At Great Tew there have usually been 16–27 although in three years there were fewer than ten. The largest local heronry is near Nuneham Park. This is subject to the greatest fluctuations from year to year with counts ranging from 12–46. The sale of the wood in which this heronry is sited was considered in 1991, and its future is uncertain. In most years a few herons nest away from the main groups in solitary sites along Thames' tributaries or near small lakes. Sometimes these show signs of developing into small heronries. Examples were at Middle Aston (five nests in 1977), and Chislehampton (three in 1965). However, all have been short-lived.

In the south-east of the county herons have nested in some years in trees on islands at gravel pits north of Reading, but regular counts were not made. There were more than 20 nests at the Henley Road Gravel Pit in 1981, but numbers are generally much lower than this.

Extreme population fluctuations are clearly connected with weather conditions during the winter and in the breeding season. The three months of continuous frost at the beginning of 1963 caused starvation, and many emaciated birds and corpses were found. Cold periods during breeding seasons, and nest damage caused by high winds have been limiting factors, and may have caused the decline in the 1980s, which, it is to be hoped, is temporary. Also, it may be no coincidence that the long, hot summer of 1976 which provided many shallow pools for easy fishing, preceded the Grey Heron's most successful years locally.

While the drainage of wet meadows and the

general tidying up of the countryside have caused problems, the species has benefited from the creation of gravel pits and reservoirs. In a rapidly changing environment the Grey Heron has shown itself to be an opportunist. It has explored new possibilities presented by trout farms, and made early morning raids on small garden ponds in built-up areas. At Farmoor Reservoir in the early months of 1991 up to four Grey Herons repeatedly descended to steal fish from Cormorants as they surfaced, even though this sometimes involved swimming.

Most importantly its survival as a common breeding bird in the county would seem to hinge upon its continued occupancy of the three major heronries. The threat to the future of at least one of these is now a cause for concern. However, old sites have been re-occupied in recent years. For example at Rycote where six pairs bred in 1989 for the first time in 20 years and a new site was occupied at Grimsbury in 1990. Grey Heron numbers will continue to be monitored comprehensively.

PURPLE HERON
Ardea purpurea

This very rare vagrant was recorded twice in the nineteenth century and seven times in the first 90 years of the twentieth century.

One was shot at Aynho in May 1928 as it left the Cherwell Valley. In the long, cold winter of 1963 one joined a party of Grey Herons at Appleford Gravel Pit from 17–20 February. An adult at Wroxton from 22 May to 1 June 1971 was among several which wandered into Britain in the early 1970s.

Other records in the 1970s were of an immature in the Cherwell Valley in August 1976, a sub-adult at Marston on 14 May 1979, and one at Bicester on 5 July 1979. The last sighting was of one over the 'scrape' at Stanton Harcourt Gravel Pit on 22 August 1981.

Table 5.5. Grey Heron.
Total nest counts at the three major heronries (Buscot, Great Tew and Nuneham) in Oxfordshire from 1964-1989.

Year	Nests
1964	56
1965	39
1966	61
1967	79
1968	67
1969	70
1970	74
1971	69
1972	73
1973	96
1974	80
1975	58
1976	72
1977	74
1978	89
1979	99
1980	86
1981	87
1982	88
1983	77
1984	85
1985	68
1986	54
1987	53
1988	58
1989	55

Family: Ciconiidae
Storks

One Stork species occurs in Oxfordshire as a vagrant from the European mainland. Although rare today, the White Stork probably bred in the county in medieval and earlier times, perhaps nesting on the tops of houses as they have done for centuries in Europe.

WHITE STORK
Ciconia ciconia

There was one nineteenth century record, and there have been at least six twentieth century records of this rare vagrant although some of the sightings are believed to be birds which had escaped from captivity. One was at Port Meadow in October 1916, two at Otmoor in May 1917 and one there in May 1928. One at Asthall on 5 August 1939 (a month before the outbreak of the Second World War), was assumed to be one of the birds brought from Germany and released in Kent earlier that year. Recent records are of singles on a ploughed field at Wheatley on 26 June 1986, and near Pigeon Lock on 18 August 1988. A much earlier record dated as medieval is of a bone found during archaeological excavations at Church Street, Oxford (Wilson 1987).

Family: Threskiornithidae
Ibises and Spoonbills

Two members of this family have been recorded in Oxfordshire. Both are vagrants from Europe. However, it is possible that, as with the White Stork, the Spoonbill might once have been a regular visitor to the valley of the upper Thames since it bred in Britain until about 1650.

GLOSSY IBIS
Plegadis falcinellus

The Glossy Ibis is a summer visitor to south-east Europe where it breeds in declining numbers. It is a rare vagrant to Britain. In the past it was a rather commoner visitor but there have been few since about 1960.

The only record of this very rare visitor is of a young female shot at Sonning Eye on 11 May 1916, after being present for several days. It is now in Reading Museum.

SPOONBILL
Platalea leucorodia

There are two records of this very rare vagrant. One was flushed from the floodwater near Taynton on 15 March 1964, flew downstream towards Burford, then returned and made off up the Windrush valley into Gloucestershire. One dropped in briefly to Stanton Harcourt Gravel Pits on 5 April 1987. After about 15 minutes it headed off steadily to the north-east.

Family: Anatidae
Ducks, Geese and Swans

Of the 38 wildfowl species which have been recorded in Oxfordshire during the twentieth century, only six breed here with any regularity. This reflects the nature of wetland in our county. Wildfowl populations in Oxfordshire must have suffered considerably during earlier centuries due to the draining of wetlands such as Otmoor and the Lower Windrush area. However wintering wildfowl numbers have undoubtedly benefited from the new reservoirs and gravel pit complexes in the county, particularly in the Stanton Harcourt and Dorchester areas. Several species which were scarce, are now regular winter visitors.

Table 5.6. Mute Swan.
The distribution by month and distance of recoveries up to 1988 of birds ringed in Oxfordshire.

Month	Distance in km		
	0–9	10–99	100+
January	71	93	2
February	63	97	5
March	78	95	6
April	76	98	1
May	47	86	2
June	60	50	4
July	50	50	9
August	60	40	8
September	84	54	0
October	114	87	6
November	89	82	8
December	65	86	6
Other	11	14	0
Total	868	932	57

MUTE SWAN
Cygnus olor

The Mute Swan is a numerous but locally distributed resident in Oxfordshire. The majority of breeding pairs inhabit rivers and streams, although an increasing proportion inhabit gravel pits. The species has had a long history of breeding in Oxfordshire, although formerly as a semi-domesticated bird. Swans were known to be breeding in 1361 when the first 'Swan-Herd' for Oxfordshire was appointed to oversee the capture and marking of owned swans (Ticehurst 1957). It is also possible that a proportion of the population was truly wild, having originated from migrant eastern European swans (Aplin 1889). Since the demise of swan ownership, the Mute Swan has bred freely in Oxfordshire for the past two or three centuries.

The first comprehensive Mute Swan census, in 1955–56, organised by the BTO, recorded a total of 387–404 swans in Oxfordshire including 84–91 nesting pairs (Campbell 1960). In the

following years the population increased considerably to an estimated 529 in 1961 (Eltringham 1963) and 550 in 1978 (Ogilvie 1981). It seems likely that this expansion was largely due to the creation of large areas of new habitat resulting from gravel extraction.

In recent years the population has fared less well, with a 27% decline down to 403 swans recorded in the 1983 census (Ogilvie 1986). A decrease in numbers of breeding and territorial swans on the upper Thames from 23 pairs in 1976 down to 11 in 1985 was particularly notable (Sears 1986). Increased boating activity may have caused significant habitat deterioration on the Thames (Bacon 1980). Lead poisoning due to the ingestion of anglers' lead weights was also partly responsible for the decline. Between 1979 and 1985 lead poisoning accounted for 44% of the known mortality of swans on the Thames in Oxford (Sears 1986). It was largely responsible for the demise of the herd of immature swans between Folly Bridge and Iffley which numbered 132 in 1955 and had dropped below ten in 1985. Since 1987, when legislation prohibiting the use of anglers' lead weights was introduced, there has been a rapid reduction in the incidence of lead poisoning. Numbers of breeding and non-breeding swans in Oxfordshire are now increasing at an average rate of 10% per annum (Sears 1989).

Fears over potential crop damage as a result of the expanding Mute Swan population in the 1960s prompted an intensive ringing study to be initiated by the Edward Grey Institute at Oxford University. By the late 1960s over 90% of the Oxfordshire breeding population was ringed (Perrins and Reynolds 1967). Detailed monitoring of the breeding success of a section of Oxfordshire's Mute Swan population has continued from 1964 to the present.

The highest breeding densities occur on the urban waterways in Oxford, Abingdon and Henley. Increased food supplies in the form of bread appear to raise the breeding success of urban swans (Scott and Birkhead 1983). Some pairs are extremely tolerant of human disturbance. For many consecutive years a pair bred on the canal in Oxford, building their nest in the middle of a very busy towpath. The increase in gravel extraction in the county has been important for the Mute Swan. In 1956, 8% of the 91 nests were on gravel pits, whereas in 1983 the figure had risen to 17% of the 58 nests (Sears 1986). Whilst these habitats provide relatively safe and undisturbed nest sites they do not appear to be very suitable for rearing young. In 1982-85 over 50% of the pairs nesting on gravel pits in the Windrush and Thame valleys moved their families onto adjacent streams within a few weeks of hatching (Sears 1986).

Movements are relatively limited particularly amongst breeding swans. Most territorial pairs in Oxfordshire remain on site for at least half the winter and only leave during cold weather when food becomes limiting. In general they then move less than 3 km from their territories (Scott 1984). The majority of cygnets raised on Oxfordshire rivers remain within the watershed for the rest of their lives, often moving between herds but rarely more than 50 km from their natal territory (Table 5.6). Winter herds of 30-90 swans have traditionally congregated on the meadows adjacent to the Thames between Lechlade and Shifford and between Eynsham and Port Meadow. Further herds are to be found on the Thames in Oxford, Abingdon and Henley, and herds of 60-100 birds have, in recent years, become a feature of the larger gravel pit lakes at Dorchester and Stanton Harcourt.

The fortunes of the Oxfordshire Mute Swan population have been closely linked to mans' activities. Local fluctuations in numbers have occurred as a result of both habitat creation and destruction and through lead poisoning. Recent measures to reduce lead poisoning appear to be successful and the population is increasing rapidly. If the present rate of growth continues there will be renewed fears concerning damage to winter crops. However it is possible that shortage of suitable territories may limit the rate of expansion.

BEWICK'S SWAN
Cygnus columbianus

This is an infrequent winter visitor. The period of records extends from 23 October to 19 April.

Flocks are generally larger than those of Whooper Swans, with several sightings of parties of between 20 and 43.

Formerly regarded as a rare winter visitor, with only eight records for Oxfordshire (pre-1974 boundaries) before 1945, a few are now seen in every winter. Most frequently parties are observed passing over, and when they do come down their visits are usually brief.

So many of the sightings in autumn are of birds moving to the west and north-west that it seems likely that at least some of these are making their way to the wintering grounds at Slimbridge where a build up of population has been encouraged by the Wildfowl Trust in the second half of the twentieth century. For example, on the morning of 20 December 1986 a party of 12 touched down at Otmoor. A similar sized group, presumably the same, was at Port Meadow at mid-day, and later in the afternoon they were seen again flying steadily west over Sutton. Several spring records also coincide with times when Bewick's Swans leave Slimbridge.

Occasionally in the first months of the year groups stay for a while feeding in flooded meadows beside the Thames or Cherwell. In the upper Cherwell valley in the vicinity of Somerton there were five in February and March 1937, 16 from December 1938 to February 1939, 11 in February and March 1972, and three in January and February 1977. A flock of up to 32 remained in the Thames meadows near Bampton from 31 January to 13 February 1982, and up to eight further downstream at Cassington from 3 January to 27 February 1987.

Although the BOS (Easterbrook 1983) commented on a general decline in north Oxfordshire in the 1970s, there is no evidence for a significant change elsewhere in the county.

WHOOPER SWAN
Cygnus cygnus

This is generally an infrequent winter visitor, although some family parties have over-wintered in damp water meadows in the county. Casual visitors drift through in most winters. Most fly over, and when they do settle visits are usually brief. Records extend from 7 October to 25 March, with most appearing in mid-winter months (Figure 5.8). The size of flocks passing

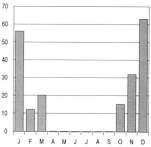

Figure 5.8. Whooper Swan.
Total numbers of Whooper Swans seen in the period 1962-1988, excluding wintering flocks (see text).

through has usually not exceeded six birds, but there were two larger parties of 24 and 12, both in December.

Earlier writers found this a rare winter visitor. Aplin (1889) called it *Cygnus musicus*, or the Whistling Swan. He described in graphic detail how at Weston-on-the-Green "in the severe winter of 1837-8 on the morning of the 6th February a flock of fifteen made a descent on the kitchen garden of these premises, evidently with the intention of attacking a bed of cabbages, from which the snow had been thawed. They did not however settle, but continued to wheel round the spot for some minutes, until a shot was fired which severely wounded one of them.".

As our county is at the southern limit of this species' wintering range, visits continued to be infrequent and the cause for much comment during the first half of the twentieth century; Radford (1966) found only about ten records for the period 1871–1945. Since then there has been a definite increase which cannot entirely have resulted from improved observer coverage. They were seen in every winter in the 1980s.

Another new and welcome development has been the over-wintering of family parties in the 1970s and 1980s. The meadows of the upper Cherwell valley in the Somerton area which are subject to extensive flooding in most winters was the main centre with herds present regularly every year from 1969–1989. At first, single families made visits, but by 1980/81 there were assumed to be four separate families present with a total of 17 mixed adults and juveniles present. They normally arrived in mid-December and stayed until February, although in some years they remained until March. There was a further extension of this behaviour when, in the winters between 1983/4 and 1987/8, single herds took up residence in the damp Thames valley meadows below Cassington. As the neighbouring county of Buckinghamshire also had Whooper Swan families staying at this time it seems that there has been a general southerly extension of the species' wintering range.

In the winters of 1989/90 and 1990/91 for the first time for 20 years no family parties were seen. Future observations will show whether this was a temporary change, possibly connected with the exceptionally mild winters, or the first indication of a permanent withdrawal.

BEAN GOOSE
Anser fabilis

A very rare winter visitor, records of Bean Geese in Oxfordshire during the twentieth century number fewer than ten. Aplin (1889) gives only one record; a bird shot near Henley on 24 January 1850. However, he did note that specimens were occasionally seen in the Oxford Market, and Clark-Kennedy (1868) and Stubbs (1903) considered the Bean Goose to be one of the commonest visitors to Berkshire. Radford (1966) adds four records, three shot near

Adderbury in December 1890, and singles on Port Meadow January 1928, on floods at Somerton in February 1937 and again on Port Meadow in March 1951.

There are five more recent records of Bean Geese in Oxfordshire, three of which were of solitary birds associating with flocks of Canada Geese. These were at Stanton Harcourt Gravel Pits, 25 February 1979, on the River Thames at Northmoor in December 1980 and at Farmoor on 17 April 1983. There was also a record of three birds at Warborough on 4 November 1989. The status and origin of the geese in these recent records is open to debate, but there seems little doubt that the party of 13 which appeared on meadows near Little Wittenham on 24 December 1987 and stayed until the end of the year were wild birds. A flock of identical size which flew over Farmoor Reservoir on 2 January 1988 were presumably the same birds.

PINK-FOOTED GOOSE
Anser brachyrhynchus

Whilst Aplin (1889) gives no records of Pink-footed Goose for Oxfordshire, Alexander (1947) gives eight from the preceding 60 years. Radford (1966) adds a further two records, one at Sonning Eye Gravel Pit in January and February 1956 and one (shot) near Somerton in October 1958. The largest number recorded stands at 60 which flew over Lower Whitley Farm near Farmoor on 16 January 1928.

More recent records include three flying westwards over Ascott-under-Wychwood on 1 January 1971, 19 westwards over the River Thames at Rushey, 4 February 1979 and 29 were present at the Stanton Harcourt Gravel Pit complex on 26 December 1981. Then on 22 January 1985, four were seen at Day's Lock and two were on Port Meadow on 14 December.

Solitary birds occasionally appear, especially on the Stanton Harcourt Gravel Pit complex, where one remained throughout 1981. Another spent the autumn of 1985 consorting with Canada Geese at Blenheim. However neither of these records of Pink-footed Geese are believed to be wild birds.

WHITE-FRONTED GOOSE
Anser albifrons

The White-fronted Goose, although still a frequent visitor during the winter months, is probably less commonly encountered than in the first half of the twentieth century. Indeed, Radford (1966) described it as a not uncommon winter visitor to the water meadows of the Thames and Cherwell, and to Otmoor, and during hard weather, skeins were regularly recorded flying over Oxfordshire, sometimes involving quite large numbers. In most years until the mid-1960s, skeins sometimes of 100–200 birds were recorded. There appears to have been a westerly or south-westerly passage in the first half of the winter period and also hard weather movements in the same direction. Presumably these geese would have moved through the Severn Estuary and Slimbridge. Some return passage was also noted in late winter.

Large parties passing over the county have now become a much less common sight, as too have wintering birds. However there have been some sizeable skeins passing over, with 300 over Tadmarton on 8 March 1978 being exceptional. Among the larger parties recorded in the 1980s were 80-90 flying eastwards over Bampton, 1 March 1983; 150 at Tadpole Bridge on 10 March 1984; between 21 and 29 on Port Meadow during January 1986; 43 heading south-west over Stanton Harcourt, 10 January 1987; and 25 on Port Meadow, 9 January 1988. In addition, small groups of up to 12 birds and solitary birds occur each winter and may remain for a while if feeding conditions are appropriate, as in the early months of 1982 and 1986.

In addition, one or two feral birds are to be found throughout the year with the Canada Goose flocks.

GREYLAG GOOSE
Anser anser

The only native breeding goose in Britain, most of the domestic breeds common here are descended from it. Despite this Aplin (1889) considered the Greylag Goose to be a very rare winter visitor to Oxfordshire and Radford (1966) gives records in only five years in the period 1933-1961. It is probable that the 1961 records refer to feral birds, possibly from Stratfield Saye in Berkshire or from Linford in north Buckinghamshire.

Since 1965, Greylag Geese have been recorded annually, with greater frequency and in increasing numbers. Breeding was first recorded at Farmoor in 1980, and a year later, ten goslings were raised at the Stanton Harcourt Gravel Pits. Breeding has occurred in every year since then, mainly centred along the River Thames from Standlake to King's Lock and between Henley and Reading.

Greylags are very sedentary in Oxfordshire, the longest movement being two which were ringed at Croughton and recovered 57 km away in Northamptonshire.

The largest flock so far recorded is 230 near Farmoor on 14 October 1984. In winters from 1985-1990, a flock of 100-150 birds has been present here, although some show features of the domestic goose. Solitary geese can appear anywhere in the county typically in the company of Canada Geese with which they have recently begun to hybridize. Occasional pairs occur in other parts of the county such as the upper Windrush valley. The presence of these resident, feral flocks makes it difficult to recognise any wild bird which might occasionally occur.

MTE 90·6

CANADA GOOSE
Branta canadensis

The Canada Goose, is a numerous, locally distributed resident in the county whose population has undergone a dramatic increase since the 1970s.

The species has been kept as a semi-domestic bird in Britain since the eighteenth century. The only known collection in Oxfordshire was at Buscot Park which was certainly present before the 1950s and during the considerable increases elsewhere, the flock of about 20-30 birds here appears to have remained sedentary and unchanged. In the rest of the county until the middle of the twentieth century, small family parties and single birds made occasional appearances, but the first breeding record, other than at Buscot, was not until 1961 when a pair nested at Sonning Eye Gravel Pits. Then in 1965 two pairs bred near Henley. This southern entry into Oxfordshire presumably represents an extension of the feral populations of Berkshire that originated from such parks as Stratfield Saye and subsequently the Kennet Valley Gravel Pits.

The OOS report of 1968 records "An increasing number of records in the north of the two counties (Oxfordshire and Berkshire) suggests a gradual spread into these areas". A party of 25-35 flying in the Blenheim area was worthy of note for 1969 as was the maximum count of 45 at Dorchester Gravel Pits between September and December 1970. On 8 November of that same year, 168 were counted at the Henley Road Gravel Pit.

The spread of the Canada Goose as a breeding bird is well illustrated in Figure 5.9, and as the Oxfordshire Atlas map shows, breeding has now been confirmed in 34 10 km squares. With only the Carrion Crow as a serious predator of their eggs, Canada Geese produce five or six goslings annually with great success. The growth

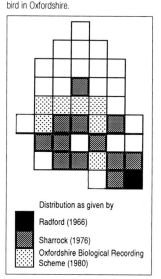

Figure 5.9. Canada Goose.
Spread of the Canada Goose as a breeding bird in Oxfordshire.

Distribution as given by

Radford (1966)

Sharrock (1976)

Oxfordshire Biological Recording Scheme (1980)

Table 5.7. Canada Goose.
Maximum counts of the autumn flock at Dorchester Gravel Pits.

Year	No. of birds
1970	45
1973	150
1974	300
1975	500
1976	550

Table 5.8. Canada Goose.
Winter count statistics, 1970-1989.

Winter Period	Mean	Max	Min
1970/71	25	58	1
1972/73	79	141	13
1974/75	113	221	67
1976/77	156	376	0
1978/79	272	562	5
1980/81	599	941	151
1982/83	708	1234	196
1984/85	467	865	97
1986/87	806	2055	140
1988/89	668	1705	215

Table 5.9. Canada Goose.
Monthly winter count statistics, 1970-1989.

Month	Mean	Max	Min
September	695	1407	3
October	661	2055	2
November	548	1186	0
December	373	1097	43
January	369	1253	1
February	225	547	7
March	188	333	6

Table 5.10. Brent Goose.
Annual number of records, 1980-1989.

Year	No. of records	No. of birds
1980	1	5
1981	0	0
1982	3	3
1983	4	5
1984	0	0
1985	0	0
1986	2	4
1987	3	10
1988	2	2
1989	3	3

of the autumn flock at Dorchester Gravel Pit (Table 5.7) illustrates this expansion.

Figures from the winter Wildfowl Counts also show the population growth on the waters of mid-Oxfordshire (Table 5.8). Individual winter flocks can be immense and on 6 November 1978, 1,400 were counted at Henley Road Gravel Pit, and estimates of 1,000-1,500 birds were on Port Meadow during November 1986.

At Farmoor Reservoir Canada Geese sometimes consort with the feral Greylag flock and in 1990 and 1991 one or two individual with characteristics of both species have been seen.

There is considerable movement within Oxfordshire of Canada Geese. For example, in some years Blenheim has a peak of up to 500 in late August through to early November when the majority then depart to the Stanton Harcourt Gravel Pit complex. Whilst it is not known whether there is any significant movement in and out of the county there is an apparent decline in the population on the main waters during the course of the winter (Table 5.9). However this may result either from winter mortalities or from birds becoming more widely distributed, and especially on to flood waters. There are no recoveries of Canada Geese ringed within the county but 35 recoveries here of birds ringed elsewhere. Of these, 33 are from southern England and two from northern England. Also, seven had made movements of less than 9 km and 23 had moved a distance of 10-99 km.

The breeding population must now be reaching its carrying capacity since pairs now occupy most small lakes and pools and occur along many stretches of river. Indeed, numbers have grown so much that they are damaging crops growing in fields close to lakes and rivers. On one particular stretch of the upper Thames the flock has become a considerable nuisance because they peck off the buds and flowers of Snakeshead Fritillaries that grow on an adjacent meadow which is a SSSI.

BARNACLE GOOSE
Branta leucopsis

Prior to 1972, the only record of Barnacle Goose in Oxfordshire is given by Aplin (1889) who mentions "one near Henley some years ago". In 1972 a bird was seen at Farmoor from 13-30 April and since then the species has been recorded in every year. However, most of these records are presumed to refer either to escapes or feral birds which frequently consort with Canada Geese.

There are four records considered to be of wild birds. Six were present in the Cherwell valley from 28 January until 28 February 1977, and in the same year two adults and an immature bird were seen at Letcombe Regis on 6 March. During 1979 a party of eight birds was present

on Port Meadow from 14-20 March and a party of ten birds was on the meadows at Farmoor from 21-25 February 1981.

There is currently no record of feral Barnacle Geese breeding in Oxfordshire but they are present throughout the year. Usually only one or two are present at any one site, normally gravel pits and lakes, and typically in the company of Canada Geese.

BRENT GOOSE
Branta bernicla

A rare winter visitor to the county, Aplin (1889) gives a single record of a bird shot at Standlake in January 1888. Radford (1966) gives a total of seven records of single birds between 1891 and 1937 but there are no further records until 1979. This interval coincides with a general decline of the Brent Goose. However the resurgence and spread of wintering Brent Geese nationally is reflected in the number of recent observations. These are usually of flocks of fewer than ten birds, but there was one exceptional record of 80-90 on Otmoor on 18 January 1979. There is a wide scatter of records, with many observations of birds in flight. The number of records and the number of birds in the 1980s is shown in Table 5.10.

EGYPTIAN GOOSE
Alopochen aegyptiacus

The Egyptian Goose is a feral but rare resident with individuals or pairs occurring at any time of the year, but most frequently in the period from February to May. Birds may remain for a few days up to several months. There are usually three or four reports each year and most records come from Port Meadow. In some years these were believed to be escapes from the collection at Worcester College, Oxford.

Breeding has occurred on the River Thames below Goring, albeit sporadically, since 1978. These breeding birds are almost certainly from the collections of the Child Beale Trust in Berkshire.

RUDDY SHELDUCK
Tadorna ferruginea

In Britain, the Ruddy Shelduck is a very rare vagrant and rare feral species although there is considerable difficulty in assessing to which category the Oxfordshire records belong. A bird shot on Port Meadow during March 1885 was believed to be a wild bird and, more recently, one which remained in the Cherwell valley at Somerton from 16-20 August 1968 was accepted by the rarities committee of British Birds. Since 1960, birds, mostly singles, have been recorded in ten years and from ten sites in the county. Some have occurred at migration times, and have passed quickly through the county, but others have remained for long periods. A pair bred at an Oxfordshire gravel pit in 1983.

SHELDUCK
Tadorna tadorna

The Shelduck occurs as a frequent winter visitor and also, to a lesser extent, a passage migrant in Oxfordshire. This contrasts with earlier times as Radford (1966) gives only 30 records of the Shelduck in Oxfordshire and Berkshire between 1885 and 1947. The majority were from Port Meadow. The increase in records reflects an increase in the national breeding population during the twentieth century. This is partly a recovery due to legislative protection since the species declined because of persecution and habitat loss. However, it also reflects range expansion inland since they have bred in a number of inland counties including Berkshire (Marchant *et al.* 1990, Sharrock 1976). Shelduck are mostly recorded from reservoirs and gravel pits, but they also occur on flood meadows, including Port Meadow in most winters.

An indication of the frequency of occurrence is given in Figure 5.10, and is very much a reflection of the entire period 1966-1989. There are indications of a spring passage from late March through April.

During the 1980s Shelduck were recorded in every month. Usually one to four birds were seen, but a party of 34 seen at Farmoor Reservoir on 12 February 1987 remains the largest. Whilst most passage Shelduck remain for a few hours, some may linger in the county for several weeks especially in the winter months; for example, four stayed at Blenheim from 15 November until 4 December 1983 whilst a pair remained at Farmoor Reservoir and Stanton Harcourt for most of April and May 1991.

WOOD DUCK
Aix sponsa

A very rare breeding bird and occasional visitor, the first Oxfordshire record is of a pair at the Henley Road Gravel Pit on 19 and 20 November 1967. There were no further records until 1977 when a pair bred at Salford, although this pair may have been introduced. Also in 1977, a female was present at Dorchester Gravel Pit

from 13-23 November and it, or another bird, appeared on the River Thames at Iffley Lock for much of December.

Since 1979 Wood Duck have been recorded annually in the county. Usually males are reported, but this may be due to the ease of recognition. Blenheim has proved a favourite locality, one male remaining from 13 February until 29 April 1987, spending much of its time with the flock of Snow Geese. In 1990, a bird stayed at Farmoor Reservoir from March to the end of May whistling at Mallards.

Wood Duck have occurred most frequently in March, October and December. It is assumed that the records relate to birds wandering from collections as no feral population seems established in Britain.

MANDARIN
Aix galericulata

The Mandarin is primarily an occasional visitor to Oxfordshire although there has been one record of confirmed breeding in recent times.

Solitary birds were seen with increasing frequency during the 1980s, with records from a variety of sites, but Shotover Park, Farmoor, and the Stanton Harcourt Gravel Pits are the most regularly used venues. The majority of records are from December and January, and from April and May. It is believed that many of the Mandarin seen in Oxfordshire may be from the feral population centred on Virginia Water in Berkshire or direct escapes from captivity.

As for the breeding records; a pair were present on the River Thames below Wallingford during May 1985, and a female with two well grown young was found on the river just above the town later in the summer. During 1986, pairs were found in two tetrads in SP50 which appeared to be prospecting for nest sites. There have been no further indications of breeding or attempted breeding.

WIGEON
Anas penelope

A very frequent winter visitor. Flocks of Wigeon (illustrated below) begin to build up in October and November and reach a peak in February and March when floods are usually most extensive. There appear to be two main groups,

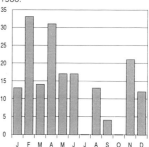

Figure 5.10. Shelduck.
Number of records, given as 'bird days' for the four years 1974, 1976, 1978 and 1980.

Table 5.11. Wigeon.
Peak counts at Dorchester Gravel Pits and Farmoor Reservoir in 1987.

Month	Dorchester Gravel Pits	Farmoor Reservoir
January	674	900
February	317	1150
March	110	230
April	34	0
September	7	11
October	162	10
November	160	300
December	440	340

Table 5.12. Gadwall.
Winter count statistics, 1976-1991.

Winter period	Mean	Max	Min
1976/77	5	10	1
1977/78	15	39	0
1978/79	17	39	8
1979/80	33	2	65
1980/81	28	58	9
1981/82	35	60	8
1982/83	46	80	30
1983/84	44	64	16
1984/85	39	77	5
1985/86	68	153	17
1986/87	64	106	25
1987/88	48	77	18
1988/89	55	89	4
1989/90	65	132	7
1990/91	85	157	8

Table 5.13. Gadwall.
Monthly winter count statistics 1970-1989.

Month	Mean	Max	Min
September	23.3	40	7
October	25.6	54	4
November	53.9	104	5
December	67.4	129	8
January	87.7	157	23
February	75.4	132	32
March	49.0	87	29

one in the Thames valley above Oxford centred at Port Meadow and Farmoor Reservoir, the other below Oxford based at Dorchester Gravel Pits. The Dorchester and Farmoor Wildfowl Count totals for 1987 give an example of the healthy state of wintering Wigeon numbers (Table 5.11). Their increase locally parallels that shown in the national indices of abundance of wildfowl in Britain from 1960-1989 given in the Wildfowl and Wader Counts 1988-1989 published by the Wildfowl and Wetlands Trust.

Occasional birds have been seen in the summer months, but there have been no indications of breeding.

The existence of Farmoor Reservoir has encouraged the increase in flocks feeding in the upper Thames meadows by providing a safe resting place. They feed by day and night on flooded fields such as Port Meadow until disturbed. There are quieter grazing areas near the Thames at Dorchester where the Wigeon flock has grown in size annually over the last 20 years. There were 1,045 present in February 1991. The large Queenford Pit has been used as a safe haven when required, and in the dry winter of 1990/1991 its well-vegetated, shallow waters also provided good feeding opportunities. (This pit was sold in 1991 for development as a leisure complex.) The Dorchester group of Wigeon seems so regular in numbers that it appears that birds here are able to over-winter without moving elsewhere.

Flights of Wigeon were once a common sight over the extensive marshes at Otmoor. Government subsidies in the 1960s sponsored the digging of deep ditches to drain much of the marsh. Although occasional flocks of up to 200 are seen there now, conditions are rarely suitable.

AMERICAN WIGEON
Anas americana

A very rare vagrant. A first-year male associated with the large flock of Wigeon at Dorchester Gravel Pits from 21 February to 14 March 1987. Other sightings elsewhere in the country of this species at this time suggest it was probably a genuine vagrant.

GADWALL
Anas strepera

Regarded primarily as a winter visitor to Oxfordshire, Gadwall have also established a small resident population on a number of the larger lakes within the county. The first breeding record for the county was in 1975 when a pair nested successfully at Blenheim. Since then, up to eight pairs have bred annually at Blenheim, but breeding has not been proven at any other site. During the Oxfordshire Atlas, this was the only site at which breeding was proven but evidence for probable breeding was obtained from five tetrads covering Blenheim, Kiddington

and Middleton Stoney Parks. In the years before the Oxfordshire Atlas, breeding may have occurred on the Rivers Cherwell and Glyme and at Dorchester Gravel Pits. Breeding could take place at any site where there is plenty of emergent vegetation.

Aplin (1889) describes the Gadwall as a rare winter visitor to Oxfordshire, and Alexander (1947) gives only four records. Radford (1966) summarised the status of the Gadwall as a scarce winter visitor becoming more frequent. She also noted that Blenheim was the most frequented site.

Since 1966, the Gadwall has continued to increase in number in Oxfordshire, reflecting the species' north and westwards expansion of breeding range across Europe. This has resulted in more being present in the county during the winter (Table 5.12), and also its inclusion on the list of breeding birds in Oxfordshire. Although the picture might be obscured a little by wildfowlers' introductions to some parts of Britain, these were few and there have been none locally (Fox and Salmon 1989).

Gadwall are present at Blenheim throughout the year, but on other waters they remain primarily a winter visitor. During the late 1970s and early 1980s, there was a pronounced autumn passage composed of two waves, one in late August and September and a second in November. However, there seems to be no consistent pattern from year to year although overall, there is a build-up to a peak in January (Table 5.13).

Blenheim no longer holds the largest winter flocks, Farmoor Reservoir and Dorchester Gravel Pits being the main centres. During January 1986 there were 63 at Dorchester, 62 at Farmoor and 51 at Blenheim. The largest flock recorded is of one just over 100 birds at Farmoor on 21 November 1988. During the winter, small parties appear on various pits, lakes and floodwaters throughout the county.

TEAL
Anas crecca

A very frequent winter visitor and very rare breeding bird. These small dabbling ducks are dependent upon shallow waters for feeding. They are most frequent at times when river valleys are flooded. For this reason the highest counts are usually in the second half of the winter (Table 5.15). Deep waters such as Farmoor Reservoir have little attraction to them. They often rest during the day in shallow streams, backwaters and in overgrown reed beds (e.g. Cassington Gravel Pits, 100-200 at times) where they can be overlooked unless revealed by their whistling calls.

The largest flock on record in Oxfordshire was of 1,200 birds in the upper Windrush valley on 2 January 1972. More usual are parties of up to 150-300 (Table 5.14) which gather at Otmoor, Port Meadow, Dorchester and Somerton, when these areas are damp. Similar numbers have occurred at Stanton Harcourt Gravel Pits when suitable shallows have been created in pits such as the 'scrape' at Stanton Harcourt. Unfortunately, in the gravel pit complexes, such habitats are only temporary since they are created by constant pumping of deep pits once excavated below the level of the water table.

Although most Teal depart in late March or early April a few remain through the summer, sometimes paired. However, breeding has only been proved twice: in 1884 at Clattercote Reservoir, and 1923 on Otmoor. The five records registered during the Oxfordshire Atlas are in the 'possible' category. Birds generally begin to return from mid-August when 'scrape' habitats such as at Stanton Harcourt are especially favoured. An example is 25-40 there from early August 1988. It is not clear whether these are family parties or non-breeders. Ringing recoveries of Teal within Oxfordshire (there are no recoveries of birds ringed here) strongly suggest that northern England is the immediate source since 51 out of 55 such birds had been ringed there. The other four had been ringed in southern England. All represented movements of more than 100 km and all had been ringed between September and February suggesting either that they were continental birds ringed on passage in England or that they included British birds driven south by hard weather.

Despite being restricted by shooting in the last century, and by a reduction in wet meadows in this, Teal still thrive. Mobility seems to be the key, enabling them to range far in search of winter feeding grounds.

MALLARD
Anas platyrhynchos

The Mallard is the commonest of our resident wildfowl and an abundant winter visitor. The results of the Oxfordshire Atlas show it breeding throughout the county except for the highest, most exposed, parts of the Downs and Cotswolds and from much of the Chilterns. Since nests are usually found close to water, it is not surprising that, in a county blessed with so many waterways and waterbodies, the species is well represented here. Although the main concentrations occur around the larger lakes and gravel pits, even the smallest pond, ditch or wet meadow may hold a pair of nesting birds. Whilst found in good numbers along the River Thames, especially close to habitation where they are attracted to food provided artificially, they are also found along the smaller rivers where suitable cover or trees (typically pollarded willows) for nesting are to be found, and where the water flow is not too swift.

In winter, Mallard are less widely distributed and congregate on the larger rivers and still waters. At this time, numbers are further

Table 5.14. Teal.
Winter count statistics, 1970-1989.

Winter period	Mean	Max	Min
1970/71	110	216	46
1971/72	169	426	56
1972/73	214	453	24
1973/74	80	281	118
1974/75	185	596	39
1975/76	134	269	33
1976/77	118	349	49
1977/78	170	304	89
1978/79	83	125	21
1979/80	156	288	13
1980/81	120	235	34
1981/82	72	146	36
1982/83	178	246	25
1983/84	166	301	61
1984/85	109	298	24
1985/86	130	281	34
1986/87	275	572	72
1987/88	210	392	17
1988/89	150	267	44

Table 5.15. Teal.
Monthly winter count statistics 1970-1989.

Month	Mean	Max	Min
September	56	151	13
October	85	135	34
November	161	406	70
December	244	606	45
January	209	426	42
February	185	349	31
March	139	392	21

Table 5.16. Mallard.

Monthly winter count statistics,
1970-1989.

Month	Mean	Max	Min
September	1460	2148	809
October	1551	2105	863
November	1668	2442	1011
December	1603	2674	959
January	1505	2770	824
February	898	1921	568
March	420	646	265

Table 5.17. Pintail.

Monthly winter count statistics,
1975-1988.

Month	Mean	Max	Min
September	1.5	14	0
October	1.0	3	0
November	2.5	6	0
December	7.7	17	0
January	15	55	2
February	29	96	2
March	7.6	33	1
April	1	4	0

Table 5.18. Shoveler.

Winter count statistics 1970-1989.

Winter period	Mean	Max	Min
1970/71	15	34	0
1971/72	19	40	0
1972/73	18	41	1
1973/74	9	17	1
1974/75	37	122	0
1975/76	11	23	0
1976/77	41	107	3
1977/78	43	126	3
1978/79	27	53	6
1979/80	63	119	11
1980/81	36	62	5
1981/82	40	55	12
1982/83	33	68	0
1983/84	68	137	6
1984/85	30	76	8
1985/86	26	45	6
1986/87	16	33	2
1987/88	32	56	0
1988/89	28	48	0
1989/90	24	45	0

Table 5.19. Shoveler.

Monthly winter count statistics,
1970-1989.

Month	Mean	Max	Min
September	4	13	0
October	12	50	0
November	28	62	4
December	34	75	5
January	43	119	12
February	48	122	4
March	49	137	7

increased by the arrival of birds from northern Britain and from mainland Europe. As Table 5.16 demonstrates, there is a build-up of numbers at the main centres during early autumn and a gradual decline through the winter period. However, it must be recognised that a relatively large proportion of the population remains away from those sites included in the Wildfowl Counts and the numbers do not represent a full count of the district. Nevertheless, large flocks can be seen at any one of the usual wetland sites and flocks of up to 250 birds occur in most winters. The largest congregations recorded are 1,051 at Blenheim in September 1937, 1,000 at Eynsham Hall Park in October 1967 and 600 there in September 1970. Large counts have been made at the Stanton Harcourt Gravel Pit complex with 600 in October 1975, over 800 in January 1976 and 900 in February 1979.

The Oxfordshire breeding population of Mallard is fairly sedentary. Of 24 recoveries of birds ringed in the county 16 were also recovered here, and the rest were in southern England. Only two had travelled more than 100 km. Similarly, 160 of the 177 recoveries made within the county had been ringed in southern England. However, 53 had travelled more than 100 km.

Whilst there has probably always been a sound Mallard population in Oxfordshire, Aplin (1889) noted that the breeding population was on the increase, a trend which he attributed to the implementation of Wildfowl and Wild Bird Preservation Acts.

The success of the species can be attributed to its ability to nest in a wide variety of lowland terrain, to its close association with man and its protracted breeding season. Young may be seen as early as March and as late as November although there is a high level of predation especially early in the nesting season. Also important is the species' ability to utilise a wide range of food. At Blenheim, beechmast is regularly taken whilst elsewhere, birds may be seen searching for fallen grain and other items on open fields. The feeding of bread and other scraps has also been important in maintaining a strong population in built-up areas as well as supplementing the diet when weather conditions become less favourable. Another factor in maintaining the high population level is the introduction of artificially reared birds for sport. Domesticated birds have also escaped and joined local flocks and, when breeding has occurred, this has often resulted in impure hybrids.

PINTAIL
Anas acuta

Although an infrequent winter visitor, Pintail have been seen with increasing regularity in the second half of the twentieth century. Indeed, Aplin (1889) described the Pintail a scarce winter visitor to the Thames and to Otmoor, and there is no mention of the species in his supplementary notes of 1915. Radford (1966) gives records of one at Blenheim in January 1923, and 12 on Otmoor in February 1924. There are a small number of records in subsequent years, mostly from Blenheim and Otmoor. From about 1935, Pintail are recorded annually in Oxfordshire. However, P.J. Campbell in the 1934 OOS *Report on the Birds of Port Meadow*, calls the Pintail a very uncommon winter visitor, noting that it had occurred only twice in the previous eight years. It was not until 1943 that Port Meadow became an important site for this species with 12 there on 1 January and 18 on 11 January.

The steady increase in Pintail numbers continued throughout the 1950s, with some exceptional totals brought about by floods and appropriate weather conditions. There were 105 on Port Meadow on 17 January 1951, with over 80 birds there on 29 January 1961 and with the highest number for the site and the county, of 300+ on 20 January 1962.

During the 1970s and early 1980s, flocks appeared in the Cherwell valley, a site now rarely used due to the lack of flood water. During the 1980s, Farmoor, and to a lesser extent the gravel pits at Stanton Harcourt have been favoured sites. Otmoor, when flooded, can hold reasonable numbers, with 35 there from 7–15 February 1988. Smaller numbers and solitary birds can occur at any pit, lake or flood water. The overall pattern of incidence in the county is one of a gradual build-up in numbers through the winter reaching a peak in February (Table 5.17) although numbers present vary considerably from year to year.

GARGANEY
Anas querquedela

An infrequent passage migrant. Spring and autumn passage visitors are present in most years, usually making brief visits of no more than a few days. There are rather more records

in spring, probably because identification is easier then, but more birds in autumn. Between 1979 and 1989 there were 26 records of 47 birds in spring but 21 records of 71 birds in autumn. This might reflect the movement of family parties in autumn. The main periods of passage are from the second half of March until mid-May, and from late August to late September, but there are occasional records in June and July. Numbers fluctuate considerably from year to year. While there were ten separate records in 1982, there were only two in the three years 1986, 1987, 1988. Usually only one or two birds are present, but occasionally there are more, with the largest flock being of 12 over Farmoor Reservoir on 9 September 1984.

There are three unproven records of breeding. Aplin (1889) mentions three young which alighted and were shot on Otmoor in August 1830. These might have hatched nearby. Breeding was suspected again at Otmoor in 1925, and in 1981 there were up to seven there on various dates in March, April, May and June. In 1948, breeding was proven at Sandford Sewage Farm. Since the British breeding population of Garganey is estimated at only 40–90 pairs (Marchant *et al.* 1990), a significant proportion must come through Oxfordshire each year.

SHOVELER
Anas clypeata

The Shoveler is a frequent winter visitor which is known to have bred on six occasions between 1928 and 1990.

In the nineteenth century, the Shoveler was considered to be an uncommon winter visitor to Oxfordshire (Aplin 1889). Alexander (1947) was able to say that the Shoveler occurred in every month of the year, mainly at Blenheim and Port Meadow. He also gave a number of breeding records: one pair on Otmoor in 1928 and three pairs there in 1937 and pairs bred at Sandford Sewage Farm in 1940 and 1944. Radford (1966) considered the Shoveler a regular winter visitor.

Breeding was proved at Dorchester Gravel Pits in 1969 and 1978 and a female was seen behaving as if she had young at the Stanton Harcourt Gravel Pits also in 1978. There have been no further records of breeding or attempted breeding in the county, but birds are occasionally seen during the summer months in most years. Family parties often appear at Blenheim in mid-August where they moult.

Winter numbers of Shoveler have increased since the 1960s. Although monthly totals vary considerably from year to year (Table 5.18), the overall trend is of a gradual build up of numbers through the entire winter period (Table 5.19). Farmoor Reservoir, Dorchester Gravel Pits and, when flooded, Port Meadow are the main centres of population and flocks typically number 40–80 birds. In some years the gravel pit complex at

Stanton Harcourt can have comparable numbers and most of the smaller lakes and pits in the county, and the rivers when in flood, will have small numbers present. The largest flock recorded is 220 at Dorchester Gravel Pit on 8 January 1980.

RED-CRESTED POCHARD
Netta rufina

A rare visitor to the county, the first Oxfordshire record is of a pair present on Port Meadow during May 1943. There is no further record until 1959 when a male was at the Stanton Harcourt Gravel Pits from 19 December until May 1960. A pair appeared at the same locality in September 1960.

Records have increased in frequency and have been annual since 1975 (Table 5.20). Usually only single birds are seen but pairs have been recorded and once, three birds were present at Stanton Harcourt Gravel Pits. Most records are from mid-September to late February (Figure 5.11) and coincide with the influx of Pochard and other wintering duck, which raises the question whether any could be from the small wild population in the Netherlands. There is a scattering of summer records.

The Stanton Harcourt Gravel Pits are the most frequented waters but there are records of Red-crested Pochard from Grimsbury and Farmoor Reservoirs, Dorchester Gravel Pits and Blenheim, and once from the River Evenlode at Cassington.

The origins of Oxfordshire Red-crested Pochard are debatable. The species is kept in many waterfowl collections both here in Oxfordshire and in neighbouring counties. It has started to breed sporadically at the Cotswold Water Park, not far over the county boundary in Gloucestershire and further west at Frampton-on-Severn. Baatsen (1960) traced the

Table 5.20. Red-crested Pochard.
Annual number of records based on first recorded dates, 1960-1989.

Year	No. of records	No. of birds
1960	4	6
1961	0	0
1962	0	0
1963	1	1
1964	0	0
1965	1	1
1966	0	0
1967	1	1
1968	3	3
1969	0	0
1970	3	7
1971	4	5
1972	3	4
1973	6	14
1974	5	10
1975	3	7
1976	4	9
1977	3	5
1978	4	5
1979	4	6
1980	3	4
1981	3	3
1982	4	7
1983	2	4
1984	3	5
1985	6	12
1986	3	4
1987	4	6
1988	2	2
1989	4	6

Figure 5.11. Red-crested Pochard.
Monthly distribution of records based on first recorded date, 1960-1989.
Grey = number of records, black = number of birds.

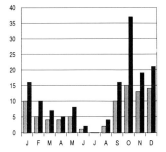

Table 5.21. Pochard.
Monthly winter count statistics, 1970-1989.

Month	Mean	Max	Min
September	252	703	28
October	531	777	130
November	891	1251	575
December	823	1240	404
January	756	1100	240
February	522	796	269
March	185	330	44

Table 5.22. Pochard.
Winter count statistics, 1970-1991.

Winter period	Mean
1970/71	477
1971/72	722
1972/73	591
1973/74	577
1974/75	467
1975/76	556
1976/77	601
1977/78	509
1978/79	496
1979/80	596
1980/81	530
1981/82	497
1982/83	652
1983/84	607
1984/85	478
1985/86	628
1986/87	640
1987/88	514
1988/89	604
1989/90	752
1990/91	818

Figure 5.12. Pochard.
Breeding distribution 1968-1972 (after Sharrock 1976).

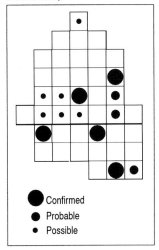

● Confirmed
● Probable
• Possible

development of breeding populations at the Cotswold Water Park and considered that many records of the Red-crested Pochard in southern Britain refer to birds wandering from this site. In particular he suggests that the Stanton Harcourt Gravel Pits, lying 40 km to the east, are well placed to receive birds using the natural flyway provided by the Thames valley. Feral populations also exist in western Europe, with some numbers in Belgium. It is likely that each of these possibilities are represented among the Oxfordshire birds.

POCHARD
Aythya ferina

The Pochard is primarily a winter visitor to Oxfordshire although there is a small resident population. Most of the wintering birds arrive in October and peak numbers are reached between November and January although, as Table 5.21 shows, the earlier date is more usual. Congregations are primarily found on the Stanton Harcourt Gravel Pits, and particularly Dix Pit. Flocks at this site regularly reach 350-700 birds but larger counts have been made and all of the largest counts for Oxfordshire are from Stanton Harcourt (e.g. up to 1,400 in November 1970, 1,000 in November and December 1971, 1,200 in October 1975, 800 in January 1976 and 725 in November 1988). The numbers present in any winter period vary widely (Table 5.22). In addition, smaller parties can be seen on any of the other waters in the county as well as along the River Thames or feeding on flood waters. In most parties, males outnumber females, often comprising 70-90% of the flock.

The Pochard has long been recognised as a winter visitor to Oxfordshire although, because of the previous lack of suitable waters in the county, numbers were never large. Aplin (1889) notes that flocks of 25-50 birds were regular and 65 was a maximum at Clattercote Reservoir.

Early in the twentieth century the species began to increase its range, albeit very slowly, and in 1923 the first breeding records for the county were made with birds nesting at Blenheim. Breeding continued at this site for over 40 years, with up to seven pairs present (1935). In the 1960s, other sites were colonised with breeding noted at Henley Road Gravel Pit in 1967 and Dorchester Gravel Pit in the

following year. Since then breeding in the county has been sporadic with only one other site utilised by nesting Pochard, namely Rycote in 1974. Birds are regularly seen during the summer months at a number of other gravel pit sites and one can only guess as to whether nesting pairs may have been overlooked. The national atlas (Sharrock 1976) noted breeding in five 10 km squares and probable in three others (Figure 5.12), although this is something of an over-representation of any single year in that atlas period since squares were not all occupied in every season.

In the course of the Oxfordshire Atlas, observers failed to find any evidence to indicate that breeding had occurred in the county although evidence of probable breeding was obtained in three tetrads. It is possible that nests or broods could have been missed but the impression gained by local observers is that this was unlikely. Subsequent to the Oxfordshire Atlas, the species bred successfully at Stanton Harcourt Gravel Pits in 1990. It would appear therefore that, following a peak in the breeding population during the middle portion of the twentieth century, and for reasons that remain unclear, the Pochard is a species in decline as a nesting bird in Oxfordshire.

RING-NECKED DUCK
Aythya collaris

A rare winter visitor, the first Oxfordshire record of Ring-necked Duck was made in 1967 when a male remained at Farmoor Reservoir from 15-24 January 1967. A second report, possibly of the same bird, came from Dorchester Gravel Pit on 5 March 1967 and both records were accepted by the rarities committee of British Birds. Since then, there have been a further nine acceptable records, some probably relating to the same individual moving from one water to another. Figure 5.13 shows the month of appearance at sites in the county.

Often the birds remain for a week or two at a site, but exceptionally one remained at Farmoor Reservoir from 15 November 1973 to 8 May 1974. Birds have been noted at seven sites, which in addition to those given, include Sutton Courtenay Gravel Pits, Abingdon, Blenheim, Stanton Harcourt Gravel Pits, and on several small fishing lakes near Swinbrook in the upper Windrush valley.

MTE 90

FERRUGINOUS DUCK
Aythya nyroca

Radford (1966) gives three records of this rare winter visitor from the nineteenth century, the last being in December 1847. There is then a break of 100 years until one was seen at Port Meadow in December 1947. Radford gives two further records, both from the Stanton Harcourt Gravel Pits: November 1963 and December 1964. Since then there have been a further 12 occurrences, all in the winter period (Figure 5.14), four of which have been at Stanton Harcourt Gravel Pits. The other records came from a wide scatter of sites.

Some hybrid Pochard x Tufted Ducks, may lead to identification problems.

TUFTED DUCK
Aythya fuligula

The Tufted Duck occurs as both a resident in Oxfordshire and as a very numerous winter visitor. Although the results of the Oxfordshire Atlas show the Tufted Duck to be generally distributed, it is a relatively recent addition as a breeder to the county list, the first confirmed breeding occurring at Blenheim in 1923. At the time of the Oxfordshire Atlas, confirmed or probable breeding of Tufted Duck was noted in 83 tetrads and possible breeding in a further 62. Gravel pit complexes feature strongly in this distribution pattern, but much smaller lakes and ponds, many of them recently excavated for angling or ornamental purposes are also frequented. Even small farm ponds and reservoirs on upland areas such as the downs may hold a nesting pair, and some stretches of each of the county's rivers, are now occupied. Farmoor Reservoir has also become an important assembly point for birds immediately after nesting, with up to nine family parties present.

Whilst only 37% of the Tufted Duck records submitted to the Oxfordshire Atlas are of confirmed breeding, the relatively late breeding season of the species coupled with the bird's propensity for nesting in dense vegetation, often some distance from the main body of water along an overgrown stream, means that further confirmed breeding may have been missed. Taking into consideration the fact that many of the 'possible' records are non-breeding birds, the distribution described could still represent breeding birds occupying up to 100 tetrads.

Prior to 1923 the Tufted Duck was regarded solely as a winter visitor, the status in which it is still most frequently encountered. Aplin (1889) called it regular but not abundant and only mentions parties of up to a dozen birds. However, at that time the species was expanding its breeding range and Aplin predicted that it would first become more numerous and, secondly, that breeding would occur in Oxfordshire.

Colonisation was somewhat slower than expected and until the mid-1960s, breeding was confined to eight sites in seven 10 km squares (Figure 5.15), with Blenheim remaining the stronghold. The species then underwent a rapid expansion of range, aided by the creation of more sites with the increase of gravel extraction. During the national atlas (Sharrock 1976) breeding was confirmed in 25 10 km squares with possible breeding in a further five (Figure 5.16). The increase continued through the seventies and data submitted to the Oxfordshire Biological Recording Scheme until 1980 showed breeding in 41 tetrads (Figure 5.17).

During the winter, birds may be seen at many of the sites where they breed but more usually they form flocks on gravel pits, reservoirs and larger lakes. The winter population of Tufted Duck is very mobile and will move from site to site according to weather and disturbance and may also move on to floodwaters in search of food. These winter flocks start to build up at the end of August, and this continues through the autumn to reach a peak in December with a decline through until the spring (Table 5.23). In addition to the increase in the local breeding population there have been more Tufted Duck overwintering in Oxfordshire. In the nineteenth century, maximum flock sizes noted were of the order of a dozen birds (Aplin 1889). By the mid-1930s, flocks of up to 120 were noted and by the mid-1960s maximum flocks were of the order of 200 birds. These figures may simply reflect the paucity of larger waters in the county and it may have been that birds were more generally distributed in smaller parties. As more large waters have become available and as the population has increased, so has the flock size. Between 1965 and 1979 the maximum annual winter flock was 300 birds and in the next five-year period flocks of up to 400 birds were reported. However, in 1987 there were 550–600

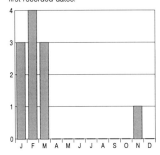

Figure 5.13. Ring-necked Duck.
Monthly distribution of records based on first recorded dates.

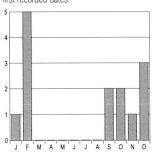

Figure 5.14. Ferruginous Duck.
Monthly distribution of records based on first recorded dates.

Table 5.23. Tufted Duck.
Mean monthly wildfowl counts, 1970-1989.

Month	Mean	Max	Min
September	413	669	119
October	607	976	298
November	840	1335	505
December	879	1387	450
January	906	1295	385
February	742	1126	425
March	531	816	288

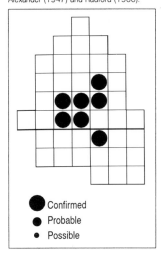

Figure 5.15. Tufted Duck.
Breeding distribution 1950-1965, after
Alexander (1947) and Radford (1966).

● Confirmed
● Probable
• Possible

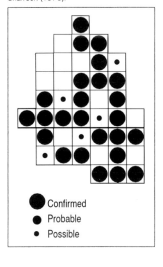

Figure 5.16. Tufted Duck.
Breeding distribution 1968-1972, after
Sharrock (1976).

● Confirmed
● Probable
• Possible

Figure 5.17. Tufted Duck.
Distribution of all breeding records before
1980. Details from OOS, BOS and
Oxfordshire Biological Recording Scheme.

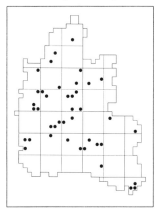

birds present at Farmoor. The following winter at Farmoor there were two monthly counts of 800 birds with a maximum of 1,150 noted in December, making this the most important site for wintering Tufted Duck in the county.

SCAUP
Aythya marila

An occasional winter visitor, the earliest Oxfordshire record is of one caught in the quadrangle of Christchurch College in December 1829. Alexander (1947) gives nine records over the period 1887-1947, seven of which were at Blenheim, whilst there are eleven records between 1947 and 1966 (Radford 1966).

Scaup have continued to increase in frequency in Oxfordshire and in the 1980s have become regular winter visitors. There have been more than 30 records since 1966. Numbers vary from year to year and small parties can occur. Ten at Farmoor, 8 February 1986 and 16 at Dorchester, 5 November 1988, are the largest parties recorded. The length of stay is also increasing, with one to three birds recorded at Farmoor Reservoir on 33 dates between 13 January and 27 March 1985. In 1988, one or two were present from 16 October to 27 October, up to four until mid-December and up to ten until the end of the year.

Most records of Scaup come from Farmoor, but records have also come from Stanton Harcourt Gravel Pits, Blenheim, Dorchester Gravel Pits, Grimsbury Reservoir and along the River Thames. Birds appear between mid-September and late April with a peak in numbers reached during January and February. One observation suggests that spring passage can occur; ten appeared at Dorchester Gravel Pit on 26 April 1981, but only one was present the next day.

EIDER
Somateria mollissima

A very rare vagrant, there are four records of this sea duck in Oxfordshire. A female and two immatures were present at Farmoor Reservoir from 5 November until 31 December 1975, a male at Stanton Harcourt Gravel Pits on 6 September 1977, a male at Farmoor, 9-16 May 1979 and two males on 26 January 1983.

LONG-TAILED DUCK
Clangula hyemalis

A rare winter visitor (illustrated below), there are only two pre-1960 records of this species, a bird shot at Standlake in 1840 and a bird on the River Thames at Kennington in 1864. Both were immature females.

Since 1967, there have been a further 16 occurrences and on two occasions more than one bird has been involved. The ratio of males to females and immatures is equal. Whilst some birds have only remained for a day, many stay for a week or more. The longest stay was by a female at Farmoor from 8 November 1980 to mid-February 1981, when presumably the same bird moved to the Stanton Harcourt Gravel Pits where it remained until 27 April 1981.

Of the 16 recent records, nine have been at Farmoor Reservoir, two at the Stanton Harcourt Gravel Pits, three at Dorchester Gravel Pits and once each at Clattercote Reservoir and Blenheim. Most records have been from November or December, with only three in January and February, with one through March and much of April.

COMMON SCOTER
Melanitta nigra

An infrequent visitor to Oxfordshire, there are only 12 records of Common Scoter from the period 1888-1965 (Radford 1966), but there have been 59 occurrences in the period 1966-1988 and birds have been noted in each month except for January (Figure 5.18). These records are usually of small parties which visit for a short time although they have stayed for up to three weeks. The largest flock recorded, was of 46 birds which were seen to arrive at the Hardwick Gravel Pit near Stanton Harcourt on 2 September 1987 at about 17.30 hrs. After flying around for some time, they settled on the water and stayed in a close flock, with much preening and diving. In flight their call was a continuous, quiet whistling; on the water they were silent. By the following day they had departed.

There have been some changes in the pattern of occurrences since 1966. Between 1966 and 1970, Common Scoter were recorded from Grimsbury Reservoir on four occasions and once from Dorchester Gravel Pit. However,

between 1978 and 1987 there was only one record from Grimsbury and one from Dorchester, but there were 22 records from Farmoor Reservoir, three from the Stanton Harcourt Gravel Pits and one each from Port Meadow and the Cherwell Valley and a single bird was found dead near Wootton.

VELVET SCOTER
Melanitta fusca

A very rare winter visitor, Radford (1966) gives three records: six killed at Henley in 1855, one killed at Cassington Gravel Pit, 20 December 1920 and a pair at Blenheim in April 1936. There are no further records until 1970, and from then until 1988 there have been nine occurrences. Of these, eight were at Farmoor Reservoir with the ninth at Blenheim on 16 February 1979. The records are as follows: 1–22 February 1970, 29 November 1973, 16 February 1979, 10 November 1984, 2–24 November 1985 and 23–25 October 1987. Numbers noted vary from one to a maximum of 11 on 10 November 1984.

GOLDENEYE
Bucephala clangula

Goldeneye are regular winter visitors in increasing numbers in Oxfordshire, showing a preference for lakes deep enough to provide feeding opportunities. They are restless creatures, frequently moving between sites during the winter, and are seen on occasions at most waters in the county. In cold weather some move on to the River Thames. Red-head (females and immatures) birds always out-number the colourful males in the local population.

There have been two or three September records, but usually the first Goldeneyes do not start arriving from their Scandinavian breeding grounds until the second half of October, building to peak numbers in January and February (Table 5.25). Many linger until late March or even mid-April before leaving, and in these months much display activity is noted. In 1979, and again in 1987, injured individuals unable to return to breeding grounds spent the summer months on the River Thames at King's Lock.

Aplin (1889) made special mention of Standlake as an area where Goldeneyes could be seen frequently. A century later this remains a favourite locality. However, this part of the lower Windrush valley has much changed since Aplin's day and is now a lakeland with 30–40 flooded gravel pits. In addition there are the two large reservoirs at Farmoor a few miles away. With the provision of a choice of suitable habitats it is not surprising that the Goldeneye has increased. While Aplin referred to one or two seen occasionally, tens were present daily during winter months in the 1980s. The extent of the local population was demonstrated when simultaneous counts of all the gravel pit lakes in the lower Windrush valley on 25 February 1990 produced a total of 40, while on the same morning there were 51 at Farmoor Reservoir.

Summaries of Wildfowl Counts (for the Wildfowl and Wetlands Trust) in the 20 winters from 1970/1 to 1990/91 demonstrate how the population has increased (Table 5.24). These simultaneous monthly counts were made in central Oxfordshire on all the waters in the Thames and Windrush valleys from Dorchester to Hardwick, and on the Blenheim Lake. The average counts per month illustrate the pattern of the Goldeneye's winter population increase (Table 5.25).

SMEW
Mergus albellus

An occasional winter visitor, Aplin (1889) describes this species as rare, especially the males, and Radford (1966) summarises this species as an uncommon winter visitor, noting 12 records from 1888–1948 with an increase from 1950. Most of these observations are from the River Thames. Most records are from the colder months in the latter half of the winter (Figure 5.19), although the severe winters of 1947 and 1963 produced no records.

Smew were absent from 1964–1974, but since then occurrences have been almost annual. Since 1974, there have been ten records from Farmoor Reservoir, seven from Dorchester Gravel Pits, and only three from the Thames. The low number of records from the river may be a reflection of observer effort. Other sites that have attracted Smew on several occasions are Wolvercote Pit, Radley Gravel Pit, and the Stanton Harcourt Gravel Pits. Numbers have also increased, with five at Farmoor on 16 and

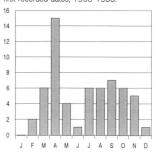

Figure 5.18. Common Scoter.
Monthly distribution of records based on first recorded dates, 1966-1988.

Table 5.24. Goldeneye.
Totals of counts in central Oxfordshire 1970-1989.

Year	No. of birds
1970/71	90
1971/72	94
1972/73	50
1973/74	113
1974/75	62
1975/76	52
1976/77	22
1977/78	75
1978/79	83
1979/80	164
1980/81	117
1981/82	175
1982/83	190
1983/84	219
1984/85	233
1985/86	215
1986/87	253
1987/88	212
1988/89	338
1989/90	266
1990/91	283

Table 5.25. Goldeneye.
Monthly winter count statistics 1970-1989.

Month	Mean	Max	Min
October	1	7	0
November	17	49	1
December	22	55	15
January	32	89	7
February	32	113	31
March	29	96	13

Figure 5.19. Smew.
Monthly distribution of records based on first dates, 1974-1989.

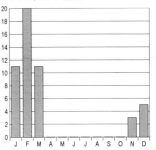

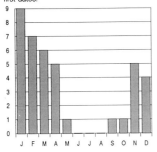

Table 5.26. Goosander.
Monthly winter count statistics
1981-1991.

Month	Mean	Max	Min
October	<1	2	0
November	4	23	0
December	14	29	1
January	34	84	9
February	52	94	3
March	38	73	12

17 February 1985 and five at Sonning Eye Gravel Pit on 8 March 1986. The very cold spell in early 1987 produced several records and good-sized parties. There were seven at Dorchester Gravel Pits on 17 and 18 January and again on 16 February. There were also six at Radley Gravel Pits on 8 February and seven there on 1 March, whilst smaller numbers were seen in the same period at other sites in the county.

RED-BREASTED MERGANSER
Mergus serrator

Whilst the incidence of Red-breasted Merganser in Oxfordshire has increased since the 1960s, it can still only be described as an occasional winter visitor.

There are four nineteenth century records of Red-breasted Merganser cited by Radford (1966). These were on Otmoor in February 1838, Cassington 1841, at Henley during January 1848 and near Wardington in January 1877. There are no further records until a female was recorded at Blenheim in November 1934. After this date Radford gives a further ten records, seven of which came from the River Thames, mostly the Port Meadow reach. The largest party noted was six at Clifton Hampden in February 1940.

From 1968–1989 there have been a total of 31 Oxfordshire records of Red-breasted Merganser. Of these, three are from the River Thames and 16 from Farmoor Reservoir. In the first four months of 1979, between one and four birds were seen in each month, with the party of four representing the largest group seen in the county, since usually only one or two birds are noted.

An unusually late record is of two at Farmoor Reservoir on 11 May 1973, whilst the earliest record for this species is 23 September, again at Farmoor.

It is generally assumed that Red-breasted Mergansers call in to the waters of the county whilst on their annual migrations from and to their breeding grounds in Scandinavia and wintering areas on the south coast. However, while this may account for spring observations, the distribution of records (Figure 5.20) shows a peak in mid-winter which more likely reflects cold-weather movements (Chandler 1981, Lack 1986).

GOOSANDER
Mergus merganser

Goosanders were once infrequent winter visitors in small numbers. Now they are regular and in some winters more than 100 are present in the county — especially in the latter half of the winter (Table 5.26). In earlier years most were red-heads (females or immatures) while males were rare (ratio of *ca.* 20:1 in the 1960s), but as the population has increased so has the proportion of males (ratio of *ca.* 4:1 in the 1980s).

Goosanders usually return from their continental breeding grounds first in late November, build to peak numbers in January and February, and leave in March. There have also been occasional records in October and April, and two lingered until 7 May at Grimsbury Reservoir in 1974. An injured female, unable to return to the breeding grounds, lived on the River Thames at Port Meadow for a total of two years and nine months, being seen last in November 1981.

The growth in numbers locally has been well recorded. Alexander (1947) noted a total of 24 records in the previous 60 years within the former Oxfordshire boundary. Since then they have appeared annually. The build-up seems to have come from the east, with most earlier records from the Thames below Oxford and the lakes at Dorchester Gravel Pits. This is not unexpected as wintering birds were well established at the gravel pit lakes and reservoirs around London before they became a familiar part of the Oxfordshire scene.

The cold winters of 1947, 1963, and 1979 appear to have encouraged this development as they marked important stages in their progress inland. After severe weather in 1947 and through the 1950s Goosanders were noted more often, although flocks rarely reached double figures.

Throughout the three bitterly cold months at the beginning of 1963 parties of 25–50 survived on the ice-free waters of the Thames below Oxford. In the following years Dorchester Gravel Pits became an annual wintering centre. Flocks here gradually grew in size (e.g. maxima of 13 in 1973, 28 in 1974, 36 in 1977, 49 in 1982). A temporary interruption occurred during the building of the Dorchester by-pass in the late 1970s which separated the lakes and came near one popular pool, but the birds soon returned when work was completed. They have always

favoured the quieter pits in the complex least disturbed by human activity. The proximity of the Thames is an advantage as Goosanders often transfer to it, especially when the lakes are ice-bound.

The next major advance came in the winter of 1978–1979 when there was an extraordinary influx of water birds from the frozen Continental shores of the North Sea (Chandler 1981). Simultaneous counts at several waters showed that at least 233 Goosanders were in Oxfordshire during this period. These immigrants were highly mobile, exploring all corners, and appearing in places where they had never before been seen. The apparent long term effect was to introduce Farmoor Reservoir as a possible wintering site which they have used regularly since. 154 in January 1985, and 138 in January 1987 were exceptional here in hard weather, but 20–50 not uncommon in most winters.

The Dorchester and Farmoor populations, by virtue of their behaviour and flight patterns, appear to be independent. The Farmoor birds are more restless. The deep waters of the reservoir provide fewer feeding opportunities, thus there is more movement daily to and from the River Thames and local gravel pits. In contrast, the Dorchester flock varies little in size throughout the winter, and can usually be found in the same corners for long periods.

The Goosander's progress as a breeding species in Britain has been well documented (Meek and Little 1977). There has been a similar spread throughout Europe. Its increase in Oxfordshire is presumably related to these factors.

RUDDY DUCK
Oxyura jamaicensis

The Ruddy Duck remains a rare resident. Ornithologists in Oxfordshire have watched its progress with interest. Table 5.27 shows the growth in numbers from 1975–1988, while Figure 5.21 shows the monthly distribution of records over the same period. It began breeding in Britain in 1960 and established thriving breeding populations in Avon, the Midlands and Cheshire. As expected it began to appear in Oxfordshire, the first record being at Stanton Harcourt Gravel Pits on 15 June 1975. The following year, on 30 October 1976, 12 were present on Farmoor Reservoir. This number has been surpassed on only one occasion when 20 were seen on Farmoor Reservoir on 24 February 1985. Although parties in excess of 100 are recorded in adjacent counties, Oxfordshire numbers remain low with most seen in the winter months on reservoirs and gravel pits.

Colonisation of Oxfordshire has been on a limited scale with breeding first noted on a secluded pool of the River Evenlode in 1980. Since then, breeding has been confirmed at Dorchester in 1983 and 1985 and ducklings were seen at Blenheim in 1988 and 1989. Breeding probably took place at Rycote in 1987 and on the Henley Road Gravel Pit in 1987 and 1988 whilst evidence for possible breeding was obtained from Clattercote in 1986 and 1988. Breeding by single pairs was suspected in the upper Windrush valley in 1990 and 1991.

Table 5.27. Ruddy Duck.
Estimated annual numbers of birds 1975-1988.

Year	No. of birds
1975	1
1976	13
1977	9
1978	12
1979	17
1980	5
1981	6
1982	22
1983	40
1984	37
1985	60
1986	44
1987	40
1988	41

Figure 5.21. Ruddy Duck.
Monthly distribution of birds 1975-1988.

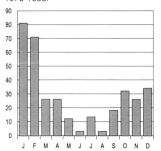

Family: Accipitridae
Hawks and Eagles

Of 17 raptor species recorded in Oxfordshire in the twentieth century, ten belong to this family. Of these, only one breeds regularly. All raptors were persecuted terribly by gamekeepers and collectors during the last century. Indeed, few nineteenth century bird records were obtained without collecting the bird itself. With the reduction in keepering after the First World War, many recovered their numbers, although several suffered again in the 1950s and 1960s from insecticide poisoning. Since then, recovery has been swift and of the species listed, only two were last seen in the county before 1980.

Table 5.28. Red Kite.
Total number of observations in the five year periods between 1959 and 1988.

Period	Observations
1959-1963	1
1964-1968	1
1969-1973	1
1974-1978	0
1979-1983	6
1984-1988	11

Figure 5.22. Red Kite.
Monthly distribution of records 1959-1988.

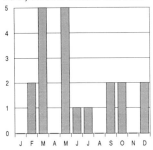

HONEY BUZZARD
Pernis apivorus

This very rare summer visitor has probably never been very common in the county, although there is a breeding record dating back to July 1838 when a female was shot off her nest at Bix, and the corpse and eggs displayed in museums. There were only two other nineteenth century records in 1841 and 1848, followed by a gap of 73 years when one was killed at Stanton Harcourt in the spring of 1921. Guns were out again later that year at Kidlington and the resulting dead bird taken to Darby, the well-known Oxford taxidermist.

After another long delay came the intriguing account of three in the air together, perhaps two adults and a juvenile from their behaviour, over the Wantage Downs on 17 September 1969. Since then there have been just two confirmed sightings of solitary birds at Harwell in May 1974 and Chinnor in April 1975. In addition, a raptor considered to be of this species was seen flying over north Oxford in August 1975.

RED KITE
Milvus milvus

Now a rare vagrant, in the eighteenth century this magnificent bird was still breeding commonly in Oxfordshire woodlands, and often seen soaring over the city of Oxford. Aplin (1889) describes in detail how it was exterminated locally in the first half of the nineteenth century, and rarely encountered in the second half. The last breeding attempt in the county was probably between 1830 and 1840.

They were totally absent in this century until 27 July 1961 when one was seen flying over Boar's Hill. At this time only a tiny relic population survived in mid-Wales.

The welcome, although sporadic, return of Kites to Oxfordshire has paralleled the recovery of the Welsh breeding population. A connection was proved when a dead bird was found under

wires near Woodstock in October 1968. The bird had been ringed as a nestling earlier that year at Tregaron. After these two records in the 1960s there was a pause until 1979, but since then they have been seen in most years. Table 5.28 shows their progress.

Although recorded in every season of the year, 50% occurred in March and May (Figure 5.22). These sightings were nearly all of birds passing over, mostly at considerable height. The timing of records makes it possible that some may be European migrants straying off course.

An interesting development was the wintering of a bird in the upper Thames valley in the Bampton/Buckland area from 2 February until 25 March 1984. A succession of observations over three years at Wychwood Forest suggests wintering birds there also.

The reasons for the Red Kite's failure to recolonise the English lowlands are unclear, but human interference is believed to be a major factor still (Marchant *et al.* 1990). Nevertheless, it could become a familiar sight in our county once again if the programme launched in 1989 jointly by English Nature and the RSPB to re-establish it in various parts of Britain succeeds (Stroud *et al.* 1989).

WHITE-TAILED EAGLE
Haliaeetus albicilla

A very rare vagrant. Wilson (1987) identified bones of this species dating back to Saxon times. Radford (1966) cited records of single birds shot on the Wantage Downs in 1793, near Henley "before 1849", at Henley about 1894 and at Combe in 1927. The 1930 annual report gives lengthy descriptions of an immense raptor, possibly this, seen in several parts of the county, once killing a puppy.

One place near the Buckinghamshire border visited by the 1930 bird was also the site of the last appearance of this species. On 22 November 1983 one was seen flying to the north over the Thame road east of Tiddington. There were rumours of a large bird of prey in the vicinity in the following month, but it was not until 20 January 1984 that a positive identification was made near Brill just over the Buckinghamshire border. Presumably this was the same individual seen earlier. It remained in the area, flying into Oxfordshire on at least two occasions, and was watched by hundreds of birdwatchers until last seen on 13 February 1984.

MARSH HARRIER
Circus aeruginosus

A rare winter visitor and passage migrant. Early writers were unusually vague about the status of the Marsh Harrier. Aplin (1889) says that "In Dr Lamb's time (1814) it was the most common hawk in the marshes around Newbury, Berkshire and it may have bred in those days upon Otmoor". However, he had no record after 1854. The decline was due to habitat loss and persecution. Jourdain (1925) described it as "no doubt formerly resident in the marshes along the Thames and Kennet valleys, it is now a rare visitor to the Thames valley." Thus it remained until its fortunes began to show signs of improvement in the mid-1970s coinciding with the progress of the species nationally. There were eight records from 1922–1975 (53 years), but 21 from 1975–1989 (15 years) (Table 5.29).

Most of the observations in the earlier period (five of eight) were in the winter months, while after 1975 the majority (19 of 21) were in the spring and autumn. The latter presented the appearance of passage through the county: birds did not linger, and were seen within a few days of each other in April and May, with a wider spread of dates in autumn from August and September (Figure 5.23). Sightings have been made in a wide range of locations, with only Otmoor (eight records) being visited more than once. Three were together at Brightwell Baldwin on 11 May 1988, otherwise all records were of single birds.

HEN HARRIER
Circus cyaneus

An infrequent winter visitor, and occasional passage migrant. The Hen Harrier is best known in Oxfordshire as a winter visitor, occurring

from November to March in small numbers at favoured sites on the Berkshire Downs and Otmoor. In these places there are wide areas of rough grass in which they can find their prey of small mammals. In the 1980s winter roosts of up to four birds were discovered on the Berkshire Downs, usually in crops such as Kale or Lucerne. These were closely observed by local birdwatchers. The birds returned as much as two hours before sunset, depending upon prevailing weather conditions, and made numerous short sorties before settling down at dusk.

They also appear in every month except June (see Figure 5.24), sometimes in unexpected places. These are usually single birds, presumably wandering through the county on passage, seen in the spring until the end of May and in autumn from mid-July. Confusion with the rarer Montagu's Harrier is possible, but there are few doubts about most records.

Summering, and even breeding was suggested by some authorities in the eighteenth and nineteenth centuries. It was believed to have bred at Compton in 1844. Clark-Kennedy (1868) describes it as "resident" though uncommon, and Aplin (1889) as "an occasional visitor of rare occurrence". Radford (1966) says that its occurrence had increased since 1958 due to the reduction in persecution and cites eight years in which birds were shot in the nineteenth century. Sharrock (1976) states that 200 years ago the Hen Harrier bred throughout Britain in such habitats as the dry chalk downs of southern England. We will never know whether some of the early records in Oxfordshire refer to this species, or the Montagu's Harrier, which was not recognised as a separate species until 1802.

MONTAGU'S HARRIER
Circus pygargus

Montagu's Harrier, the smallest and rarest of Britain's three harrier species, occurs rarely in Oxfordshire usually as a passage migrant and with one instance of proved breeding this century. The paucity of Oxfordshire records is understandable for a species at the very edge of its European range, having a British population that fluctuates in numbers due to climatic change, and which currently does not exceed single figures (Elliott 1988, *Red Data Birds in Britain* 1990). The species has always been rare in the

Table 5.29. Marsh Harrier.
Total number of records per decade.

Decade	No. of records
1920s	3
1930s	0
1940s	0
1950s	3
1960s	1
1970s	6
1980s	17

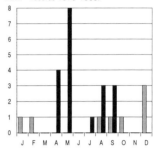

Figure 5.23. Marsh Harrier.
Monthly distribution of records.
Grey = records 1922-1975,
black = records 1976-1989.

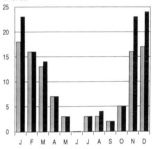

Figure 5.24. Hen Harrier.
Monthly distribution of records 1980-1989.
Grey = number of records, black = number of birds.

I.L.'90.

county (at least since recording began). Aplin (1889) gives only three records of birds shot, and Radford (1966) lists a further 14 between 1900 and 1966.

The preferred breeding habitat of this ground-nesting bird was once considered to be large tracts of open land ranging from heaths, moors, reedbeds or even young conifer plantations, well removed from human settlement. None of these exist in any quantity in present-day Oxfordshire. On the continent most recent records of breeding have occurred in large cereal fields, being superficially similar in appearance to reedbeds (Day 1988, Elliott 1988). It was in just such a situation that in 1986 a pair was found breeding in Oxfordshire.

Atlas workers reported birds in a widely spaced group of five tetrads, probably relating to the breeding pair which were known to hunt over an extensive range. Territorial behaviour and nest building in a field of barley were observed and subsequently four eggs were laid at the beginning of June. During incubation an immature male joined the pair and was tolerated in the territory for several days. The adult male often spent long periods away from the nesting area, returning with prey only for short periods. He provided the female with food throughout the incubation period and until the young were 15–20 days old after which she too began to take an active part in supplying food to the young. Food usually consisted of open-country bird species such as Meadow Pipits, Corn Buntings and young Starlings as well as occasional small mammals. With the protection given by RSPB wardens and local watchers, together with the generous support of the farmer concerned, successful fledging of two young was achieved at the beginning of August.

Wintering in Africa south of the Sahara, Montagu's Harriers usually arrive here by mid-May but are occasionally recorded as early as the end of April. Departure for their winter quarters

begins in September with birds sometimes seen into October. A resurgence of records in the 1980s offers some hope for this splendid raptor but may be partially attributed to increased observer awareness.

Egg collecting and persecution by gamekeepers was a limiting factor on the population in the earlier half of the century. Several of the relatively few local records from that time refer to birds trapped, as at Kingston Bagpuize in late April 1902 and again there in 1921, also one was shot at Watlington in April 1935. Breeding possibly occurred in 1934 in Berkshire in what is now part of south Oxfordshire as three brown harriers were seen in October after a pair had spent the summer locally. There was a reduction in sightings after the 1950s when the national population collapsed as with other predatory species in the pesticides era (Elliott 1988).

A major threat to the breeding success of Montagu's Harriers nesting in cereal fields is the harvesting operations which for barley usually takes place around the end of July when the young are still in the nest. On the continent in recent years the problem has been overcome by removing the young birds as the harvester passes, returning them later to a protective den of straw bales until fledging (Day 1988, Elliott 1988). Nesting success in Oxfordshire was achieved by leaving an area of barley uncut around the nest site.

Since the species is on Schedule 1 of the Wildlife and the Countryside Act (1981), it is of course essential that a certain degree of secrecy over the whereabouts of nesting birds is maintained. However it cannot be stressed too highly that, if their presence is kept a total secret either from the landowner or the RSPB who can take the appropriate protection measures, the inevitable result will be their destruction come harvest time.

GOSHAWK
Accipiter gentilis

The history of this species in Britain generally is poorly known (Sharrock 1976). A rare resident, Radford (1966) gives only two Oxfordshire records for Goshawk, these being in 1882 and 1950. Between then and 1974 there is only one further report. However, from 1975–1989, there have been 56 reports, including the Oxfordshire Atlas data. Birds have been noted in every year except 1983 (Table 5.30), in all months of the year (Figure 5.25), and from all parts of the county. The monthly distribution of records suggests slight peaks in late winter and in passage periods. The majority of records are of single birds but three reports are of pairs in the breeding season. Breeding records are rare with only two confirmed instances of nesting, in 1984 and 1990 in woodland south of Oxford. Two of the reports of pairs were during the period of the Oxfordshire Atlas; one from the west, one from the south-east of the county where display over woodland was observed. Of the eight sightings of single birds in the Atlas period, four are possible breeders. In 1991, breeding behaviour was noted at two sites in east Oxfordshire. However, because of the large territories occupied and the general difficulties in locating birds, the accuracy of this figure is difficult to assess. Nevertheless, the limitations imposed by the paucity of large tracts of woodland (the species' preferred habitat) means that there are unlikely to be many more.

The main reason for the marked increase, which has also been noted in other parts of Britain, e.g. Devon, (Sitters 1988), is generally considered to be the deliberate release of Goshawks to the wild or the escape of falconer's birds. The local figure has presumably been improved by increased observer cover and it is possible that there may have been some instances of misidentification with large female Sparrowhawks which are now more frequently seen.

Many records of Goshawks in Oxfordshire include observations of prey items taken with Grey Squirrels, corvids, Woodpigeons and Collared Doves all noted. Kenward (1979), in a study using released Goshawks in an area near Chipping Norton, found that Rabbits, Woodpigeons and Moorhens were the most commonly taken prey. However, commenting on the use of these raptors to control Woodpigeons and so lessen the damage caused to growing crops, the author concludes that any effect would be slight. It is apparent that a wide range of prey, including gamebirds, is taken and Lack (1986), notes that the species will take whatever large birds or medium-sized mammals are readily available and easily taken.

The Goshawk is a protected species and because of predations by egg-collectors and falconers and persecution by keepers, no distribution map is presented.

SPARROWHAWK
Accipiter nisus

Although the Sparrowhawk currently enjoys a widespread distribution, in the past its fortunes in the county have been mixed. Aplin (1889) and Alexander (1947) both described the bird as fairly common although the former did note that it was decreasing because of persecution. The population increased during the period 1939-1945 as game-rearing diminished, and remained at a consistently high level until the fifties. However, during the latter half of that decade and into the 1960s, the population crashed until records in Oxfordshire were a mere handful. This decrease was part of a widespread decline, particularly noticeable in southern Britain and especially in predominantly cereal growing regions. It has since been attributed to the use of a range of organochlorine seed-dressings such as Aldrin and Dieldrin, which accumulated in the body tissues of birds. These had both direct toxic effects and sub-lethal consequences such as reduced fertility and egg-shell thinning leading to a decreased reproductive rate. A ban on this type of pesticide was introduced in 1962 and since then the Sparrowhawk has returned although the process initially was a very slow one (Newton 1979, Marchant et al. 1990). In 1971 the OOS report regarded it as uncommon whilst the BOS decennial report of 1974 described it as scarce over the period 1962-1971.

The National Atlas (Sharrock 1976) demonstrated that the bird was certainly increasing its range and entering districts which, for the past decade had been unoccupied but was still at a low level in many areas. Comparison of the distribution in 1968-1972 (Figure 5.26) with the Oxfordshire Atlas, demonstrates just how marked this change has been. The Oxfordshire Atlas shows that the distribution is not continuous over the county and is related,

Table 5.30. Goshawk.
Annual number of records 1975-1989.

Year	No. of records
1975	1
1976	3
1977	2
1978	2
1979	3
1980	6
1981	2
1982	8
1983	0
1984	6
1985	7
1986	2
1987	4
1988	2
1989	4

Figure 5.25. Goshawk.
Monthly distribution of records 1975-1989.

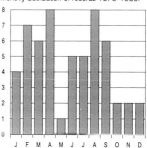

Figure 5.26. Sparrowhawk.
Breeding records 1968-1972 (after Sharrock 1976).

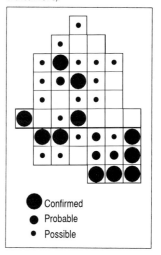

● Confirmed
● Probable
• Possible

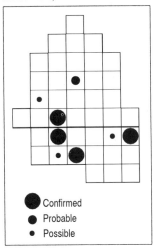

Figure 5.27. Buzzard.
Breeding records 1968-1972 (after Sharrock 1976).

● Confirmed
● Probable
• Possible

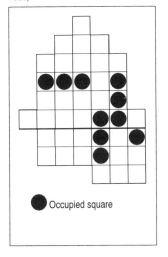

Figure 5.28. Buzzard.
Oxfordshire distribution 1983 (after Taylor 1988).

● Occupied square

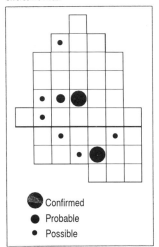

Figure 5.29. Buzzard.
Breeding records 1985-1988, results of the Oxfordshire Atlas.

● Confirmed
● Probable
• Possible

in part at least, to the bird's close association with woodlands. Mixed or coniferous woodlands are particularly favoured with a high proportion of nests located in Larch, pines and other conifers. The north-west/south-east band of registrations across the county reflects this, although there are a number of woods in which no birds were found. This may be due in part to low observer coverage, particularly in the Chilterns, whilst there is evidence that in some areas Sparrowhawks may still be subject to persecution. Conversely, some birds nest away from the typical woodland site and nests have been found in standard trees along hedgerows as well as in tall hedges themselves. It is surprising that so few records were of a confirmed breeding. The Sparrowhawk is probably the easiest raptor to locate in the breeding season. The conspicuous aerial nuptial display in late February/early March is helpful whilst adults carrying prey to the nest and the very vocal nature of the young on and around the nest should lead to the higher category of breeding evidence. Such fieldwork does require extra time and hence a general study of the nature of the Oxfordshire Atlas is not the most suitable way of obtaining data on the Sparrowhawk and a specific study is needed. Also, through the period of fieldwork for the Oxfordshire Atlas, the spring weather was often unfavourable and it was difficult to locate pairs displaying.

Whilst many of the 'possible' breeding records may relate to birds passing through a tetrad (hunting territories may be large), it is felt that a high proportion of nests may have been overlooked. If one assumes though that column '2' and '3' records give the most accurate picture, and one assumes a density of one pair per tetrad, a minimum breeding density of six pairs per 100 km² is obtained. In suitable habitat birds may nest at high densities. The BOS has reported nests as close as 400 m, and Wiggins (1984) reports five pairs in Bagley Wood, a density of over two pairs/km². This is a similar density to that reported for Wytham by Gosler (1990).

A number of local observers have commented that in the latter 1980s, the Sparrowhawk was possibly the commonest raptor in the county. In the absence of any full, county-wide study, this is difficult to assess although it is certainly a species which has become very conspicuous. It is regularly seen in the urban environment, coming in to hunt small birds in gardens, allotments and parks. The bird table in particular has provided an apparently irresistible attraction and Sparrowhawks pick off finches, sparrows and tits. Here and elsewhere a wide range of prey have been seen to be taken; wagtails, Starlings, Fieldfare and Redwing from roost sites, and the female Sparrowhawks, the larger of the sexes, will take Collared Doves or Woodpigeons. Indeed birds have been seen attempting to catch the Feral Pigeons in central Oxford.

Since the species still appears to be expanding

locally, it is not surprising that recent ringing returns have all been of local recoveries with 95% of Oxfordshire-ringed birds recovered here (the rest were all from southern England). The longest movement noted is of a bird ringed as a nestling at Woodstock found 92 km to the east at Hoddesden, Hertfordshire, the following February.

The species was the subject of two major studies at Wytham. Geer (1979) looked at the effect of Sparrowhawk predation on the tit population of the wood, noting that whilst birds of all age-classes were taken, predation was greatest when the tits fledge. However, oddly, he found little evidence that the hawks took the young tits in preference to adults. Gray (1987) studied aspects of the feeding ecology in winter looking at a resident winter hawk population of 25 birds (12 males; 13 females) using Wytham as a roost site. Woodland was the favoured hunting area, but females made more use of farmland than males. This difference was related to the exploitation of different prey populations. In each case, habitat edges were most often used. On average, 25% of the day was spent hunting with 18% of observed attacks successful. Adults were more successful than first-year birds and most hunting took place in the early morning, with 88% before noon. It was noted that as the winter progressed the mean body-weight of the hawks decreased, relating to the diminishing numbers of prey, so that an individual having a higher body-weight at the start of winter had an increased chance of survival.

The problems which faced British birds of prey during the 1950s and 1960s are now over and the re-establishment of the Sparrowhawk is well advanced. Provided that there are no further problems with agrochemicals and that persecution remains low, there is no reason why the species should not continue to grace the county with its spirited hunting dashes and graceful soaring flights.

BUZZARD
Buteo buteo

In many parts of north and west Britain the sight of a Buzzard hunting or soaring over open countryside would possibly elicit no more than a cursory glance. However, it's appearance in Oxfordshire still causes a degree of excitement amongst local birdwatchers for here it is a rare breeding species although it does occur more frequently as a visitor, typically during periods of passage.

During the Oxfordshire Atlas, breeding records were obtained from 14 tetrads and the highest grade of evidence in each 10 km square is shown in Figure 5.29. Since some of these records form distinct clusters, it is believed that the data represent no more than five occupied territories and nesting in only three sites in any one season. All nests have been in medium to large tracts of woodland including the Chilterns, the Downs and a number of sites in central to west Oxfordshire.

Until the early nineteenth century, the Buzzard was widespread over much of the country including Oxfordshire but, due to persecution by gamekeepers, it became restricted to more remote areas. Aplin (1889), could give no evidence of breeding for 40 years and, similarly, Alexander (1947) described it as merely a visitor to the county. Reduction in gamekeeping during the second world war was followed by records of breeding in two sites through until the late 1940s and early 1950s, but nothing later (Radford 1966). Nationally, the Buzzard population suffered at this time from the use of organochlorine pesticides and the affect of *myxomatosis* on Rabbits. The National Atlas (Sharrock 1976) found breeding to have occurred in four 10 km squares (Figure 5.27), and a BTO survey in 1983 (Taylor *et al.* 1988) revealed birds to be present in ten 10 km squares (Figure 5.28) but there was no confirmation of breeding. This latter study showed that since the 1968–1972 survey although there had been a national increase in the number of breeding pairs, there had been very little eastward expansion. Since the late 1960s breeding has been sporadic with up to three pairs present in any year. Since completion of the Oxfordshire Atlas, it is believed that breeding probably occurred at six sites in 1989.

Buzzards are recorded in the county throughout the year and from a wider scatter of locations. Whether these are local breeding birds, non-breeding individuals or birds moving into or through the area from elsewhere is difficult to ascertain, possibly they represent a combination of all three. There is one ringing recovery from Oxfordshire. A bird ringed as a nestling at Bossington Porlock, Somerset on 18 June 1941 was recovered at Freeland, (154 km ENE) on 27 August the same year. The

occurrence of birds through the year is provided in Figure 5.30 which shows a peak in the autumn. Many of these autumn sightings are of birds drifting eastwards across the county.

The reasons for the apparent reluctance of Buzzards to extend their breeding range eastwards are a matter of some debate. Continued persecution may be of some significance despite the bird's protected status although some Oxfordshire birds do nest close to keepered woodlands. Another cause is likely to be the lack of suitable hunting grounds. Since Buzzards are birds of open countryside, preying upon Rabbits and other small mammals in grassland habitats, Oxfordshire's arable landscape seems far from ideal with much of the preferred habitat having disappeared under the plough many years ago. With changes in the agricultural land-use likely in the final decade of the twentieth century it will be interesting to see if any expansion of range occurs. Additionally, the explosion in the Rabbit population in 1990-91 could provide new feeding opportunities.

ROUGH-LEGGED BUZZARD
Buteo lagopus

This is a rare winter visitor to Oxfordshire, seen between October and April. In the early years of recording in the county the species seems to have been rather more regular, with single records in winter 1825, 1840, November 1888, November/December 1906, autumn 1920, 1921, January 1927, March 1935, March 1936, March 1938, April 1942 and October 1947. Four of these records came from Cholsey Down.

Since then there have been years when they have appeared in greater numbers. As part of noted influxes into Britain in the winter of 1966-1967 there were three separate individuals reported in Oxfordshire (Aston Rowant, mid-December 1966 and January 1967, Henley, 26 February 1967) and in 1973 there was one (Shotover on 14 October).

But the most impressive period was the winter of 1974/75 when there were five certain records (including one of two birds) and two unsubstantiated reports. These were at Aston Rowant, 27 October to 16 November, at Watlington Hill, 10 November, two at East Ginge Downs on 10 and 11 November and 'possibles' there on 22 November and 7 December, West Ginge Down on 8 February, Cholsey Fair Mile on 3 and 31 March, a 'probable' there on 16 February, Wytham, 15 April and Steeple Aston, 29 August. This followed an autumn influx of unprecedented size on the east coast where groups of up to 45 were seen in the air simultaneously (Christie 1975).

After this excitement the normal pattern has been resumed locally, with just two more occurrences, of two at Goring in December 1980 and one there in October 1983.

It is known that these birds wandering into

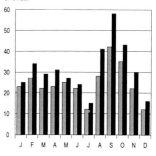

Figure 5.30. Buzzard.
Monthly distribution of records, 1975-1989. Grey = number of records, black = number of birds.

ILN90.

Britain originate from Fennoscandian populations arriving through the east coast, and our observations have a decidedly easterly bias: nine of the 13 records since 1966 have been on the eastern fringe of the county. It would seem that we are at the edge of their wintering range.

GOLDEN EAGLE
Aquila chrysaetos

Only one confirmed record. One seen on Wantage Downs in July 1924 and shot. It is now in Reading Museum.

Family: Pandionidae
Osprey

Despite an extensive world-wide distribution, the Osprey is still uncommon in Britain and breeds here only in Scotland. This is itself one of the best known of conservation success stories since the species was persecuted to extinction in Britain by 1916. It returned to breed on Speyside in the mid-1950s. With the protection of the RSPB, it has, since then, expanded its breeding range so that there are now more than 50 pairs.

OSPREY
Pandion haliaetus

This infrequent passage migrant was regarded as a rare visitor before 1960. Up to then there had been only nine or ten twentieth century records and Aplin (1889) lists only a further six, but by the 1980s small numbers were seen annually both on spring and autumn passage at various watery places, with Farmoor Reservoir replacing Blenheim Lake as the main site. The steadiness of the increase is demonstrated by Table 5.31. This development parallels the re-establishment of breeding in Scotland, so some of the Ospreys we see may be British birds.

Periods of records are from 9 March to 11 June, and from 5 July to 19 November, with peaks in April/May and August/September (Figure 5.31).

In some years Ospreys have lingered on passage for several days, even weeks, especially in the autumn. One making twice-daily fishing visits to Farmoor Reservoir in August and September 1989 attracted many interested spectators. It flew off on several occasions towards Wytham Wood where it probably roosted. More usually visits are no more than brief pauses over watery places. In recent years passage birds have been seen migrating at low altitudes, and there are two records of Ospreys passing over open country far from water.

The frequency of their appearances at certain west Oxfordshire sites in the spring in several years in the early 1980s, and the way some individuals did not hurry on, gave rise to the speculation that they might spend the summer in the county as in neighbouring Wiltshire (Pollard 1982).

Table 5.31. Osprey.
Number of records in each 5-year period 1960-1989.

Period	No. of records
1960-64	0
1965-69	3
1970-74	6
1975-79	10
1080 81	17
1985-89	19

Figure 5.31. Osprey.
Monthly distribution of records 1949-1989, based on arrival dates.

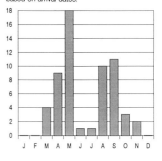

I.L.~90

Family: Falconidae
Falcons

Of the five falcon species recorded in Oxfordshire, two breed regularly, two are regular winter or passage visitors and one is a vagrant. The history of falcons in the county closely parallels that of the hawks described above. After persecution in the last century, a partial recovery and significant declines in some species due to pesticides, they are now probably as abundant here as at any time for more than 100 years. This has resulted from the ban on organochlorine pesticides, intensive protection efforts and a more enlightened attitude from keepers in the country as a whole.

Figure 5.32. Kestrel.
Ringing recoveries involving Oxfordshire.

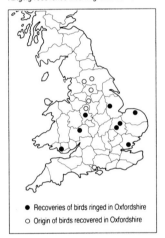

● Recoveries of birds ringed in Oxfordshire
○ Origin of birds recovered in Oxfordshire

Figure 5.33. Kestrel.
Number of roadside sightings in 1985 (after Overall 1985).

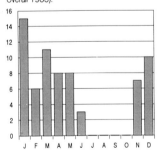

KESTREL
Falco tinnunculus

Widespread and numerous, the Kestrel is surely the most familiar resident diurnal bird of prey in the county. It's habit of hovering over roadside verges in search of small mammals often allows easy viewing as well as instant recognition. The Oxfordshire Atlas revealed birds present in 65% of tetrads. However, more than half of these records fell into the 'possible' category. This is not too surprising since the difficulty of locating nest sites is well known and has been noted in other atlas studies (Sitters 1988). Indeed, even in an intensive study by the BOS in 1984 across 475 square kilometres (not all in Oxfordshire), only 16 nest sites were located although additional observations suggested a minimum of 35 pairs. Careful observation of birds carrying prey to nests is the most satisfactory way of confirming breeding although the large hunting area used by a pair makes the tracking of birds difficult. Also, Kestrels are very wary

around the nest site and will remain silent and hidden if an intruder approaches. Gaps in the distribution come, as might be expected, from areas of intensive agriculture, the heavily-wooded Chilterns and from some built-up areas.

The BOS survey showed that nest sites were divided almost equally between cavities in trees and old crow nests, particularly those of Magpie or Carrion Crow. Occasionally Kestrels nest on buildings. Although the loss of old trees may therefore be a problem, birds will readily take to nestboxes, which, if situated well away from thieving hands and other disturbance, can be very successful. Boxes in parts of west Oxfordshire for example have been occupied regularly for more than 12 years. Despite the value of cavities in old Elms as nest sites in the BOS area, the loss of trees due to Dutch Elm Disease did not have a significant effect on the population in that area (Easterbrook 1983).

Most nests are found along hedges and in copses on farmland and also in woodlands, but more usually at their edges. One feature of the 1984 BOS survey was the demonstration of the importance of permanent pasture in the vicinity of the nest site. In each of the 1 km squares occupied by Kestrels there was a significantly smaller area of arable farmland present than in other squares surveyed. This observation is related to the feeding preferences of the species. Analysis of pellets has shown the Short-tailed Field Vole to be the principal prey although other voles and mice are also caught. These small mammals are found in grassland habitats of all types whether meadow, field-edge or along roadsides, thus dictating the feeding areas of the kestrel. Occasionally, individuals may enter woodlands to hunt. This is especially true of the Beechwoods along the Chilterns. Such woods generally have a high, closed canopy with reduced shrub and field layers and in these situations, hunting from perches rather than by hovering is more usually practised.

The species will actually take a wider range of prey than small mammals, including large invertebrates and small birds. Although feeding on this latter group seems to result from opportunism. Hence Linnets in reedbed roosts and sparrows on bird tables have been observed falling prey to Kestrels. Similarly, one July nest contained the remains of many juvenile Starlings whilst the observation of one Kestrel carrying a Blackbird must represent the maximum size of prey taken.

After the breeding season the young birds disperse around the country. Birds ringed in Oxfordshire as nestlings have been recovered, prior to their first breeding season, at points east and west of Oxfordshire and there have also been recoveries in the county of birds ringed in northern England (Figure 5.32).

It is difficult to document any long-term changes in the Oxfordshire Kestrel population since most of the previous authorities regard the species as a common resident. However, there is evidence of an increase in the 1940s, possibly due to a reduction of game-keeping. Radford (1966) suggested that a decline had occurred in recent years (presumably due to pesticide use) but that this was much less than in other areas and than observed in other species. In the short-term, Aplin (1889), considered that most birds left the district in winter although in recent decades, observers have been aware of influxes into the county in December and January. Throughout the year of 1985, whilst driving around a large part of the county, Roy Overall (OOS report 1985) noted all roadside Kestrel sightings. These findings are shown in Figure 5.33. The interpretation of these results, particularly their absence from July to October is a little speculative (i.e. are they breeding away from roads? Is the grass on these verges too tall for successful hunting? Are there more Kestrels in the county in winter?). Whilst the reporting of sightings is valuable up to a point, there is obviously scope for further study into the population ecology of the Kestrel in Oxfordshire.

The regular appearance of hunting Kestrels along verges is almost certainly due to a lack of good feeding opportunities in the wider countryside rather than a particular affinity for roads. With potentially beneficial changes to the agricultural landscape such as 'set-aside' likely in the 1990s, it may be that birds will utilise these opportunities as and when they arise. Natural nest sites could also be an important limiting factor and the provision of boxes in suitable areas could be a useful exercise in practical conservation.

RED-FOOTED FALCON
Falco vespertinus

There are two records of this very rare vagrant. A first-summer male showing signs of moult, in foraging flight, pausing to hover, over Wolvercote Gravel Pit on 12 June 1983. Another male hawking insects over Standlake Gravel Pits on 27 and 28 May 1987.

MERLIN
Falco columbarius

This is a regular winter visitor (illustrated below) and passage migrant in small numbers in Oxfordshire. On three occasions two have been seen together, but all other reports are of single birds. They are highly mobile, so instances of birds remaining in one area for more than a few days are unusual, although individuals appeared to have over-wintered at Churn and Dorchester. Records came from various parts of the county, but mostly from the more open, hilly districts.

Records range from 13 August to 1 May. There is a clear peak in mid-winter as shown in Figure 5.34. The origin of Oxfordshire Merlins is unknown although the nearest breeding population is probably Staffordshire (Harrison *et al.* 1982).

These little raptors can usually be seen perched on a post, or chasing into a flock of finches or buntings. Despite a recent decline in numbers of these prey items locally, there was an upsurge in Merlin sightings in the 1980s which could indicate a real improvement in status.

HOBBY
Falco subbuteo

The status of this summer visitor is something of a mystery, at least over the greater part of Oxfordshire. Its spectacularly acrobatic, aerial feeding technique aid identification but even with the intensive survey for the Oxfordshire Atlas an accurate assessment of the breeding population cannot be made.

Aplin's long account of 1889 suggests that the species was probably widespread in the nineteenth century but was never common due probably to severe persecution. Clark-Kennedy (1868) says that if it "were not persecuted and

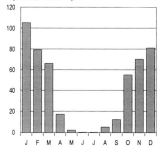

Figure 5.34. Merlin.
Monthly distribution of records 1959-1989. (Except 1981 when records in the annual report were undated).

Table 5.32. Hobby.

Period of first arrivals to Oxfordshire 1975-1989.

7-day period commencing	Number
28 March	5
4 April	0
11 April	1
18 April	3
25 April	6
2 May	1

its nest robbed it might become numerous". One can only wonder today as to what possible threat keepers perceived from this eater of Swallows and Dragonflies!

Radford (1966) was able to provide very few accounts of proven breeding although the species was believed to breed in small numbers each year. In the county bird reports since 1965, up to eight nests, but more usually four to six, have been reported in the county in any one season although records of sightings may number ten times as many. The reason for this lack of nesting information is linked to the generally secretive nature of the species and the fact that whilst over much of southern Britain it is associated with commons and heaths, in Oxfordshire it is a bird of farmland. This habitat is largely ignored by the average birdwatcher, and so whilst offering a secure nesting habitat (Hobbies are notoriously easy to disturb and are still subject to depredations by egg-collectors) it does lead to the paucity of the higher grades of nest recording. However, the work of a Hobby Study Group operating in the north of the county has shed light upon some aspects of the biology of the species (Fuller *et al.* 1985). Considering that this study area is almost at the northern breeding limit of the species and that it does not differ greatly in landscape from the rest of the county, the findings may be extrapolated to much of the county.

The Oxfordshire Atlas showed a very wide spread of records from around the county and while concentrations of records around the central area may represent an observer bias, records have come from all corners of the county. In the four year survey, birds were noted in 89 (11.8%) tetrads and, of these, 75% were 'possible' breeding records. By assuming that clusters of records represent nesting birds, an additional eight pairs are likely to have bred. If these results are compared with those obtained by the north Oxfordshire survey (Fuller *et al.*

1985), the shortcomings of a general atlas study becomes apparent. That study obtained a density of four pairs per 10 km square a figure which was maintained into the period of the Oxfordshire Atlas.

The Hobby is one of the latest summer migrants to arrive in Oxfordshire. First arrivals have been noted between 28 March and 5 May with an average of 16 April (Table 5.32), but the main influx of birds occurs towards the end of that period. In the north of the county, the BOS give the earliest arrival as 25 April and an average first date of 6 May. The late arrival is linked to the species' feeding habits since it feeds mainly on aerial insects such as Dragonflies and a range of small bird species, but especially those of open country such as hirundines, Swifts, pipits and larks. The arrival is timed so that the young (which are fed mainly on small birds) will be in the nest during the period of peak availability of juvenile hirundines in July and August.

Hobbies leave Oxfordshire in late September or October. The period for last records range from 20 September to 24 October with a mean of 7 October. The latest record in the BOS area is 13 October and the mean departure date 24 September.

One of the best times to locate potentially nesting birds is shortly after their arrival since they tend to be seen in the near vicinity of the nest tree. It would appear likely that a subsequent period, spent feeding on high-flying insects, is necessary to achieve full breeding condition since adverse weather in May and June leads to a poor breeding season. In the agricultural landscape of Oxfordshire, most nests, which are usually disused Crow or Magpie's nests, are situated in solitary trees or in a hedgerow. Woodlands and copses are also occupied although nests tend to be towards the edges of these habitats. In general nests are well away from human habitation and even roadsides are avoided as much as possible. Thus, a pair nesting close to Oxford's railway station on one occasion was somewhat unusual. However, Hobby nesting density is also, in part, apparently related to the availability of hirundines, especially House Martins. In areas of prey abundance, pairs may nest at intervals of 3–5 km (Cramp and Simmons 1976). In north Oxfordshire the Hobby favours higher ground up to 150 m although it has only once been found higher than this at 180 m.

Egg-laying usually takes place in June, the young hatch in July and fledge towards the end of August. This is another period when birds are easy to locate and although birds will remain around the nest site for a while, family parties may move to other sites such as gravel pits or reservoirs where prey such as Swallows and martins may congregate and subsequently attract as many as six Hobbies. The sight of young Hobbies attempting to catch Swifts on the wing is both amusing and exciting to watch. This is the peak time for records of the species.

As a protected species there is an obvious need to remain informed as to the status of this most welcome summer visitor. Indeed it was the inability of the OOS to satisfy a request from a national conservation body for an estimate of the county population, which was one of the prime motivations to embark on the Oxfordshire Atlas. Any monitoring and reporting must however be done in such a way as to ensure that disturbance is prevented, hence we do not provide a distribution map in this account. Given the effort needed to locate nests, it is unlikely that we could ever obtain an accurate estimate of the county population. We hope that in the future, local field ornithologists may be able to study selected areas in the southern half of Oxfordshire intensively and give a little more insight into this attractive falcon.

PEREGRINE
Falco peregrinus

An infrequent visitor. In the last century many were shot, and most records this century have been of birds briefly passing through. Apart from 1971 and 1972, when there were none, a few have been noted annually.

Although seen in every month, they are much more likely to appear in autumn or winter. 82% of all records are in the period August to January (Figure 5.35)

The national decline of this species in the 1960s and early 1970s due to poisoning by organochlorine pesticides accumulated from prey items, and their subsequent remarkable recovery when these chemicals were banned, is reflected in the number of Oxfordshire sightings (Table 5.33).

Peregrines usually make no more than fleeting visits, although some early observations hinted at the possibility of individuals occasionally over-wintering. Firmer evidence of this came in recent years with a series of records centred around the Stanton Harcourt and Farmoor area from 30 September 1973 to 25 January 1974, from 13 November 1987 to 3 January 1988 (a first-winter female), and from 29 August to 3 December 1988 (an immature). The origin of Oxfordshire Peregrines is unknown.

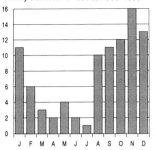

Figure 5.35. Peregrine.
Monthly distribution of records 1960-1989.

Table 5.33. Peregrine.
Sightings during five year periods from 1945-1985.

Period	Sightings
1945-49	24
1950-54	21
1955-59	18
1960-64	12
1965-69	10
1970-74	8
1975-79	17
1980-85	11

Family: Phasianidae
Gamebirds

Of the seven gamebirds recorded in Oxfordshire during the twentieth century, only three, the Black Grouse, Grey Partridge and the Quail, are native to Britain. The others have all been introduced deliberately for sport or have escaped from captivity. All except the Quail are resident throughout the year.

Table 5.34. Red-legged Partridge.
Total number of sightings by J.W. Brucker 1985-1990.

Year	Grey Partridge	Red-legged Partridge
1985	115	135
1986	70	208
1987	58	105
1988	38	90
1989	59	116
1990	49	112

BLACK GROUSE
Tetrao tetrix

A very rare vagrant. Jourdain (1926) considered it was once indigenous to Berkshire, and quoted two nineteenth century records of "stragglers" shot at Forest Hill in 1836, and at Tackley in 1880. The only record this century was of one in a north Oxford garden after a cold spell on 19 March 1928. B.W. Tucker suggested the Wyre Forest in Worcestershire as the most likely place of origin of this bird.

RED-LEGGED PARTRIDGE
Alectoris rufa

The Red-legged Partridge is a numerous resident of a sedentary nature. It is therefore found in greatest concentrations near to the places where they were released. They show a preference for arable fields bordered by dense hedgerows, and dry, wild areas around gravel pits and limestone quarries.

Totals of sightings made by J.W. Brucker during a similar amount of watching annually from 1985-1990 in a variety of habitats throughout central and south Oxfordshire show them to be more than twice as numerous as the Grey Partridge (Table 5.34). The Oxfordshire Atlas found them in 75.8% of tetrads as compared with 57.5% for the Grey Partridge. Hence if we assume that John Brucker's counts are representative of the county

as a whole, either the Red-legged Partridge occurs in larger coveys than the Grey, or it is more conspicuous.

Aplin (1889) traces the steady progress from their first appearance in the Chilterns in 1835 to their occupation of many parts of west and north Oxfordshire in the following half century. This population was supported by introductions during the first half of the twentieth century, although on a limited scale as their habit of running away rather than springing to flight made them unpopular with sportsmen.

As numbers of Grey Partridges declined through the twentieth century due to changes in agricultural practice, Red-legged Partridges were "put down" increasingly as substitutes, with the result that by the 1970s they had became widespread and common. It is unlikely that the species would continue to survive in such numbers without these annual supplements (Marchant *et al.* 1990). Some display their origins by extreme tameness, such as a pair which nested (unsuccessfully) in a herbaceous border in a Marston garden, and the pair which lived for a time in the playground of a Woodstock school.

There are several population controls. Organised shooting accounts for many each year. Natural predators have increased during the second half of the twentieth century with Magpies and Foxes known locally to have taken eggs and chicks. Low spring temperatures and cold, wet summers cause temporary declines as in 1987 and 1988. See also Chukar.

CHUKAR
Alectoris chukar

Some of these southern European gamebirds have been introduced on occasions since the mid and late 1970s. They associated with coveys of Red-legged Partridges, and inter-breeding has occurred to such an extent that it has become impossible to be sure whether birds of either species found in the wild are of pure stock. In April 1977, for example, there were several birds at Blenheim showing characteristics of both these species and also of the Rock Partridge *A. graeca*. Other sightings of Chukar, or hybrids have been made at Horton-cum-Studley and Stanton Harcourt Gravel Pits.

The further introduction of these species was banned in the 1980s, but it is likely that their characteristics will be noted in Red-legged Partridge types for many years to come.

GREY PARTRIDGE
Perdix perdix

The native Grey Partridge may still be described as a fairly common, highly sedentary resident in Oxfordshire, but occurring in much reduced numbers. It is most numerous in the cereal growing areas of the Berkshire Downs, the Vale of the White Horse, and on the Oxford Clays, but is more sparsely distributed in more wooded parts of the Chilterns and Cotswolds. The only precise counts on record were made in January 1979 when parties were conspicuous after snowfalls: there were 254 in 26 coveys seen from the 17 km of roads between Ewelme, Watlington, Stadhampton and Little Milton, and 102 in 4.5 km between Stanton Harcourt and Northmoor.

This was once such a well known resident that Aplin (1889) commented that in his part of north Oxfordshire, "as many as twenty or thirty brace can be bagged in a day". It remained a common, widespread bird for most of the first half of the twentieth century, but Radford (1966) gave the first hint of a possible decline. Annual reports since 1960 show a sharp reduction in numbers in the 1960s, some evidence of a partial recovery in the 1970s, but a continued disappearance from many places in the 1980s. Recent fluctuations in numbers appear partly attributable to weather conditions, with a succession of cold, late springs in the 1980s causing breeding failure. The extent of the overall loss may be illustrated by the figures given in the log books showing totals shot each season on one large estate in central Oxfordshire. In 1929/30 the total was 998, by 1961/62 it had fallen to 607, and in 1987/8 only seven birds were killed.

Grey Partridges are confronted by a number of natural hazards. Stuart-Whortley (1893) stated that the Red Kite must have accounted for the young when they were common in the country, and also described how a friend was taking a walk near Oxford "when a beautiful Hen Harrier singled out a fine partridge and struck it dead at his feet". These species offer no threat today, but the abundance of Magpies, Carrion Crows and Foxes in recent years resulting from a reduction in gamekeeping, presents a new, and considerable danger, especially at nesting time.

Agricultural changes were the main cause of the decline. Destruction of hedgerows and verges has reduced areas of suitable nesting cover. A survey conducted by the RSPB in west Oxfordshire showed that 17% of hedgerows were lost between 1946 and 1986 (Joyce *et al.* 1988). The use of pesticides limited the availability of insects vital for feeding chicks. Local gamekeepers mention the importance of ant-hills and grasshoppers which were once very much more abundant. The practice of burning stubbles (banned from 1991), the reduction in the amount of weed seed resulting from the use of herbicides, and the clearing of waste ground, all combined to heighten difficulties in the Grey Partridge's search for autumn and winter food. Among the few helpful habitat changes have been the closure of many railway lines, leaving green paths across the countryside, and the waste ground left around gravel pit sites.

On many estates in the late 1980s the practice began of supplementing natural stocks by the introduction of hand-reared birds. As Grey Partridge chicks need a diet of insects in the first six weeks of their life it was once considered impossible to keep them. However new foods with a high protein content have made this practicable, and an increasing number are being released into the wild when they have grown past the critical period. Some farmers have even banned or restricted the use of insecticides to help them survive. One or two unusually tame Grey Partridges encountered recently were presumed to have been hand-reared. In addition, 'Set aside' fields in the

Table 5.35. Quail.

Approximate number of Quail records per year in Oxfordshire from 1925-1989.

Year	No.	Year	No.
1925	1	1958	15
1926	1	1959	23
1927	2	1960	29
1928	1	1961	28
1929	2	1962	6
1930	2	1963	21
1931	5	1964	85
1932	3	1965	34
1933	1	1966	15
1934	2	1967	26
1935	2	1968	2
1936	1	1969	9
1937	5	1970	32
1938	3	1971	18
1939	3	1972	18
1940	10	1973	10
1941	9	1974	2
1942	3	1975	5
1943	0	1976	12
1944	14	1977	21
1945	1	1978	8
1946	3	1979	9
1947	3	1980	3
1948	23	1981	5
1949	16	1982	16
1950	11	1983	30
1951	8	1984	12
1952	25	1985	8
1953	65	1986	11
1954	16	1987	27
1955	22	1988	8
1956	4	1989	37
1957	20		

early 1990s have proved, at least initially, to produce new supplies of weed seeds for this species and the banning of stubble-burning after 1991 is a promising development. The Grey Partridge's progress will be watched with interest.

QUAIL
Coturnix coturnix

The Quail is our only migratory gamebird occurring in the county as a summer visitor. It is very rarely seen and most records in Oxfordshire relate to calling males.

The Oxfordshire Atlas map is particularly revealing as it emphasises some aspects of Quail behaviour in Oxfordshire. The distribution of records, with concentrations in the north and on the chalky soils of the Downs and the foothills of the Chilterns, is typical of the pattern of occurrences throughout the present century. Also, the fact that breeding was confirmed in only one tetrad out of a total of 38 in which it was recorded highlights the elusive nature of this bird and the reliance on calling males for recording purposes. Contributory factors to this low proportion of confirmed breeding records are the Quail's liking for hiding in fields of cereals, especially barley, and observers' desire to avoid disturbing such a scarce species. It must also be remembered that the map is a composite picture of four years' records and the number of occupied tetrads in any one year is likely to be a fraction of those depicted.

In some years Quail are first encountered in April, as in 1985 and 1988, but more usually in May or June. Most records are from June and July with a few in August and September. One late record is of two near Leafield in October 1978. There are some exceptional cases of Quail over-wintering in Oxfordshire. Aplin

I.L.'90.

(1889) cites sightings of birds on 10 November 1846 and 9 December 1848. More recently, Quail have been recorded in mid-November 1969 and one was flushed by a hunt on 20 February 1961.

The number of Quail recorded in OOS reports from 1925–1989 are shown in Table 5.35. The data are subject to a number of problems of interpretation due to inconsistencies in recording and to the need to rely on calling males to establish their presence. This causes difficulties for the following reasons:

i) a number of males calling together has a ventriloquial effect on the listener and the actual number of birds present is difficult to determine;

ii) one of the functions of the males' calling is to attract females. It will, therefore, be suppressed when a mate is found (Moreau 1951);

iii) another function of calling is to establish territories and to exclude other males (Marchant *et al.* 1990), so this, combined with the Quail's tendency to concentrate in small areas (Sharrock 1976), may result in over-recording in years of high population;

iv) unpaired males have a tendency to move considerable distances (Sharrock 1976) and could be recorded in different places;

v) calling can be suppressed in cold weather (Radford 1966), resulting in under-recording. However, even bearing the above in mind, Figure 5.35 shows two aspects of the Quail's population changes in Oxfordshire during the past 65 years.

First, it shows a general long-term increase in the number of Quail records since the 1940s. This is a national trend (Sharrock 1976) and could be attributed, in part, to an increase in the amount of cereals being grown in recent years or to an increase in the number of birdwatchers.

Secondly, and much more striking, is the fluctuation in Quail numbers from year to year. The years in which especially large invasions occurred reflect those noted on a national scale (Marchant *et al.* 1990). Note especially good years in 1964, 1970, 1983 and poor years in 1968, 1974, 1975, 1980 and 1985.

The causes of these large fluctuations in numbers are unclear but they could be due to, for instance:

i) 'overshooting' on migration in favour-able weather conditions;

ii) a high European population resulting from a good breeding season the previous year;

iii) unsuitable conditions on the continent;

iv) a result of events in their wintering grounds.

Any one of these ideas, and others, would benefit from a special study. The last suggestion is particularly difficult to investigate, however, due to a lack of ringing data it is not known where Oxfordshire's Quail winter. It is thought that the majority of British Quail winter in Africa, south of the Sahara (Cramp and Simmons 1976).

PHEASANT
Phasianus colchicus

Common, except in urban areas. Pheasant rearing is an important commercial enterprise to which many acres of woodland and parkland throughout the county are devoted. Thousands are bred and released annually to maintain stocks of game, but there is also a thriving population of naturalised birds which continue a separate existence.

Because of the sedentary nature of this species they tend to be more often found in the vicinity of the management areas, although some have moved to places where the sound of gunshot is rarely heard. Proof that the wild population could survive independently was demonstrated during the 1939-1945 war when reasonable numbers remained despite bans on pheasant rearing.

The earliest record is of bones dating from medieval times (Wilson 1987). The greatest number were introduced during the last two centuries. Various races have been brought in including *P.c. colchicus* and *P.c. torquatus*, and as they interbreed freely, few today are of pure stock. One local gamekeeper calls them his 'liquorice allsorts'. Total albinos are found from time to time, as are sandy coloured and melanistic birds.

There are some data for breeding densities in woodlands in Oxfordshire. Gosler (1990) estimated 15-45 males/km^2 in Wytham Woods. Harper suggested fewer than 22 males/km^2 in Bagley and Wiggins fewer than 38 males/km^2 at Little Wittenham (both Wiggins 1984). Ford (1987) found no effect of woodland size on the likelihood of occurrence or density of Pheasants in Oxfordshire woods.

While birdwatchers have paid scant regard to this species, there is an appreciation that game preservation has caused the protection of many habitats, and the provision of foods and cover valuable for other species. Unlike so many of their predecessors many gamekeepers in Oxfordshire today are enlightened naturalists, and are not inclined to break the law by shooting all raptors on sight.

GOLDEN PHEASANT
Chrysolophus pictus

Attempts have been made to introduce the Golden Pheasant into the wild at one site, and possibly others. Its distribution is not understood clearly because of its skulking habits, but it seems to have survived for many years in Wychwood Forest where birds were released some time before 1967, and on occasions after this date. A small breeding population was established there in the late 1970s and early 1980s.

It is also frequently found in collections. The keeper at Bix Hall Estate kept Golden Pheasants in the early 1970s. Both males and females escaped, and managed to survive and breed in the neighbouring woods at the BBONT Warburg Reserve at Bix. They were still present in April 1990 when three cocks were seen chasing through the thick scrub of Great Hill.

Other records are of one which remained in the Hartslock area from August 1984 to May 1985, and one in a Burford garden in May 1985.

LADY AMHURST'S PHEASANT
Chrysolophus amherstiae

In addition to Golden Pheasants these were kept by the keeper on the Bix Hall Estate in the early 1970s, and males and females escaped several times. Since then pure specimens of both species have been encountered on the Warburg Reserve, as have brightly coloured hybrids of the two. Nests have been found twice in thick bramble scrub, but it is uncertain to which of the two species they belonged. In 1990 the warden, Nigel Phillips estimated the population, mostly hybrid, of six to eight males, and a similar number of females. Silver Pheasants *Lophura nycthemera*, also escaped at Bix, but although seen since, have not shown signs of breeding. In the west of the county they have wandered away from local collections and have appeared on occasion in Wytham Woods and Wychwood.

Family: Rallidae
Rails

Five species of Rail have occurred in Oxfordshire during the twentieth century. Of these, three are resident and breed here, one formerly bred in good numbers but has been driven to extinction in the county by unsympathetic farming practice during the last fifty years and the last is a vagrant which probably bred in the past. Rails are generally good indicators of habitat quality and especially of wetlands and the history of the group in Oxfordshire is a valuable barometer of habitat change.

WATER RAIL
Rallus aquaticus

A scarce resident and frequent winter visitor, the Water Rail is among the most secretive and enigmatic of the birds breeding regularly in the county. Its propensity to inhabit waterlogged, often inaccessible situations, seeking the dense cover afforded by aquatic plants such as *Phragmites, Typha* and *Carex,* offers limited opportunities for study.

Whilst known to be a regular breeder, proof that nesting has occurred is sporadic. Nests are notoriously difficult to find as borne out by the limited stock of Nest Record Cards for the species held by the BTO. Between 1939 and 1984, only 50 such cards had been obtained nationally — fewer than for the Dotterel! Nonetheless, it is remarkable that in Oxfordshire 120 years elapsed between the discovery of a nest with eggs in 1863 (Aplin 1889) and the next such discovery, at Wolvercote, in 1983.

More often, Water Rails are located by their

high-pitched squeals and pig-like grunts, known as 'sharming' which is both distinctive and far-carrying. In the absence of a visual observation, this is often the only reliable indication of site occupancy. Most evidence of breeding is of birds seen with young. Nest sites need not be extensive and small reedbeds, often under two hectares, may hold a pair (Bayliss 1984).

Aplin (1889) considered the Water Rail to be "generally distributed in fair numbers". Radford (1966) comments that locally, the species faces a bleak future as a regular resident due to widespread drainage and the destruction of habitat. However, between 1968 and 1972, the National Atlas (Sharrock 1976) located Water Rails in 22% of all 10 km squares in the British Isles and it was suggested that numbers could be higher than at any time during the twentieth century. The Oxfordshire Atlas gives confirmed or probable breeding in ten tetrads and possible breeding in a further eight. The elusive nature of the species means that this is likely to be an underestimate, and an evaluation based on the Oxfordshire Atlas data and the experiences of a number of local observers would suggest a population of around 20 pairs. The increase in breeding records since Radford may represent either a real increase or it may represent a greater awareness of, and interest in, the species during the 1970s and 1980s.

In winter, a wholly different picture emerges with the arrival of immigrants which, on the basis of national ringing data, originate from continental Europe. Whilst they may remain generally elusive, a prolonged spell of hard weather may force birds into the open. They may then be seen at a wide variety of sites including sheltered ditches and damp waste-ground. In January 1982, during particularly severe conditions, up to four individuals were seen at Fiddler's Island near Port Meadow, with other birds noted at Iffley, Hinksey Pools, Osney, Trap Grounds, Godstow, Wolvercote and north Oxford and involving perhaps a dozen or more birds. During the late 1980s, Water Rails have also been seen coming to feed around bird-feeding stations at suitable wetland sites such as at BBONT's Lashford Lane Fen Nature Reserve. By the end of March, these visitors have departed leaving just the resident population.

The long-term future for the Water Rail as a local breeding species is by no means assured. Although the extensive mineral workings in the county may have partly compensated for the loss of wetlands, to be of value to nesting Water Rails these need to develop the necessary vegetation cover and to be allowed to exist with minimal disturbance, particularly from recreational activities. If we are not to witness a decline in the number of Water Rails breeding in the county, extreme vigilance will need to be exercised to retain the remaining established wetland sites.

SPOTTED CRAKE
Porzana porzana

Now a rare visitor, although nineteenth century writers used phrases such as "frequently killed on the banks of the Thames" (Clark-Kennedy 1869), and "seen occasionally in some numbers in autumn" (Aplin 1889), suggesting that it was more common then. Indeed Aplin suggested that it might breed in the county because of the presence of immatures in August.

There have been ten records of single birds during this century: in November 1901 near Banbury, two records in June 1931 near Iffley, in October 1931 on Otmoor, in April 1941 at Sandford Sewage Farm, in January 1942 at Clifton Hampden, in July 1957 at Great Milton and August 1957 at Cholsey, September 1957 near Wallingford, in December 1983 on Port Meadow and in April 1985 on Blewbury Down. As can been seen, these are evenly distributed through the year and come from a wide scatter of sites.

Breeding has not been proved, but a freshly killed specimen on the road at Great Milton on 17 July 1957 was an adult female with a very large ovary suggesting she was breeding or had bred.

Some records of this elusive bird indicate the possibility that it might overwinter, as shown by the one found in a ditch near Port Meadow on 19 and 26 December 1983, while others may be on passage like the one hit by a vehicle on a farm track near Blewbury Downs in April 1985.

CORNCRAKE
Crex crex

Once a common breeding bird in the Oxfordshire Thames-side meadows, this is now a rare passage migrant. Neither Aplin (1889) nor Warde Fowler (1886) writing at the end of the nineteenth century detected any reduction in numbers. Indeed the latter even remarked on hearing it occasionally in Christchurch Meadows

in the centre of Oxford. By 1926 Jourdain described it as "not plentiful, but breeding annually in varying numbers, chiefly in the low lying, grassy districts". Alexander's assessment in 1947 was that "during the last sixty years numbers have steadily decreased, and it is doubtful whether any now breed in the county".

There has been no evidence of breeding since the summer of 1953 when presumed juveniles were seen at Ipsden and Woodstock. The decline in passage records since then has continued, and the last record was of one heard at Kingham on 3 July 1977 (Table 5.36).

Causes of the disappearance of Corncrakes from most of Britain were well considered by Norris (1947) who traced the first signs of the decline to the mid-nineteenth century in southeast Britain and linked it to the introduction of the mowing machine though it is now considered that this was not the only problem (Marchant *et al.* 1990). In Oxfordshire their favoured handscythed hay meadows have not existed for a considerable time. Another factor suggested by Norris is that they are liable to fly into overhead cables; at least three local records are of birds presumed killed in this way.

Recent research based on surviving Corncrake populations in Ireland and Britain by O'Meary (1979), and Cadbury (1980) makes depressing reading, indicating that although mechanisation of agriculture is an important factor there must be other reasons for the decline which are not yet understood. For example, habitat destruction in their African winter quarters might also have contributed to their decline. There is little cause for optimism for any recovery in the near future unless substantial changes in land-use were to come about.

MOORHEN
Gallinula chloropus

The Moorhen is our most widespread and probably most common breeding waterside bird — a status unchanged for 100 years. With its low profile, flicking tail and sharp call, it is well known on all of the county's lakes, gravel pits and rivers, and is also common along smaller streams and on even the smallest of farm ponds. There are good numbers along the Oxford Canal corridor, being recorded in 76% of the 1 km segments of it's length (Collins, 1983). Nests are built on the edges of these waterways in reeds and other bankside vegetation and on low, over-hanging boughs, but birds are just as likely to be found on damp, rushy meadows or in overgrown ditches and drainage channels. The Oxfordshire Atlas map reflects this ability of the Moorhen to utilise a wide range of wet habitats, and although, in the main, high ground is avoided, small ponds on the Downs or Cotswolds can host a pair or two.

The breeding season is often a long one and nests with eggs have been recorded as early as 23 February, or as late as mid-September. Weather

Table 5.36. Corncrake.
Total number of records by five-year periods 1960-1990.

Period	No. of records
1960-65	6
1966-70	6
1971-75	4
1976-80	2
1980-85	0
1985-90	0

conditions have an important effect on breeding success; wet weather leading to spate conditions, may destroy a large percentage of riverside nests while hot summer weather may cause smaller ponds to dry out and, as a result, young birds may perish. Replacement broods are commonplace and losses are often recovered quickly as was particularly evident after the drought in 1976.

River management is instrumental in maintaining a high breeding density and success rate. Where banks are devoid of vegetation or the adjacent land is intensively farmed or urbanised, pairs are thinly distributed. On the Thames, heavy boat traffic, and the wash created by it, may cause some problems and lead to the loss of nests. Where suitable habitat exists, pairs may nest close together, even to the point of being on the same overhanging bough.

Outside the breeding season birds tend not to stray far from nesting areas. Of 14 recoveries of birds ringed in Oxfordshire, 12 were within 9 km of the ringing site. However, they show a tendency to form medium-sized flocks in winter. 105 were counted at Banbury Sewage Farm in November 1987, and over 50 noted at Blenheim in January 1987 and January 1988. In severe weather, birds have been known to enter gardens to feed.

In the absence of any comparative data, it is difficult to assess accurately any population trends over the county as a whole. Waterways Birds Survey and CBC information shows fluctuations from year to year for the reasons outlined above. The Cherwell Valley WBS though does reveal an overall long-term decline (Knight 1985), and in the south-west of the county, Perry (1986) also showed a decrease. Elsewhere some observers have cited predation by Foxes, and more often Mink, as having had a major part to play in local declines. Members of the crow family may also be implicated in this. However, over much of the county, numbers remain high. Winter counts along the Thames around Oxford have recorded an average of 16 birds/km of river, and the status as defined by the Oxfordshire Atlas suggests a high local population.

COOT
Fulica atra

Widespread in its distribution, the Coot is a regular breeding bird on lakes, gravel pits, larger ponds and along the wider stretches of the county's rivers. The resident population is augmented by immigrants in the autumn.

The Coot is a very conspicuous and a highly vocal species, its characteristic rounded, humped shape is easily recognised, and its nest bulky and untidy. Nests are always built at the water's edge, either in fringing and emergent vegetation or on limbs of trees that sag or have fallen into the water. Their conspicuousness increases the likelihood that the Oxfordshire Atlas gives an accurate reflection of the species' distribution. In addition to the increase along rivers, the creation of the numerous gravel pits in the county has contributed to the increase in the population as demonstrated by the Oxfordshire Atlas map.

Coot breeding success varies from year to year and is affected by a host of factors. Coot are normally single-brooded and losses due to flood damage or predation are not always made up. The BOS, in their annual breeding season survey of 1977 showed that between 37% and 49% of young were lost in the first three weeks after hatching and that fledging success could be as low as 10% on some waters. Horsfall (1981) studied various aspects of the breeding biology of the Coot on a number of waters in the county. He demonstrated that by supplementing their food supply, the birds could be induced to lay earlier and to lay a larger clutch. Also, the

earlier in the year that chicks hatched, the higher was their survival rate.

The Coot falls into that category of commoner bird species that, through their very familiarity, are treated with a degree of disdain by birdwatchers. Relatively little detailed information is available about the size of the Coot population in Oxfordshire, but it is clear that it has increased, both as a breeding species and in its overwintering flocks. The OOS report for 1921 noted that it was breeding on all the larger waters and also on a few parts of the River Thames and a survey in 1937 yielded 48 breeding pairs and a winter population of around 600 birds. Until the 1960s numbers and distribution did not change significantly. Since then it has become a breeding bird along the greater length of the Thames as well as the rivers Cherwell, Thame, Evenlode, Windrush and Cole. Nesting is seen in the heart of Oxford and on busy sections of the River Thames at Abingdon, Henley and Wallingford.

In October there is a large influx of birds to the county. Counts as high as 2,000 have been made at the Stanton Harcourt Gravel Pits in the first half of October with a concentration of birds on Dix Pit. This single water has consistently high counts throughout the winter period and a December 1988 census totalled 935 birds. Dorchester Gravel Pits are also used regularly (e.g. 1,100 in October 1979 and 1,145 in November 1984). This latter site, as well as providing abundant natural food for Coot, also had food artificially provided by way of discarded potatoes dumped by a local farmer, which the birds were quick to exploit. High numbers also remain along rivers in winter especially where feeding of swans and ducks takes place. From the combined figures obtained from the winter wildfowl counts, and taking into account the population along the county's rivers, a winter population well in excess of 3,000 is calculated. Table 5.37 shows the monthly count statistics for the winters of 1984/85 to 1989/90. The Coot population may suffer dramatic losses during severe winter weather. In 1963, the margins of Blenheim lake were littered with Coot corpses, but within 12 months, numbers had returned to normal.

Table 5.37. Coot.
Monthly winter count statistics 1984-1989 for central Oxfordshire waters.

Month	Mean	Max	Min
September	793	1046	617
October	970	1110	865
November	1043	1726	604
December	964	1253	906
January	1032	1336	901
February	889	1336	605
March	545	674	338

Family: Gruidae
Cranes

Only one species of Crane is found in Europe and this is a summer visitor to most of that area. Although it bred in Britain in former times, the Crane has been absent as a breeding bird for more than 300 years. However, as a vagrant it is not uncommon, especially in the south and east of England. There is every reason to expect it to occur again in Oxfordshire.

CRANE
Grus grus

A very rare vagrant. Cranes were resident in Britain in ancient times, and Wilson (1987) reports bones of this species found in Oxfordshire dating back to Mesolithic, Romano-British, Saxon, Medieval and post-Medieval times. Since then it has occurred very rarely.

There were two early nineteenth century records. In addition, one was shot at Adderbury in 1913. A flock of 27 large birds which passed over Enstone in August 1914 were considered by Alexander (1947) probably to have been of this species. On 30 October 1963, 36 were seen circling above Thame. There was a considerable passage noted in several parts of Britain at this time.

MTC 92 16

Family: Haematopodidae
Oystercatchers

One species of Oystercatcher occurs in Britain, and although principally a coastal and upland breeder, this can occur almost anywhere in the country on passage since it winters chiefly on the coast.

OYSTERCATCHER
Haematopus ostralegus

A frequent passage migrant, there was a striking increase in Oystercatcher records during the 1980s, reflecting the increase in this species nationally. There were 22 records in the 1960s, 24 in the 1970s and 91 in the 1980s. Birds have been seen in every month, with peaks in March, April and August and at several sites including Port Meadow and Stanton Harcourt Gravel Pits. Most records refer to one or two birds but, very occasionally, parties in double figures have been noted (Figure 5.36). A large proportion of the records have been of birds in flight, no doubt as a consequence of the species' distinctive and vociferous call. Seven of these flight records have been of birds flying over the centre of Oxford.

Most records relate to birds present for only one day. However, in recent years there have been several occasions on which birds have been present in the spring for a week or more. With the species' increasing use of inland breeding sites in Britain it is possible that the Oystercatcher could be added to the list of breeding birds in Oxfordshire at some point in the future.

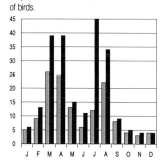

Figure 5.36. Oystercatcher.
Monthly distribution of records 1960-1989.
Grey = number of records, black = number of birds.

Family: Recurvirostridae
Stilts and Avocets

The Avocet is the only member of this family of exquisite waders to occur in Oxfordshire. The species formerly bred in England until about 200 years ago but was absent as a regular breeding bird until the 1940s when it returned to breed in East Anglia. With protection from the RSPB, its numbers have grown dramatically since then.

AVOCET
Recurvirostra avosetta

A rare visitor to Oxfordshire, the first known record is of six killed at Sonning in 1794. There were no further records until 1964 when four were seen at Somerton on 23 March. Since then there have been an additional nine records: singles at Dorchester on 10 October 1970, at Sonning on 6 December 1970, at Stanton Harcourt from 8–13 May 1981, Farmoor on 10 November 1984, Port Meadow on 7 December 1986 and Farmoor on 9 April 1989. Two birds were on Port Meadow on 4 June 1979, there

were seven at Stanton Harcourt on 27 March 1983 while the largest party, one of ten birds, was at Farmoor on 28 April 1978. Although there is no seasonal pattern evident, stormy or wet weather appears to have been a factor on most occasions.

The increase in records almost certainly relates to the species' re-establishment as a breeding bird in Britain in recent decades and some of the records may be of birds moving between their East Anglian breeding grounds and wintering quarters in the south-west of the country.

Family: Burhinidae
Stone Curlews

The Stone Curlew is the only member of this small family which occurs in Europe. In Britain it is on the edge of its range, but it was formerly very much more abundant than it is today. In Britain, its breeding distribution closely follows that of the major chalk downland areas of southern England so that Oxfordshire borders its range.

STONE CURLEW
Burhinus oedicnemus

A very rare breeding summer visitor. A small population survives on the Oxfordshire/Berkshire border, but in the late 1980s and early 1990s no more than one or two pairs bred in our county. Passage birds also are found occasionally.

At the end of the Second World War in 1945 the OOS, looking to the future, asked C.F. Tunnicliffe to draw them a bird to serve as an emblem for the society. They chose the Stone Curlew because many members enjoyed seeing and hearing it on annual excursions to the hills near the county boundaries at Swyncombe Downs and the Fairmile.

Unfortunately this species has been decreasing for some time. While Aplin (1889) reported it breeding in hills and arable land of north and west Oxfordshire in places such as Kingham, Great Rollright and Weston-on-the-Green in the second half of the nineteenth century, the BOS (Easterbrook 1983) has no record for the Banbury area since it was known to be breeding in the Chipping Norton area in 1871.

By 1926 Jourdain found it restricted to the western slopes of the Chilterns and the Berkshire Downs. There were still some to be seen in these locations in 1947, when Alexander estimated there to be fewer than twenty in the old county of Oxfordshire and "numerous pairs" breeding on the Berkshire Downs.

For a time, two or three pairs lingered in the Chilterns. Breeding was last proved there in 1980, and since 1985 none has returned. The situation is only marginally better in the Berkshire Downs. A small relic population survives, mostly in Berkshire. Counts of post-breeding season flocks here show the decline. In the early years of this century there were more than 100 on occasions. Alexander (1947) mentioned flocks of 50–80. By 1960 there were in the region of 20–30, and in the 1980s the largest flock was of ten birds.

A young bird ringed on one OOS trip in 1923 was recovered in the following year in Landes, France. Ringing between 1933 and 1952 produced more evidence of their migratory journeys with recoveries in the last three months of the year in Gironde and Landes, France, and Estremadura in Portugal. Return in the spring is usually from the end of March, with the earliest Oxfordshire record being 13 March. Most leave in September, but there have been a number of October records, and the latest date is 4 November.

In the 1920s egg collectors were a problem, but a major factor accelerating the decline locally in the second half of the twentieth century was habitat loss. When sheep grazed these hills the short grassland produced provided ideal feeding grounds. The present vast acreage devoted to cereal cultivation is of little use to Stone Curlews as the crop generally grows too fast to allow successful nesting. An understanding of this bird's requirements led

the RSPB to launch a scheme in 1990 to recreate suitable conditions. Working closely with farmers and local ornithologists they aim to increase the population by at least 50% over ten years. Learning from the experience of a similar successful exercise in the Norfolk Brecks, they intend to encourage the restoration of chalk grassland, to protect nests and promote the value of set-aside and the growing of appropriate game crops to provide feeding and nesting sites.

The success or failure of this scheme may determine whether it will be appropriate in future for the OOS to continue using its Stone Curlew symbol.

Family: Charadriidae
Plovers

Oxfordshire boasts an impressive list of waders for a land-locked English county with 39 species occurring during the twentieth century. Of these, eight are plovers. These consist of three breeding or occasional breeding species, two regular wintering species and the rest vagrants or passage migrants. As in the sandpipers which follow, the occurrence of plovers generally in the county has increased during this century. However, the presence of certain breeding species depends on the maintenance of rare or temporary wetland habitats such as pumped gravel workings which provide 'scrape' conditions.

LITTLE RINGED PLOVER
Charadrius dubius

The diminutive Little Ringed Plover, the smallest of our regularly breeding waders, is a summer visitor to Britain, wintering in a zone south of the Sahara. Arrival in Oxfordshire is in mid-March/early April, with a passage of birds making usually brief stop-overs at gravel pits, reservoirs and wet meadows until mid-May.

Until the late 1940s it was a rare species in Britain. Its colonisation of the British Isles was part of a gradual spread through Europe which reached England in 1944 (a breeding record in 1938 was believed to be an isolated occurrence) with the first breeding in Oxfordshire recorded in 1954. During the 1950s, nesting in the county was sporadic but since 1961 it has bred annually.

On the continent, the Little Ringed Plover nests on shingle banks along rivers. In Britain it has utilised the shingle and bare ground resulting from mineral excavations, especially

sand and gravel. With a plentiful supply of such sites coinciding fortuitously with a gradual expansion of its range, the colonisation of Oxfordshire can be regarded as part of a continued spread northwards from the Home Counties as birds take up residence in new mineral workings. In Oxfordshire, these gravel pit and other quarry sites are utilised, and very occasionally breeding, or attempted breeding, has taken place at other bare ground sites such as around factories. Gravel pits are however in a state of continual change as new ones are excavated and others in-filled and, as a consequence, individual sites may only be occupied for a few seasons before they become unsuitable. For this reason, the Oxfordshire Atlas which found birds in 13 tetrads, gives a slightly exaggerated picture and in any one season a maximum of 11 pairs is more realistic. Indeed, the numbers occurring in each season vary as do the number of sites that are occupied. The maximum figures were noted in 1978 when 14 pairs were seen at seven sites. On average though, three to five sites holding between eight and ten pairs is more usual. It is felt that the population has reached a peak in Oxfordshire, as indeed it has elsewhere in southern Britain (Parrinder 1989), and may have begun to decline. For example, one quarry site which in the early 1970s held at least five pairs and where the physical characteristics do not appear to have altered markedly, now hold only one or two pairs. This decline has coincided with the appearance of breeding Foxes and Magpies.

There are four ring recoveries of Little Ringed Plover involving Oxfordshire. Two are short movements to Berkshire, one concerns a bird ringed as a chick in Shropshire which was in Oxfordshire the following year, and another ringed as a chick in Oxfordshire on 31 May 1966 was at Minsmere, Suffolk (214 km ENE) on 11 July the same year.

Although care must be taken to minimise disturbance to this protected species, it is a relatively conspicuous bird and easy to monitor within it's restricted habitat. Locations for nesting may be shared with the closely related Ringed Plover. Whilst in most instances both species appear to be successful, some observers have reported inter-specific chases, and observations elsewhere in Britain have suggested that this competition has been to the detriment of the smaller species.

As discussed with respect to the Ringed Plover, long-term continued nesting success in artificial habitats of this nature can not be assured. While birds can tolerate a degree of disturbance and will lay replacement clutches, trampling of the site or flooding obviously cannot be tolerated. Although sand and gravel extraction will continue in the county for many years, more efficient methods of extraction are being used and suitable areas are available for shorter periods than before.

RINGED PLOVER
Charadrius hiaticula

In Oxfordshire, the Ringed Plover occurs as a passage migrant with a few pairs remaining to nest. Although nationally, the Ringed Plover is primarily a coastal-breeding species (Sharrock 1976), it is estimated that approximately 10% of the breeding population nest inland. In southern Britain, the post-war boom in mineral extraction, especially of sand and gravel, has seen the colonisation of these inland habitats by this species. Breeding was noted in Oxfordshire for the first time in 1976, when, at a disused quarry site, two broods were believed to have been raised. Since then, up to four sites, holding a maximum of nine pairs, have been occupied annually. With the exception of the original quarry site, all have been in gravel pits.

Birds arrive at breeding sites in February or March and the first young may be seen in April or, more usually, May. If early clutches are lost, replacement eggs are often laid. In most seasons, pairs are double-brooded.

The Ringed Plover is also well known in Oxfordshire as a passage migrant, appearing at gravel pits, reservoirs, rivers and flood-meadows. Records come mainly from the period February to October, with few from other months or from June. Migrant parties are generally small (one to four) or of single birds and are often seen accompanying other migrant species such as Dunlin. Thus flocks of 18 at Radley Gravel Pits on 4 July 1983 and 26 at Dorchester Gravel Pits on 15 September 1974 are exceptional.

Whilst the migrant status of the Ringed Plover in Oxfordshire is unlikely to alter, there is concern for its continued success as a breeding species. Gravel pit sites occupied by the species in Oxfordshire are rather transient in nature as they are produced by pumping, are subject to disturbance and under constant threat of flooding or in-filling. The creation of a pit maintained in such a way as to provide permanent shingle beds and managed so as to minimise disturbance could encourage the Ringed Plover to remain as an Oxfordshire breeding bird.

KENTISH PLOVER
Charadrius alexandrinus

Jourdain (1926) records that two of these very rare vagrants were shot on Port Meadow prior to 1849. Subsequently there have been only two records: a female at Farmoor on 15 May 1970 and a male at Dorchester on 26 April 1978.

DOTTEREL
Charadrius morinellus

The Dotterel is a rare passage migrant, sometimes recorded from the Downs and other hilly areas of the county in spring and, very rarely, autumn. Since 1960 there have been nine records of 19 birds.

Formerly, the status of the species was markedly different. In the early nineteenth century records were annual during both spring and autumn passage. On occasions, 'trips' in excess of 50 birds were noted. By the 1860s, numbers had diminished in autumn but spring records remained common. From the late 1880s spring records also declined. Between 1910 and 1960 there were no records at all (Radford 1966).

Records since 1960 have been predominantly from the Berkshire Downs. Single birds were at Aston Tirrold on 16-17 April 1960, at Chilton on 16 May 1984 and at Ilsley on 11 October 1984. Two were at Churn on 13 August 1986, five there on 22 April 1988 and two at Harwell on 7 April 1988.

Away from the Downs there were four at Swyncombe on 5-7 May 1971, one at

Woodstock on 18–19 May 1977, two at Sibford Ferris on 18 August 1980 and two at Glympton on 5 May 1991.

GOLDEN PLOVER
Pluvialis apricaria

A frequent winter visitor and passage migrant, birds have been recorded in the period 21 July to 12 May. Most occurrences in the early autumn have been of single birds or small parties, often on the Downs. From late September, the main arrival occurs, with wintering birds remaining until March or April, unless moved on by hard weather. From mid-March numbers are augmented by passage birds.

In recent years, the size of flocks and number of birds wintering in the county appears to have increased. In 1971, flocks of 600 and even 100 were described as "exceptionally large", whereas in most years during the mid-1980s flocks in excess of 1,000 birds have been seen at various locations. Exceptional was a gathering of over 5,000 at Aldfield Common on 3 April 1983.

Wintering flocks are often noted as occupying traditional sites. To be more precise, they appear to occupy extensive ranges within which several 'traditional sites' can occur. These ranges are generally associated with river valleys, notably the Thame, Ock, Cherwell and Thames and the Ray at Otmoor. The number of birds within them varies substantially from year to year, although exact numbers can be difficult to ascertain when a flock splits into groups at several sites. It is not known why these traditional wintering areas are preferred to others which appear equally suitable (Knight 1977). Variations in numbers from month to month, and from winter to winter are caused, at least in part, by weather conditions, with birds leaving quickly on the advent of freezing temperatures. Table 5.38 shows the number of birds counted each month at all sites in the winter of 1986/1987 and clearly shows the drop in numbers from December to February due to hard-weather movements out of the county and the return of birds on passage in March.

It is also the case that traditional sites can be abandoned for long periods and then re-adopted. For instance, Port Meadow, which was an important site in the 1930s and 1940s, had a "greatly diminished" flock in the mid-1960s

(Radford 1966). This remained true until the mid-1980s. However, since then, the flock has built up to substantial proportions, with 870 on the meadow in December 1989, approximately 1,500 there in January 1990 and over 2,000 in January 1991.

GREY PLOVER
Pluvialis squatarola

An occasional passage migrant, the first Oxfordshire record of this species came in 1921. There have been 58 subsequent records up to the end of 1989, almost half in the period 1984–1989. This increase probably reflects better observer coverage, important for a species usually present for only one day. A bird at Port Meadow from 14–22 January 1986 was an exception.

Records have come from all months except July (Figure 5.37) and marked peaks occur in passage periods and also in December. Records in the latter month are normally associated with hard weather and presumably reflect a southwards movement of birds wintering in north-west Europe. 80% of records refer to single birds, with the largest party reported being of six birds at Shipton in October 1967.

Eighteen locations have been visited by the species, an unusually high number when compared to that for most other uncommon passage waders, and include flooded meadows along river valleys in addition to the usual reservoir and gravel pit sites.

SOCIABLE PLOVER
Chettusia gregaria

The only record of this very rare vagrant from the eastern Palearctic was of a bird in the Cherwell valley on 14 September 1980, associating with a flock of Lapwings.

LAPWING
Vanellus vanellus

The Lapwing is a widespread and numerous resident with numbers increased in winter by a large population of visitors. As might be expected of a bird breeding on open farmland, the Lapwing has a very wide distribution in the

Table 5.38. Golden Plover.
Totals of monthly counts at all sites in 1986 and 1987.

Month	No. of flocks	No. of birds
September	2	285
October	2	114
November	8	1486
December	8	501
January	8	623
February	6	183
March	11	1632
April	2	403

Figure 5.37. Grey Plover.
Monthly distribution of records 1960-1989. Grey = number of records, black = number of birds.

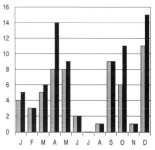

Table 5.39. Lapwing.
Number of Lapwing along a 25 km transect
from Hordley to Burford 1962-1980.

Year	Pairs
1962	7
1963	10
1964	10-14
1965	16
1966	19
1967	16
1968	29-34
1969	24+
1970	19
1971	18-23
1972	23
1973	25-29
1974	22
1975	25-29
1976	20
1977	11-15
1978	no data
1979	13
1980	17-20

county. The Oxfordshire Atlas survey recorded Lapwings in 467 tetrads (62%) of which 382 were of confirmed or probable breeding. Breeding is fairly evenly distributed throughout the centre of the county with notable gaps in the built-up areas of Oxford and Witney. The breeding distribution is sparse in the Chilterns, where there are large areas of woodland, and Lapwings appear to be more thinly distributed in the north of the county than in the south.

Given dry weather conditions, display can start in late February or early March with the first eggs being laid in the middle of the month. These early clutches are especially prone to destruction by farming operations. However, many pairs will have further breeding attempts under these circumstances, although Lapwings normally raise only a single brood (Knight *et al.* 1980). Failure due to predation can also lead to second breeding attempts as occurred in the Ascott-under-Wychwood area in 1970. Breeding more usually takes place in April but can extend into June or early July when autumn flocks of the earlier breeders begin to build up.

The size and stability of the breeding population of Lapwings in Oxfordshire has been the subject of two recent surveys. The first, a one year study, was done in the north of Oxfordshire by the BOS who chose the Lapwing for their annual breeding survey in 1980 (Knight *et al.* 1980). It was found that the breeding density in the area was 25.7 pairs per 10 km². An extrapolation of this figure gives an estimated population of over 750 pairs in the county at that time. This survey also found that Lapwings showed a marked preference for land sown with spring cereals and avoided ley grassland. Birds breeding on the former category also had a high success rate (92%) compared to fallow land with only a 28% success rate. The commonest reasons for failure were disturbances due to cultivation of some kind.

The second survey was by B. Campbell who

recorded the number of Lapwings breeding each year in fields along a 25 km stretch of road between Hordley and Burford from 1962 to 1980 (Table 5.39). This survey showed the relative stability of the population in that area during those years, building up from low numbers after severe winters in 1962 and 1963. However, this period of stability has since come to an end as poor breeding seasons were noted in 1985, 1986 and 1987 with a slight recovery in 1988. This pattern reflects the national trend. During the 1970s and early 1980s the national CBC index remained remarkably constant, but by 1988, had dropped to 50% of that in 1985 (Marchant *et al.* 1990). One possible reason for this decline is changes in farming methods such as the trend towards sowing cereals in the autumn rather than in the spring. Lapwings find that by the next spring, autumn-sown crops are too tall for use as breeding habitat (Marchant *et al.* 1990). The drying out of wetlands and a run of cold, wet springs may also have contributed to the decline. Declines in the breeding population of Lapwing in Oxfordshire have also been noted in the past and are mentioned by Aplin (1889), Jourdain (1926) and Radford (1966).

As previously mentioned, Lapwings start to gather into flocks from late June onwards. The size of these flocks varies. Over 500 at Witney on 13 July 1974, 300 at Port Meadow on 26 June 1977 and 2,000 in the Cherwell Valley on 7 July 1985 are some recent examples. These early flocks are made up mainly of local birds with a few immigrants. Later in the year large numbers arrive from the continent, mainly Scandinavia, Denmark, Germany and the Netherlands (Lack 1986). A number of the locally bred birds emigrate to France and the Iberian peninsula as shown by recoveries of Oxfordshire-ringed birds in France (11), Spain (seven) and Portugal (four). Of these 22 recoveries, 20 were between November and March and probably represent hard-weather movements.

Lapwings depend on soft ground for their food and are quick to move on in cold weather, usually in a southerly or south-westerly direction. Some cold weather movements can be quite dramatic. An estimated 70,000 crossed a 12 km front near Whitehorse Hill on 10 January 1959. More recently, a flock of 1,010 present at Farmoor on 28 December 1976 before snow was reduced to two birds on 31 December after snow had fallen. Other examples of movements in advance of cold weather are 6,000 over Wallingford on 9 December 1978 and over 5,000 in a day over Didcot on 10 January 1987. Short periods of frost result in the birds returning soon after (Lack 1986). Long freeze-ups can, on the other hand, result in Lapwings being absent for long periods such as in early 1985 when the birds left on 1 January and did not return until the end of February. Large flocks are rare after the end of February when Lapwings disperse to their breeding grounds.

However, overall the county gains more Lapwings in winter than it loses, as indicated by the size of some flocks in recent years. Flocks of over 1,000 birds are encountered in most years and some of up to 5,000 birds have occurred fairly regularly. The largest flock numbered "about 10,000" on Otmoor, 26 November 1986. Favoured sites over the years have been, among others, Stanton Harcourt, Cherwell valley, Otmoor and Port Meadow. These large flocks compare well with those noted in the past by Radford (1966) and Aplin (1889) who reported flocks of 3,800 and 1,500 birds respectively as being noteworthy. Flocks were smaller in 1987 and 1988, however, perhaps reflecting the run of poor breeding seasons.

The Lapwing has suffered a drastic decline as a breeding species in Oxfordshire since the mid-1980s and it is possible that the wintering flocks are also smaller than they were in the previous two decades. This trend is also occurring nationally and it is thought to be due to changes in farming practices, drainage of damp meadows and, possibly, climatic changes.

Family: Scolopacidae
Sandpipers and Snipe

Of the 39 wader species occurring in Oxfordshire during the twentieth century, 28 are scolopacids, and of these, only one has not been seen since before 1980. This reflects a marked increase in the numbers of waders being recorded annually in the county during this century. Whilst this partly reflects the increased number of observers, it is also due in large part to the greater presence of suitable habitat in the form of gravel pits and reservoirs. However, whilst passage records have increased, so the numbers of breeding birds have declined. The presence of waders in the county reflects, as much as any group of birds, the current state of land use.

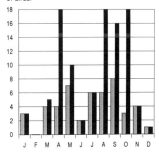

Figure 5.38. Knot.
Monthly distribution of records 1960-1989. Grey = number of records, black = number of birds.

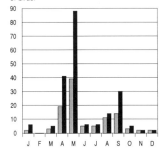

Figure 5.39. Sanderling.
Monthly distribution of records 1960-1989. Grey = number of records, black = number of birds.

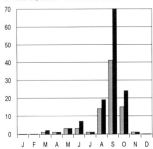

Figure 5.40. Little Stint.
Monthly incidence, 1960-89. Grey = number of records, black = number of birds.

KNOT
Calidris canuta

An infrequent passage migrant, there is a single nineteenth century record, none until 1940, and just eight in the following two decades. From 1960-1989, there have been 48 records of 101 birds (Figure 5.38). Most occurred singly or in small flocks, but there have been three flocks of 14-16 birds. Records have come from 15 sites across the county and although birds seldom stay for more than a day, one at Farmoor Reservoir was present for ten days in January 1985.

In most years there have been only one or two records. Exceptions are 1970 (four records of 20 birds), 1976 (seven records of 14 birds) and 1985 (seven records of 33 birds). However, the increased incidence in these years appears not to reflect any trend in movements since records were spread throughout the year.

SANDERLING
Calidris alba

Prior to 1960 there were only four records of this infrequent passage migrant. Three were on Port Meadow, 1931, 1933 and 1943 while Aplin (1889) gives only one authenticated nineteenth century record. He comments, " the Sanderling rarely wanders inland, being, as its name denotes, devoted to the sands, and during its stay on our coasts is seldom seen far from the tide edge".

The increase in records is notable. There were ten records in the 1960s, 33 in the 1970s and 53 between 1980 and 1988. In 1989, one to four birds were seen on 13 dates between 5 April and 23 May, and one to three on 14 dates between 30 July and 24 September. This reflects both improved observer coverage and the increased availability of suitable habitat in the form of the banks of reservoirs, lakes and gravel pits. 62% of records have come from Farmoor Reservoir, 17% from Stanton Harcourt Gravel

Pits and 11% from Grimsbury Reservoir. Figure 5.39 gives the monthly incidence of records and the peak appears to coincide with migrating birds have been subjected to adverse or changeable weather.

Whether these birds were passing over Oxfordshire in Aplin's day but could find no acceptable place to call in, is an interesting point for speculation.

LITTLE STINT
Calidris minuta

An infrequent passage migrant, especially during the autumn, the Little Stint was recorded only twice in the nineteenth century. However, they began to appear with increasing frequency at sewage farms from the 1930s until modernisation reduced the attractiveness of such sites in the 1950s and 1960s.

Between 1960 and 1989, there were 80 records, two-thirds of which were between the last week of August and the first week of October (Figure 5.40). The number of birds indicated in the graph must be an underestimate. At key sites, the autumn passage can be protracted, with birds present in varying numbers; on occasions up to seven have been seen together, for a week or more. The actual numbers passing through a given site are therefore difficult to assess.

Birds have been recorded at ten different sites since 1960, but in the 1980s the overwhelming majority of records have come from Farmoor Reservoir (74%) and, to a lesser extent, Stanton Harcourt Gravel Pits (18%).

TEMMINCK'S STINT
Calidris temminckii

A rare passage migrant, prior to 1974 there had been just three occurrences: on Port Meadow in August 1848 and September 1852, and from Sandford Sewage Farm in late April 1943.

Since 1974 (to the end of 1991), there have been eight records: Farmoor on 12 May 1974 and two there on 28 May 1974; then singles at Dorchester on 2 May 1976, Cherwell Valley on 21 June 1979, Dorchester from 30 August to 1 September 1980, Stanton Harcourt on 11 May 1981, Day's Lock from 10–13 May 1988 and Farmoor Reservoir on 5 May 1991.

PECTORAL SANDPIPER
Calidris melanotos

A very rare vagrant, the first record of Pectoral Sandpiper in Oxfordshire came from Farmoor Reservoir on 1–2 September 1973. Two more records came soon after and at the same location on 10–14 May and 4–7 September 1974.

Hopes that these records presaged the start of regular occurrences proved rather optimistic and there has been only one subsequent record: a bird at Stanton Harcourt Gravel Pits and Farmoor from 19–24 April 1985.

CURLEW SANDPIPER
Calidris ferruginea

An occasional passage migrant, there is one rather dubious nineteenth century account, but the first definite Oxfordshire record was in 1950 when five were seen at Sandford Sewage Farm. Five years later, a party of six were present at Stanton Harcourt.

From 1960–1989 there were 28 records, the majority of which were in August and September (Figure 5.41). Most records have been of single birds — a record of five at Abingdon Sewage Farm in 1960 was, therefore, exceptional. This site provided all four of the records during the 1960s. In the 1970s, there were seven records from five sites, of which Dorchester Gravel Pits was the most important. The 1980s saw 17 records, all but one from Stanton Harcourt Gravel Pits or Farmoor. Several records refer to birds present for relatively long periods — up to three weeks in one instance.

PURPLE SANDPIPER
Calidris maritima

Before 1976, there was only one record of this rare passage migrant — Aplin (1889) refers to one shot near Oxford "many years ago". Since 1976 there have been nine records: all but one of them in autumn and all but one being present only briefly. Seven records came from Farmoor Reservoir: on 2 September 1976, 28 July 1977, 6 September 1982, 27–29 September 1987, 5 November 1988, 15 September 1989, and 29 October 1989. The other two records came from Dorchester Gravel Pits and Stanton Harcourt Gravel Pits on 10 November 1979 and 17 May 1987 respectively.

DUNLIN
Calidris alpina

Dunlin (illustrated below) are frequently seen in the county as passage migrants and winter visitors, mainly to open wet meadows and to reservoirs and gravel pits.

In the nineteenth century the Dunlin was described as "not very common" although with occasional large flocks such as around 50 on Port Meadow on 25 April 1887 (Aplin 1889). Radford (1966) noted that, "since last century it has certainly been much commoner" and described its status in the 1960s as a "regular passage migrant". The main change subsequently has been the presence in most years of wintering birds on Port Meadow, a site which has hosted most of the large flocks recorded in the county with 50 in November 1935, 61 in December 1938, 60 in February 1956, 63 in December 1974, up to 80 in January 1975 and 89 in January 1986. However, in terms of the numbers of birds passing through in the main spring and autumn passage the principle site in the county is Farmoor Reservoir.

The pattern of Dunlin records in the county is well exemplified by looking at a particular year. In 1987 for instance, wintering birds remained on Port Meadow until late March, with a maximum of 22 in March and up to 15 in January and February. Otherwise there were only occasional records of single birds at Farmoor and Stanton Harcourt during this period. The main spring passage was recorded at Farmoor where at least 37 birds occurred in April and May. There was also passage during these months at other sites such as Day's Lock, Stanton Harcourt, Grimsbury and the Cherwell valley. Late May to mid-July saw no records apart from a single bird at Farmoor in June. From late July onwards passage occurred

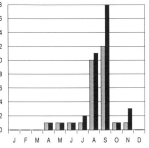

Figure 5.41. Curlew Sandpiper.
Monthly distribution of records 1960-1989. Grey = number of records, black = number of birds.

strongly, with Farmoor again predominant. In August at least 62 birds passed through the site, with a further 15 in September. By October records were much scarcer at Farmoor and elsewhere. November and December saw the return of up to seven winterers on Port Meadow, but very few records elsewhere in the county.

RUFF
Philomachus pugnax

Although it has been recorded in every month of the year, the Ruff must be regarded primarily as a regular passage migrant, the main passage occurring from March to May and August to September. Wintering birds occur irregularly, mainly on Port Meadow, from late November through to April. During the 1960s, in the heyday of Abingdon Sewage Farm, wintering was more regular.

Numbers occurring vary considerably from year to year. Over the past two decades the numbers recorded annually have ranged from 8-93. The latter figure was exceptional and reflected an influx between 15 and 17 April 1987 when there were at least 61 birds present: at Dorchester Gravel Pits (23), Chimney (20), Taynton (seven), Port Meadow (four), Rushey Mead (four) and Stanton Harcourt Gravel Pits (three). In more normal years numbers recorded range from 20-40.

The spring passage now tends to be the stronger. In 1987, for instance, when the spring passage exceeded 70 birds, the autumn passage yielded only two singles. This reverses the position in the early 1960s when Abingdon Sewage Farm autumnal records dominated the picture. It was, however, in spring, on 30 March 1965, that this site produced the largest flock recorded in the county with a party of 43 birds. There have been two recoveries of Ruff ringed in Oxfordshire. Both were ringed as first-year males at Abingdon in the autumn of 1963. One was recovered near Calais, France (237 km ESE) on 17 July 1965, the other near Kholmogory, Russia (2,815 km ENE) on 14 May 1964.

Ruff have been recorded from a wide variety of sites in the county with wet meadows, gravel pits and sewage farms preponderant. Over 40 locations have hosted the species in the past three decades.

JACK SNIPE
Lymnocryptes minimus

A frequent but secretive winter visitor, almost invariably seen in flight rather than on the ground. Records occur between late September and April, with passage being marked between October and November and in March. At these times parties in double figures have been recorded at favoured sites although such numbers have not been seen in recent years. In November 1925 an extraordinary record of over 100 in a flock with Snipe came from Eynsham (Radford 1966).

Jack Snipe tend to be more selective in their habitat requirements than Snipe. Shallow pools with emergent vegetation, such as occur at former gravel workings, are particularly favoured. This type of habitat has provided several of the regular wintering sites noted over the past 30 years at, for instance, Cassington, Stanton Harcourt and the Cherwell valley. Change in the vegetation cover at some of these sites has, however, led to their abandonment, whilst others have been lost by site development.

Numbers reported vary from year to year. This can be a reflection of weather conditions, with harsh winters leading to an increase in the number of records as birds are forced into more open areas. However, there does appear to have been a decline in the numbers recorded since the 1970s, with fewer records and smaller parties occurring even at favoured sites. This trend has been noted in some other counties, and may reflect a real decline.

There is one recovery of a Jack Snipe ringed in Oxfordshire. A bird ringed at Wallingford on 24 December 1953 was at Heras, Spain (932 km SSW) on 5 February 1954.

SNIPE
Gallinago gallinago

Whilst the population of Snipe resident in the county is probably no more than 50 pairs, numbers are augmented by large numbers of winter visitors and there is a considerable passage of birds through the county in spring and autumn.

The basic habitat requirements of the Snipe are for a soft, organic soil, rich in invertebrates, into which it can probe with its long, sensitive bill. An additional requirement during the

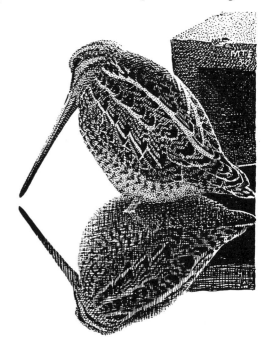

breeding season is for frequent clumps of tall grasses or rushes, providing cover for nesting whilst still affording good visibility for the sitting bird. In Oxfordshire, these conditions are provided by unimproved, damp pastures and it is the effect on this habitat of changes in agriculture which have had the greatest influence on the Snipe.

Nests and chicks of Snipe are notoriously difficult to locate. Fortunately, the presence of displaying birds is a reliable indication of breeding. So although in the Oxfordshire Atlas, breeding was only confirmed in ten tetrads, the 27 tetrads in which probable breeding was recorded should be added to this total. Possible breeding records are thought to relate to passage birds. The Oxfordshire Snipe population is rather thinly distributed with most breeding sites being occupied by only one or two pairs. Otmoor is the only area where they ever reach double figures, and then only in good years. There are certainly no more than 40–50 pairs nesting in the county, and this is a tiny fraction of the estimated British population of 5,000–10,000 pairs (Smith 1983), most of which are to be found in upland habitats. Of the lowland population in Britain, of approximately 2,000 pairs, over half breed at five major sites. Most of the decline in lowland Snipe populations has occurred at smaller sites such as those in Oxfordshire so that their abundance here has been affected disproportionately more than the total national population.

A boom in land drainage during Victorian times led to a decline in the breeding Snipe population. At the end of the nineteenth century they were believed to have bred near Stanton Harcourt although there were no confirmed records (Aplin 1889). With the agricultural recession at the end of that century, Snipe returned to breed in many lowland areas of England and Wales. By 1922, breeding was noted at a number of sites in the county including Otmoor, Somerton and Standlake. By 1931, a survey by members of the OOS located 40–50 pairs within an 11–13 km radius of Oxford. However, by this time, a new wave of agricultural intensification had begun which has continued to the present day so that by 1982 and the BTO's Breeding Lowland Wader Survey, only 15 pairs were located in this same area and only 33 pairs in the entire county (Smith 1983). For a detailed account of the results for Oxfordshire see Knight (1982). The BTO survey was repeated in 1989. The results of this suggest a continued decline due mainly to losses in the Windrush valley but these are partly offset by an increase on Otmoor.

The numbers of Snipe present in the county appear to be at their lowest in late summer when most of the favoured feeding areas have dried out. By October winter visitors are arriving in strength and by December large flocks are often present. A peak is reached towards the end of February or the beginning of March before numbers decline rapidly again as birds return to breeding grounds (Table 5.40). Many of the local breeding sites such as Otmoor, also hold small wintering flocks and are often thinly spread in these areas. However, in recent years, Port Meadow has been the most important site in the county — a flock of 1,100 there in February 1984 was the largest ever recorded in Oxfordshire. This does not necessarily reflect an overall increase in Snipe numbers, but is more likely to be connected with the reduction on availability of suitable sites. Until their replacement by modern treatment works, sewage farms were favoured feeding areas. Flocks of over 100 birds were regularly seen (e.g. 500 at Banbury Sewage Farm on 23 December 1973).

Snipe are more widely distributed in winter particularly during periods of unusually dry or cold weather when the frozen soil forces them to disperse from their favoured feeding areas. Prolonged spells of such conditions leave two options. The majority of birds migrate south and west in search of milder conditions, but a small number remain to feed along ice free river banks and ditches and in extreme conditions have even been found in gardens. The numbers of Snipe that visit the county in winter varies and seems to depend on general weather conditions. Unless conditions are especially severe, the largest flocks are recorded in colder and wetter years.

Of all the breeding waders of lowland habitats, the Snipe is most dependent upon a high water table and damp soils. Unlike other species it has been unable to adapt to breeding in new habitats and as a consequence has suffered dramatically during the decades of agricultural intensification. Although there is currently much less emphasis on increasing crop production, sites are still being damaged or lost and remain under threat as pressures from housing, industry, road-building and leisure activities become more acute. A further decline in the breeding population appears inevitable.

GREAT SNIPE
Gallinago media

A very rare visitor. Radford (1966) describes it as having been recorded in Oxfordshire as follows: near Oxford in 1839, 1851, 1857, Benson 1858, Bampton 1878, Chimney 1924, Shifford 1928, and Eynsham 1932. Most nineteenth century records were of birds shot. The only recent report is of a bird at Minster Lovell on 28 August 1974 considered "probable" by the Rarities Committee owing to the early date. The observer knew the species in Africa.

WOODCOCK
Scolopax rusticola

In Oxfordshire, the Woodcock is an uncommon resident, the distribution of which is very localised and related to its woodland habitat.

Table 5.40. Snipe.
Monthly totals recorded at all sites during 1986 which are typical.

Month	No. of sites	No. of birds
January	10	923
February	10	84
March	1	1
April	4	29
August	4	11
September	7	35
October	2	146
November	4	169
December	7	35

Figure 5.42. Woodcock.
Monthly distribution of all records in Wytham
Woods (After Gosler 1990). Grey = all
records, black = roding records.

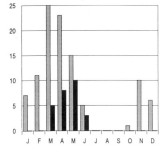

Numbers present during the winter months are increased by an influx of visiting birds.

With its superbly cryptic plumage, the Woodcock is one of the most elusive breeding birds. Virtually invisible among the leaf litter of the woodland floor, birds sit motionless and silent, taking off only at the very last second when almost trodden under foot by the unwary. Whilst the Woodcock has long been known as a regular, but not plentiful, winter visitor to Oxfordshire, as a breeding species there are rather few past records. Aplin (1889) regards the bird primarily as a winter visitor and listed only four breeding sites: Caversham, Ditchley, Eynsham Hall Park and Waterperry. Jourdain (1926) gives a similar description and added a further two sites, Bagley and Tubney. In the OOS report of 1935, Alexander added Glympton, Nuneham and Wychwood (where breeding was first noted in the mid-1920s), and Radford (1966) adds Blenheim, Wytham, Chinnor Hill and other parts of the Chilterns to the list of breeding sites. It is these sites that make up many of the occupied tetrads given in the distribution map compiled during the Oxfordshire Atlas. It is difficult to know whether the apparent gradual increase in occupied sites described in the literature reflects a genuine increase in the local population or whether Woodcock have been consistently overlooked during the breeding season.

The Woodcock is probably the most difficult species for which to obtain confirmation of breeding. The best that can be expected without intensive studies is to look and listen for 'roding' males. Since these flights are most often performed at dusk, it is vital that field visits are timed appropriately. Although the distribution map shows a scattering of records from along the Chilterns, this area has probably been under-recorded and a number of territory-holding birds missed. With this exception, the distribution map can probably be regarded as

accurate. It shows most of the squares in the BOS area as unoccupied but Woodcock have always been scarce in the north of the county with the only past breeding records occurring at sites with birds present at the time of the Oxfordshire Atlas.

The study of the breeding and feeding behaviour of Woodcock is mostly beyond the scope of most amateur birdwatchers. A few diligent individuals have been able to locate nests in some of our woodlands but any extensive study is ruled out by the limited access to most suitable woods and also by the time required. In the 1970s, Hirons (1981) studied the feeding ecology of the Woodcock in Wytham Woods. Males were found not to maintain exclusive territories but to display by low 'roding' flights across the tree-tops in search of a receptive female. Once paired, the male then remains with the female until breeding occurs. He then recommences roding. The most successful males were found to spend the longest time displaying and although females breed in their first year, first-year males did not breed. Only the female incubates and although the young are able to fly after 19 or 20 days, the broods remain together for about 35 days. The breeding success rate of birds is limited by two factors. Predation is the most important cause of nest failure and during Hirons' study, 42% of nests started by marked birds failed for this reason. The second important factor is food. Woodcock probe for invertebrates in soft soils. In the summer feeding is done mainly during the day within woodland and the main food items are earthworms. It was found that the distribution of Woodcock in woodlands was positively correlated with the abundance of earthworms. This is only important in the summer since in winter, birds often feed away from woods, usually on pasture and usually at night.

In winter the resident population is joined by birds from northern Britain and from continental Europe. Gosler (1990) shows the distribution of all records of Woodcock from Wytham Woods (Figure 5.42). Ringing data, although limited, have shown two birds to have come from the former USSR, one from Sweden and one from Scotland. Winter records, usually of singles or pairs of birds, are more scattered than the records during the breeding season and birds are noted along streams and ditches, in woodlands and on damp meadows. It is likely that an influx of birds occurs during November or December although there is some variation in numbers seen each year which is probably governed by weather conditions. Often moderately sized flocks are noted: 15 at Cokethorpe in January 1980, 20 at Ditchley and 20 at Cogges Wood in January and February 1981, ten at Kiddington in December 1982, while nine were flushed from springs at Sandford St Martin in January 1987. Many of the winter records are made during the course of shoots on various estates in the county although it must be noted that one other important conclusion of

Hirons' work was that shooting had little overall effect on the resident population because such a large part of the winter population were winter visitors.

BLACK-TAILED GODWIT
Limosa limosa

Now an almost annual and frequent passage migrant (illustrated below). Apart from two birds shot in the early nineteenth century, there were no reports until March 1939.

Black-tailed Godwits occur between March and May or July and October. Although 60% of records were made in the earlier period, the most birds, 54%, occurred in the autumn passage. The disparity results from the inclusion of several large parties during the autumn passage, the maximum being 27 at Abingdon Sewage Farm in August 1960.

The spring passage takes place earlier than that of the Bar-tailed Godwit, with a peak in March to early April. Autumn passage is mainly concentrated in July and August, with occasional stragglers as late as October. There have been no winter records. Since 1960, records in spring have shown a sharp increase, whereas those in autumn have shown a decrease. The reasons for this have been analysed (Daniel 1988) and the conclusion tentatively drawn is that spring passage primarily represents birds of the nominate race, *L.l. limosa* while the autumn passage is composed of birds of the Icelandic race *L.l. islandica*.

Over 20 locations have yielded records since 1960, with Port Meadow the principal site. Wet meadows and gravel pits have been the most common type of habitat in which birds have been recorded.

BAR-TAILED GODWIT
Limosa lapponica

An occasional passage migrant, the first definite record of Bar-tailed Godwit was on Otmoor in May 1936, followed by one near Eynsham in May 1938. There were no further reports until 1957 since when there have been 53 records, almost three-quarters of them between 1978 and 1989 (Figure 5.43). The increase probably reflects the number of observers: crucial for a species which is most common on spring passage

(60% of records) and which rarely stays longer than a day. Peak passage is in late April and in May — rather later than for Black-tailed Godwits. Autumn passage extends from July to October, with peak passage in late July and August. There have also been occasional records in winter.

Most records have been of single birds, the maximum party noted being of 12 at Farmoor Reservoir in July 1978. Farmoor has provided most records (40%) with Stanton Harcourt and Dorchester Gravel Pits, and Port Meadow prominent among the other 12 sites represented since 1960.

WHIMBREL
Numenius phaeopus

The Whimbrel was considered a "scarce visitor on migration" by Radford (1966) although Aplin's (1889) description implies greater regularity. However by the late 1980s it was being seen annually. It is most often seen from late April to May, and in late July and August (Figure 5.44).

The majority of records are of birds seen in flight rather than on the ground. This fact, coupled with increased observer coverage explains the recent upsurge in records. Over 60% of all the records between 1960 and 1989 have occurred since 1980.

The preponderance of flight records also explains the wide variety of locations from which reports have come — although Farmoor is the principal site for this as for so many passage waders. Large parties are reported on occasion, the maximum being 26.

CURLEW
Numenius arquata

The Curlew may be seen in Oxfordshire as both a passage migrant and a locally distributed summer visitor or resident in some years. Its inclusion on the list of breeding birds is a relatively recent development; Aplin (1889) described the Curlew as an "occasional but not uncommon spring and autumn visitor" but made no mention of it ever having bred in Oxfordshire. During the twentieth century, the Curlew extended its breeding range from strongholds in the uplands of northern and western Britain into the Midlands and parts of

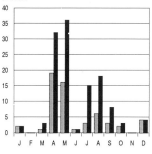

Figure 5.43. Bar-tailed Godwit.
Monthly distribution of records 1960-1989. Grey = number of records, black = number of birds.

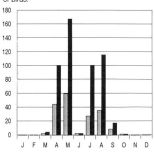

Figure 5.44. Whimbrel.
Monthly distribution of records 1960-89. Grey = number of records, black = number of birds.

Figure 5.45. Spotted Redshank.
Monthly distribution of records 1960-1989.
Grey = number of records, black = number
of birds.

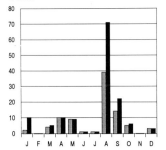

southern England. Breeding was first proven in Oxfordshire on Otmoor in 1925 and, by 1949, four pairs were present there. Following the first colonisation slow, steady progress was made with pairs moving into the valleys of the upper Thames, Windrush, Thame and Cherwell. During the BTO survey of waders in lowland wet meadows in 1982, 36 pairs were recorded in Oxfordshire (Knight 1982, Smith 1983). However in the 1980s, Curlew have not been confined to breeding in this habitat and have colonised downland and arable situations which were not covered in the 1982 survey.

During the Oxfordshire Atlas, confirmed or probable breeding was recorded in 59 tetrads suggesting a rather higher population than was previously perceived. These figures may represent an overestimate since Curlews perform their display flights over large areas, possibly covering several tetrads, particularly when breeding at low densities as in this county. Taking the two surveys together, the true population is probably in the region of 45–60 pairs.

The Curlew's breeding habitat requirements are not well understood. In Oxfordshire the majority of breeding pairs are found on unimproved damp pastures and meadows. While many other species dependent on this habitat have declined in the second half of the twentieth century due to changes in agricultural land-use, Curlews have increased. The reasons for this apparent paradox seem to be that Curlews are less dependent on damp conditions than other lowland waders and indeed, are capable of breeding in completely dry habitats such as chalk downland and arable fields. They also tolerate, and in fact may even prefer, the tall dense vegetation found in hay fields, unimproved grasslands, and crops where they are able to use their long bills to probe into herbage in search of insects. Other points which may have been instrumental in their success are that they are relatively catholic in diet and are prepared to range far in search of it.

The first birds return to their breeding grounds in mid-February or, exceptionally, in late January. By mid-March almost all sites are occupied. In recent years an interesting phenomenon has been observed at Banbury Sewage Farm, namely communal roosting in the early spring. For instance, up to 23 birds were noted between 13 March and 26 March 1987. Although this could represent a roost of wintering or passage birds, it is more likely that

these are birds which breed locally and which then disperse to their established territories later in the season.

Passage of birds through the county occurs in both the spring and autumn and these records often involve large flocks. Parties of 24 at Farmoor on 22 April 1981 and 29 on Port Meadow on 12 May 1977 are the largest flocks to be seen in Oxfordshire.

In winter, British Curlews move south-west into France, Iberia and Ireland. An individual ringed as a pullus on Otmoor in June 1949 was recovered at Finistere, France in October of that year. Nationally, ringing data show that there is also a movement of birds into the British Isles from the Baltic states and from the Low Countries. However, very few of these birds are seen in Oxfordshire, except on passage, preferring to winter on coastal marshes and estuaries.

In spite of agricultural intensification the Curlew has shown itself to be an adaptable species and there seems to be no reason why the trend observed during the last 20 years should not continue.

SPOTTED REDSHANK
Tringa erythropus

During the nineteenth century, the Spotted Redshank was considered a rare species to Oxfordshire, but Radford (1966) called it a "regular passage migrant". The species is most often seen in August and early September but it is also recorded in winter and on spring passage. At these latter times birds almost invariably occur singly whereas in autumn, parties of up to seven have been noted (Figure 5.45).

In the 1950s, most were seen at Sandford Sewage Farm until it was modernised. On 23 August 1962, eight flew low over the eastern by-pass near the former site of Sandford Sewage Farm at Littlemore. The birds circled and called, apparently looking for a place to land and eventually flew off south-west towards the River Thames. The sewage farm had been closed for four years and one wonders whether some memory of the place attracted them to the area? In the early 1960s almost all records came from Abingdon Sewage Farm, which hosted small numbers regularly each autumn. The loss of this site led to a marked drop in the number of records and also in the duration of stay; many

subsequent records have been of birds present for only a short time.

In total, birds have been seen at 18 locations since 1960. Apart from records at the well-watched reservoirs and gravel pits there have been reports from a wide scattering of water meadow sites by the Rivers Thames, Cherwell and Windrush. Dry autumns, with a consequent increase in exposed mud by rivers, appears to be a factor here.

REDSHANK
Tringa totanus

A resident species nesting on open, wet meadows, Redshank also occur as passage migrants and winter visitors to Oxfordshire. During the Oxfordshire Atlas, Redshank were recorded as confirmed or probably breeding in 38 tetrads. Some passage birds may have been included in this total and other birds may have territories overlapping tetrads, so the Oxfordshire population is estimated at 30–40 pairs.

The fortunes of the Redshank as a breeding bird have ebbed and flowed, reflecting changes in agricultural practice. The massive increase in land drainage schemes which occurred in the nineteenth century led to the loss of much breeding wader habitat so that by 1889, Aplin regarded the species only as an occasional visitor to the county. Towards the end of that century, and in the first quarter of the twentieth century, as an agricultural depression set in, further drainage ceased and the efficiency of those systems already installed, declined. Subsequently, Redshank populations throughout England gradually recovered and in 1920 the annual report of the OOS noted that they were "still increasing in a remarkable manner" with new sites being occupied every year. Land drainage was resumed during the late 1930s and then accelerated during and after the second world war. This second phase involved not only re-drainage, but also the draining of wet pastures which had not previously been touched. The situation was worsened by the loss of sewage farms which had previously been popular breeding sites. A serious decline in the Redshank population then followed. The population peaked in 1939 when there were 122 pairs breeding in the county (Wood 1939). By 1982, only 15 pairs remained breeding on damp pastures in Oxfordshire (Knight 1982, Smith 1983). O'Connor and Shrubb (1986) demonstrated how this rise and subsequent fall was related to the amount of rough grazing in the county. There has been some compensation for this decline on agricultural land by the colonisation of new industrial sites such as gravel pits. In 1978 for instance, 14 pairs were recorded at eight gravel pit sites.

The long bill of the Redshank is rarely used for probing — most food is located by sight and pecked from the surface. For this reason they prefer to feed in areas of short vegetation or open mud adjacent to water. The precise nature of the vegetation is less important than a combination of an open aspect and a high water table. It is interesting to note that Redshank only returned to Otmoor to breed after the resumption of hay-cutting on the wetter areas which had previously been dominated by tall, coarse grasses. Although Redshanks do prefer to nest close to the feeding area this is not essential and the two sites may be up to 1.5 km apart.

In winter and during spring and autumn passage, Redshank tend to concentrate at a few favoured sites. The winter birds do not usually appear before January, and numbers build up gradually until mid-March, when they are joined by passage and breeding birds. Flocks can be quite large. Fifty were present at Wallingford Sewage Farm on 14 March 1957 and 22 were at Port Meadow on 15 March 1979. The autumn passage is much lighter, and usually comprises small flocks and single birds. Few are seen between August and the end of the year.

The recognition of agricultural over-production has reduced the demand for additional drainage schemes for agricultural purposes and one might expect a brighter future for the county's breeding Redshanks. However, even since the Oxfordshire Atlas, at least one breeding site has been lost to housing development and there is the threat that other housing, industrial or road-building schemes may pose further problems. Also, the future long-term after-use of gravel pits is not clear and without appropriate management, these sites which have helped maintain a viable county population, may not be able to do so in the future. There are encouraging signs of a more sensitive approach to management at some key sites in future which could help to maintain the county population.

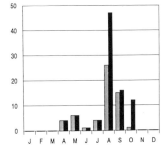

Figure 5.46. Wood Sandpiper.
Monthly distribution of records 1965-1989.
Grey = number of records, black = number
of birds.

GREENSHANK
Tringa nebularia

Now a frequent passage migrant, in the nineteenth century Greenshank records were rare: Aplin (1889) cites only three definite occurrences. The position was little changed in the early twentieth century. However since the 1930s records have been much more common.

Birds have been seen in every month of the year, but the great majority during autumn passage. This can extend from mid-July until late October, but August and September are the peak months. During this time there may be varying numbers of birds at favoured sites for several weeks at a time although precisely how many actually pass through is very difficult to assess. The speed of passage is indicated by a recovery of a bird ringed at Abingdon on 15 August 1963. Three days later it was recovered at Medoc, France, 682 km S.

Spring passage by comparison is usually thin, with only occasional reports of singles, usually in April or early May. Appearances are usually fleeting and are widely spread.

There are only ten records during the period November to March between 1960 and 1989. None remained for long and some are undoubtedly birds returning early or else are late stragglers, with very few reflecting movement within Britain of wintering birds.

In the early 1960s the favoured site was Abingdon Sewage Farm. Subsequently the most reliable venue has been the Stanton Harcourt/ Standlake Gravel Pit complex and its future presence here will depend upon the availability of suitable habitat.

LESSER YELLOWLEGS
Tringa flavipes

There have been two records of this American vagrant: one at Stanton Harcourt from 1-18 October 1970 and one at Grimsbury Reservoir from 2-18 December 1983.

GREEN SANDPIPER
Tringa ochropus

Whilst Green Sandpipers are recorded in every month of the year, they are primarily regular passage migrants and winter visitors. Peak numbers are usually recorded between July and September, with the maximum seen together being 22 at Stanton Harcourt Gravel Pits on 28 July 1984. Numbers vary from year to year; in 1985, for instance, the maximum count at Stanton Harcourt was eight.

Wintering birds are often found singly, although they can occur in small groups at favoured sites such as Ewelme cress beds or Stanton Harcourt Gravel Pits. For instance in November 1988 there were up to five at Ewelme. Spring passage (March to early May) is

usually less marked, and most sites host only one or two birds, at any one time. There is one recovery of a bird ringed in Oxfordshire. One ringed at Abingdon on 15 August 1963 was at Lire, France on 27 December 1964, 482 km S.

During recent years numbers of both passage and wintering birds have shown some decline. This may be attributed to the reduced availability of suitable habitat although some formerly popular sites which apparently have undergone little change, also attract fewer birds.

WOOD SANDPIPER
Tringa glareola

The Wood Sandpiper is a passage migrant to Oxfordshire. It has been recorded in each of the months between April and October although almost 50% of records are from August (Figure 5.46).

Radford (1966) noted that there had only been six records up until 1945 but that the frequency of records had increased since that date and that sewage farms were the favoured sites. From 1965-1989 records were obtained from 15 sites and there were just three years without any records.

Most records are of single or pairs of birds and the number of records in any single year seldom exceeds four. Notable exceptions include a party of 12 at Dorchester Gravel Pits in October 1967, whilst in 1976 there were a total of eight records submitted. In this latter year, five of these records were from Dorchester Gravel Pits, with between one and five birds noted at various times in the second half of August. In such circumstances it is difficult to know if this referred to a single fragmented group making a long stop-over or a steady passage of single birds and small groups.

COMMON SANDPIPER
Actitis hypoleucos

Although it occurs in the county as a rare summer visitor and as a rare winter visitor the Common Sandpiper is mainly known as a regular passage migrant. Birds are seen during both the spring passage from mid-April to mid-May, and again during a more protracted period from the end of June through until October. Stop-over sites include gravel pits, such as those at Dorchester, Radley or in the lower Windrush valley, and at Farmoor and Grimsbury Reservoirs. River banks are also particularly favoured.

During the spring most of the records are of small parties, usually no more than six birds, but groups of up to 13 have been reported. During the autumn migration larger assemblies may be reported and loose flocks of up to 20 birds have been seen (e.g. at Farmoor Reservoir on 29 July 1985 and at Grimsbury Reservoir in August 1970). These autumn flocks possibly represent family groups. There is one distant recovery of a bird ringed in the county. One ringed at Abingdon on 2 August 1975 was at Lake Eldarn, Sweden on 1 July 1978, 1,211 km NE.

In addition, there have been records outside the main passage periods. Since the late 1970s, one or two birds have been present on occasions during some winters (November to March) at sites such as Farmoor Reservoir or the Stanton Harcourt Gravel Pits. The few Common Sandpipers noted throughout the summer months were assumed to be non-breeders. However the presence of family parties during July has led local birdwatchers to suspect local breeding. Alexander (1947) noted a few instances of confirmed breeding along the rivers Thames and Evenlode although these are not added to by Radford (1966). Birds may have bred in the Chalgrove area in 1972 but the next instance of proven breeding came during the Oxfordshire Atlas. In 1985 breeding was confirmed at Stanton Harcourt and in 1986, birds were holding territory at the same area of gravel pits. Two other records, both of possible breeding, were obtained in the Atlas period, from Chinnor and from a stretch of the River Windrush near Minster Lovell.

SPOTTED SANDPIPER
Actitis macularia

There are two records of this very rare American vagrant. The first, an adult in full summer plumage sporting a fine spotted breast, was found in company with five Common Sandpipers at Farmoor Reservoir on 1 May 1989. It had departed by the following morning. The second was at Farmoor Reservoir on 3 and 4 July 1990. This bird arrived on the same day as the first returning Common Sandpipers, raising the possibility that it was a bird which had been in Europe for some time, possibly migrating with the Common Sandpipers.

TURNSTONE
Arenaria interpres

Until 1962 there were only four records of this passage migrant, two of them from the mid-nineteenth century. Subsequently there have been 73 records of 150 birds (Figure 5.47)

mostly at reservoirs and gravel pits. Forty-seven of these records have come in the 1980s, suggesting a real increase in occurrence. This may be attributed to increased availability of suitable habitat in the form of reservoir surrounds.

Records are concentrated in April–May (50% of the total) and August (30%). The majority, two-thirds, have occurred at Farmoor reservoir with most of the remainder at Stanton Harcourt and a scattering at a further seven sites.

Several parties of up to five have occurred and the maximum seen together was 23 at Farmoor in May 1978. Duration of stay is often prolonged (e.g. one at Farmoor in 1986 was present from 7 August to 2 September).

RED-NECKED PHALAROPE
Phalaropus lobatus

A very rare passage migrant, there have been six records, all of single birds. The first was a bird found exhausted in winter 1834 at Shotover. The others were at Sandford Sewage Farm from 30 September to 1 October 1944, Marsh Baldon village pond from 27 June to 7 July 1960, Stanton Harcourt on 27 June 1969, Farmoor Reservoir on 17 May 1974 and the same place on 8 June 1974.

GREY PHALAROPE
Phalaropus fulicarius

The Grey Phalarope (illustrated below) is a rare visitor to Oxfordshire, usually seen after strong westerly winds in autumn.

Records of Grey Phalarope have seen significant changes over the past two centuries. Aplin (1889) referred to 15 nineteenth century occurrences in the county. This included five on Port Meadow and a scattering at other locations including Bloxham, Henley and Newbridge. October was the commonest month, with January and February also well represented (Aplin 1889).

However, from the late nineteenth century until 1960 there was just a single record, at Cassington from 6–8 October 1940. As Radford (1966) pointed out, this decline was surprising, given the increase in observer coverage, and must have reflected a real reduction in incidence.

Since 1960 numbers have again increased,

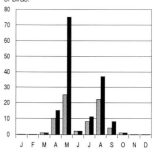

Figure 5.47. Turnstone.
Monthly distribution of records 1960-1989. Grey = number of records, black = number of birds.

with 13 records up to 1989. All were of singles, with more than half occurring in September. The September figures include three records of birds present during the same period of 1981 on different waters, at Farmoor, Dorchester and Blenheim. Birds have also been noted in October (two), August, November and December.

The favoured site is Farmoor Reservoir, with five records during the period. Two have occurred at Dorchester Gravel Pits, and the others at Abingdon Sewage Farm, Somerton, Henley Road Gravel Pit, Blenheim, and Stanton Harcourt Gravel Pits. The other record, from Kiddington, was of a bird found freshly dead.

Family: Stercorariidae
Skuas

Skuas are essentially marine species and the four which occur in the county are accidentals whose appearance usually coincides with rough weather. Like the other vagrant seabirds considered, they probably originate on the west coast and come to us via the Bristol Channel but there is no evidence of this. Unidentified skuas were noted at Farmoor Reservoir on 29 August 1985, 18 August 1986 and on 16 October 1987.

POMARINE SKUA
Stercorarius pomarinus

A very rare visitor. In the nineteenth century there were records of single birds in February 1834, November 1848, October 1877 and December 1890. The only occurrence this century was of an immature at Farmoor Reservoir on 13 October 1988, identified from a photograph.

ARCTIC SKUA
Stercorarius parasiticus

A rare visitor (illustrated below with Black-headed Gulls). There were four nineteenth century records. The first twentieth century record was in early October 1976 when one was picked up at Dorchester Gravel Pits nearly blinded by leeches. In the same month another bird appeared at Farmoor Reservoir. Sightings at Farmoor became more frequent with identifications of this species there on 29 April 1982, 16 April 1989 and 11 August 1989. Also one was seen at Grimsbury Reservoir on 3 and 4 May 1978. There is a clear connection between the existence of large bodies of water, as at Farmoor Reservoir and the recent increase in the number of records.

LONG-TAILED SKUA
Stercorarius longicaudus

A very rare visitor. This was once considered by coastal birdwatchers as the most pelagic of skuas, but immatures are being found increasingly inland in August, often in an exhausted state. One such individual was found at Farmoor Reservoir on 30 August 1980. It was cared for until it regained strength, when it was released on the Welsh coast. Another was seen trying to join the gull roost at Farmoor Reservoir on 10 August 1989. It was harried by gulls, and was apparently absent the following morning.

GREAT SKUA
Stercorarius skua

A rare visitor. One was picked up dead at Barford in October 1917. The next record was on 25 September 1971 when one appeared at Blenheim. The individual seen later that day and the following morning at Dorchester Gravel Pits was probably the same individual. On 22 September 1985 one was picked up exhausted at Appleton Common. The final record is of one briefly at Farmoor Reservoir on 12 September 1986.

MTE '92

Family: Laridae
Gulls

Most species of gull were rare inland in 1889. Today one species breeds and is resident, another four are regular winter and passage visitors, and the rest (five species) are irregular visitors but in growing numbers. This reflects a growth in the populations of several species during the twentieth century. An important development in the last 30 years has been the build-up of large gull roosts on major waters in the county. The birds are attracted inland by the presence of several large landfill refuse sites where they can feed. Notable amongst these are Stanton Harcourt, Sutton Courtenay and Wally Corner, Dorchester.

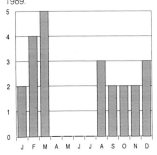

Figure 5.48. Mediterranean Gull.
Monthly distribution of records to the end of 1989.

Table 5.41. Little Gull.
Annual number of records.

Year	No. of records
1970	4
1971	5
1972	2
1973	4
1974	53
1975	3
1976	2
1977	12
1978	14
1979	2
1980	3
1981	13
1982	9
1983	50
1984	38
1985	18
1986	16
1987	33
1988	12
1989	40

Figure 5.49. Little Gull.
Monthly distribution of records, 1970-1987.

MEDITERRANEAN GULL
Larus melanocephalus

A rare visitor, but increasingly reported. Mediterranean Gulls have been found most often at roosts at Farmoor Reservoir, Dorchester and Stanton Harcourt Gravel Pits, or feeding at the Alkerton Tip.

There is an even scatter of sightings from August through the winter until March (Figure 5.48). Autumn birds are in juvenile or first winter plumage, while the majority of winter birds are adults.

The expansion in the range of this species in Europe in the second half of the twentieth century has been well documented. It was extremely rare in Britain before 1940, but by 1963 had been recorded so often that it was taken off the list of species considered by the British Birds Rarities Committee. First breeding in Britain was proved in Hampshire in 1968. Most sightings in the early years were near the coasts in southern Britain, but this was followed by a steady spread inland and to the north.

The first accepted Oxfordshire record was of an adult at Port Meadow in November 1976. The next was on 2 December 1984 when an adult visited Stanton Harcourt Gravel Pit. There was a first winter bird at Port Meadow on 16 March 1986. 1988 produced a minimum of eleven records, and 1989 at least five.

It is certain that the appearance in the county of dedicated gull watchers in recent years, has contributed to the increase in records. Two or three birdwatchers are responsible for the bulk of recent records.

Mild winters in the late 1980s may have accelerated their spread. It will be interesting to observe whether they progress further.

LITTLE GULL
Larus minutus

An infrequent visitor. Until 1968 the Little Gull was considered a rare vagrant having been seen on only five previous occasions. Since then it has made annual visits in increasing numbers (Table 5.41).

Farmoor Reservoir is undoubtedly the most popular water with 67% of all records for the period 1979–1989 occurring here. Other locations include Port Meadow, Grimsbury Reservoir, Banbury Sewage Farm, Dorchester Gravel Pit, Stanton Harcourt Gravel Pit and Otmoor. Two factors have presumably contributed to the increase: there has been an expansion in European populations in recent years, and the presence of newly created water bodies locally has provided more opportunities for Little Gulls to feed and rest. They seem capable of surviving here for a while, sometimes lingering for a few days to catch rising insects either on the water surface, or in the air.

Although now recorded in every month of the year there are clear peaks in the spring and autumn at migration times (Figure 5.49). Suggestions that this species deliberately migrates across central Britain have been resisted, but the pattern in Oxfordshire is becoming so regular that it seems their passage may be as much by design as accident.

The largest groups have all been in spring. There were 30 on 1 May 1983, 19 on 3 May 1974, and 15 on 24 April 1987. Spring dates are mostly confined to the last week in April and the first week in May, but autumn visitors come in at various times throughout August and September.

BLACK-HEADED GULL
Larus ridibundus

A very frequent visitor, especially in winter, and an occasional breeding bird. It is common throughout the county except in wooded areas from August until April, with the main concentrations at low-lying sites. A few stay to breed in summer, and a few others, mostly immatures, wander through the county at this time.

Black-headed Gulls are now a familiar part of the Oxfordshire scene. From roosts established in the second half of the twentieth century they move out daily into the surrounding countryside. These roosts usually break up in April and May and are formed again in late July. Spring movements to the north usually peak in mid-March with large numbers moving through quickly. Returning birds re-appear from the first week in July passing over the county by day in groups of up to about 15 birds. They probably fly on through the night as movements continue at dusk. Most have been seen within five miles of the Thames, so they may be following the valley. Nearly all July records are of adults, with juveniles appearing in August. At this time of year, the birds typically are seen feeding on recently ploughed fields or following the plough. Some will have flown a considerable distance (e.g. one found injured at Radford in 1963 had been ringed as a nestling in Lithuania in June of the same year). More recent results from ringing have confirmed that the majority of the Black-headed Gulls visiting the county have come from the Baltic states (Gosler 1987b, 1987c). Table 5.43 gives a summary of recoveries of birds ringed in Oxfordshire.

A number remain in the county in August when they are typically found surveying rivers and canals for consumable debris. A feature of this behaviour is that individuals patrol their own patch and do not work co-operatively. On 12 August 1987, 21 were counted spaced out thus along the Thames between Abingdon and Folly Bridge

Sometimes a few stay to breed. The first record, probably unsuccessful, was at Otmoor in 1932. One or more pairs nested successfully at Sandford Sewage Farm from 1953–1956, and at Abingdon Sewage Farm in 1963 and 1964. Recently breeding has occurred on island sites in gravel pits in the Windrush valley near Stanton Harcourt and Standlake. One chick

MTE 90

was produced in 1985, five in 1986, there were ten pairs present in 1987, 13 pairs in 1989 and more than 30 birds displaying breeding behaviour in 1990. When they returned in 1991 the colony was destroyed. Many birds were lying dead on the island. The cause is unknown to ornithologists.

The progress made by this species during this century may be demonstrated by the careful and enthusiastic way in which W.H.B. Somerset and H.F.I. Elliott noted every sighting in their personal diaries on visits to Port Meadow and Blenheim in the 1920s and 1930s. Their reactions to seeing such a relatively uncommon species were similar to those of Aplin in the second half of the nineteenth century.

Inland roosts formed at the Middlesex Reservoirs in the early 1900s had some influence on the mid-Oxfordshire population, but Alexander (1947) stated that, although it had become... "a regular and abundant visitor to the Thames below Pangbourne, comparatively few ascend higher".

During the 1950s and 1960s they increasingly made daily trips in winter to the upper Thames valley, although flights did not proceed far west of Oxford as time had to be allowed for the long journey back to roost before dark. Only very occasionally were nights spent on the floods at Port Meadow.

It was the establishment of more permanent roosts on newly created large lakes in Oxfordshire which changed the situation considerably. By 1965 up to 4,500 gulls, mostly this, were roosting at Sonning Eye Gravel Pit and another 2,000 at Dorchester Gravel Pit.

In the following year some roosted at Farmoor Gravel Pit, and before 1970 other roosts were formed at Dix Pit, Stanton Harcourt, and the new Farmoor Reservoir. Until recently these roosts remained undisturbed and continued to grow, and gulls ranging from these bases on foraging flights became common sights throughout the county. A count of all gull roosts in central Oxfordshire on 22 January 1983 (Table 5.42) showed Black-headed Gulls easily the commonest gull species with some 12,800–13,650 present. It is fairly typical that there were more than twice as many Black-headed Gulls present than all other species together. Since then the population has grown considerably. Gosler (1987b) found some 40,000 gulls, mostly of this species roosting on Farmoor Reservoir and Queenford Pit, Dorchester, in the winter of 1986/87. Some 10,000 of these had been feeding at the Sutton Courtenay landfill site, while many of the rest were feeding at landfill sites at Stanton Harcourt and Wally Corner.

The population explosion of Black-headed Gulls has caused some concern. On occasions there has been anxiety about the number showing signs of botulism dying at Farmoor Reservoir. However, since this presents no risk to the public water supply, of greater concern has been the risk to aircraft from bird-strike. Of the 10,000 gulls that Gosler found feeding at

Table 5.42. Black-headed Gull.
Summary of Gull roost counts. January 22 1983. While one team of counters at Farmoor Reservoir assessed numbers flying in, the other counted the numbers settled on the water. Both counts are given.

Black-headed Gull			
Farmoor Reservoir		Dorchester Gravel Pits	Stanton Harcourt
Flying	Settled	All	All
7350	650	3800	2500

Lesser Black-backed Gull			
Farmoor Reservoir		Dorchester Gravel Pits	Stanton Harcourt
Flying	Settled	All	All
2220	2500	520	540

Herring Gull			
Farmoor Reservoir		Dorchester Gravel Pits	Stanton Harcourt
Flying	Settled	All	All
1680	1000	180	250

Common Gull			
Farmoor Reservoir		Dorchester Gravel Pits	Stanton Harcourt
Flying	Settled	All	All
60	75	80	1

Great Black-backed Gull			
Farmoor Reservoir		Dorchester Gravel Pits	Stanton Harcourt
Flying	Settled	All	All
20	13	2	32

Glaucous Gull			
Farmoor Reservoir		Dorchester Gravel Pits	Stanton Harcourt
Flying	Settled	All	All
1	1	0	0

Table 5.43. Black-headed Gull.
Summary of ringing recoveries.

State	No. of recoveries
South-west England	7
Southern England	3
South Wales	1
Netherlands	6
Denmark	5
Germany	4
Baltic States	2
Norway	1
Sweden	1
Finland	1

Sutton Courtenay, some 4,000 flew north to roost at Farmoor Reservoir. This flight took them directly across RAF Abingdon (Gosler 1987b). During the following winter, efforts to disperse the gulls from the landfill site were monitored and found to be successful except in cold weather when the attraction of food outweighed the perceived threat from a Verey pistol. Also gull numbers jumped back to many thousands at the tip within 48 hours after scaring stopped, although they dropped again with equal speed when scaring was resumed (Gosler 1988).

In 1989 a bird-strike at RAF Abingdon which caused a Tornado bomber to crash was attributed to gulls passing over on roosting flights to Farmoor. As a consequence, in 1990, a programme of roost prevention was undertaken at Farmoor Reservoir to see whether it was possible to disperse the roost. The project was funded by Thames Water Utilities and carried out by members of the Institute of Terrestrial Ecology, the Edward Grey Institute and the Aviation Bird Unit. The work involved broadcasting the appropriate distress calls of the gulls as they came in to roost. It was found that so long as Dix Pit was available as an alternative roost site, the birds quickly learnt to avoid Farmoor. Within a week the number of gulls visiting Farmoor was reduced from many thousands to a few hundred, and the number over-flying RAF Abingdon was reduced to single figures. The method ceased to be effective in very hard weather when Dix Pit was frozen and no longer available as a safe roost site. Regular wildfowl counts at Farmoor showed that there was no significant change in the numbers of duck using the reservoir since they simply did not respond to the gull distress calls. However, this might not have been the case if stronger roost prevention measures had been used during the severe weather early in 1991.

Undoubtedly the success of this species results from its opportunistic foraging strategies. The ever-growing availability of domestic refuse at tips is the most important single attraction, and the dumps at Sutton Courtenay, Port Meadow, Stanton Harcourt, Dorchester and Alkerton have all seen large feeding flocks.

In addition to refuse-feeding, flycatching techniques are adopted in spring to take rising chironomids at Farmoor Reservoir and in summer for flying ants over towns and villages. One small party was even reported picking ripe elderberries while hovering, and there is an account of another group stripping haws like Fieldfares. When Lapwings and Golden Plovers are worm-catching, Black-headed Gulls frequently join them and steal their finds. Recently they have become more bold, coming into gardens for large items of food, and making carefully timed visits to school playgrounds after playtimes, and early morning visits to fish and chip shop courtyards. These are all in addition to their more traditional feeding grounds in fields which are flooded or under the plough.

COMMON GULL
Larus canus

A very frequent winter visitor, and passage migrant. Most often found in higher parts of the Cotswolds in north Oxfordshire and the Chilterns on both pasture and arable fields. Aplin (1889) called it "a frequent visitor which often occurs". There has been a general increase since his day, but on a much less dramatic scale than the other numerous gull species.

The pattern of its distribution is markedly different from other regular gull visitors. The largest numbers are seen in the spring from late February until early April in a well defined passage movement, often visible by day, towards the north-east. This was first noted by Aplin (1889), and was still observed in the 1960s and 1970s in the Cotswolds with frequent accounts in the annual OOS reports of flocks of more than 100 appearing on a line approximately from Burford to Sibford Ferris. In the 1980s similar movements were observed along the Chiltern Scarp. Near Cowlease Wood an annual gathering place on sheep pastures was noted from 1987 until 1991. On 18 March 1990 more than 500 were seen leaving this site at mid-day, gaining height in thermals, and heading off to the north-east.

Common Gulls are rarely seen in the summer months, but return movements up the Thames valley take place during July and early August. This is less conspicuous than spring passage, mostly involving single birds drifting along with the stream of Black-headed Gulls moving at this time. Larger concentrations like the flock of ca. 100 at Chipping Norton on 27 August 1975 are unusual.

During the winter they are mostly reported from the chalk hills of the Berkshire Downs and the Chilterns. For example, in the 1980s regular parties of up to 60 were present in the Stonor valley. Feeding parties are usually well spaced out, but overall totals may be considerable as suggested when a flock of ca. 700 assembled on a field being harrowed at Aston Upthorpe in February 1982 with birds coming in small groups from all directions. At this time of year they sometimes wander into the Thames valley dropping in to bathe in the nearest open waters particularly at the Dorchester Gravel Pit complex.

They have been less attracted to rubbish tips than other wintering gulls although they make occasional visits and this is an increasing tendency. For example, One large flock of ca. 500 at the Alkerton Tip on 15 March 1984 at the peak of spring passage was considered exceptional but Gosler (1987, 1988b) found that about 8% of 10,000 gulls visiting the Sutton Courtenay landfill site in the 1986/87 winter were of this species. Some join the large mixed-species gull roosts in the county (see Black-headed Gull), but numbers are not high, and it is possible they also go elsewhere.

Seven were ringed in two cannon-netting catches on 7 March 1987 and 5 March 1988.

One Oxfordshire ringing recovery indicating the longevity of the Common Gull was a bird found at Off Vannoy in Norway (2,338 km NNE) in June 1961, which had been ringed at Wallingford in April 1951, making it more than ten years old. Another ringed in Gloucester on 28 November 1987 was at Abingdon on 17 June 1988 (70 km ESE) suggests movements from the Bristol Channel area.

LESSER BLACK-BACKED GULL
Larus fuscus

Now a very frequent visitor, the increase of this species locally shows many parallels with that of the Black-headed Gull. It is now the second most commonly noted gull here. Less trusting of man, it has fewer feeding alternatives than the Black-headed Gull, and is mainly to be seen at rubbish tips, in open fields, or taking carrion from roads in the early morning.

Aplin (1889) described the Lesser Black-backed Gull as an occasional visitor and in the first half of the twentieth century it was known mostly as a passage migrant. The northerly flights of small parties passing over during the day-time in May were always considered worth reporting. These movements continue today, although less remarked upon now because the sight of this species is no longer unusual.

In the second half of the century there has been a considerable increase. By the 1960s parties of up to a few hundred began making daily feeding trips, mostly to the eastern part of the county from roosts at the reservoirs around London. Local roosts formed in the 1970s and 1980s at Dorchester, Farmoor, and Stanton Harcourt encouraged a further growth in numbers. In these decades a wintering population estimated in excess of 3,000– 4,000 was maintained, although there were fluctuations according to weather conditions, with declines during cold periods.

In June a few immatures were noted wandering over, usually in a northerly direction, possibly straggling behind the breeding migrants which passed through during the previous month. By 1990 these were forming summer assemblies of 50–120 at rubbish tip sites. The numbers wintering are very much larger than this. For example, counts carried out during the 1990/91 winter found up to 4,400 Lesser Black-backed Gulls roosting at Farmoor

Reservoir in a roost of some 15,700 between roost-prevention trials (A. Gosler pers. comm., see also Black-headed Gull).

Gosler (1987b, 1987c, 1988) studied the attendance, feeding and roosting behaviour of gulls using the Sutton Courtenay Landfill Site in the winters of 1986/87 and 1987/88. He found that about 1,200 of the 10,000 gulls present were of this species (see Black-headed Gull). He also found that these birds were divided into two more or less discrete flocks depending on race. One flock contained only birds of the dark-backed continental race *L.f. fuscus* and these roosted on Queenford Pit at Dorchester. The rest, which roosted at Farmoor Reservoir, belonged to the British race *L.f. graellsii*.

On 7 March 1987, 21 Lesser Black-backed Gulls were ringed at Sutton Courtenay. None of these has yet been recovered. However, birds ringed in the county have been recovered in Manchester, France and Iceland, while birds recovered here which were ringed in the UK have been ringed at Bristol, Skokholm, Skomer, Walney Island and Anglesey. This pattern indicates that *graellsii* birds are largely from the west coast colonies and probably travel inland via the Bristol Channel and Severn valley.

HERRING GULL
Larus argentatus

A very frequent visitor. Herring Gulls visit this inland county chiefly from mid-November to the end of February, with some in October and March. Most are seen at times of extensive flooding of river valleys when they feed on the litter and debris at the water's edge. In cold winters they are more restricted to living near rubbish tips. One immature bird at Taynton in December 1986 spent more than an hour trying to catch rabbits as they emerged from their burrows.

The highest counts have been *ca.* 5,000 at Farmoor Reservoir on 20 February 1969, 1,430–2,110 there on 22 January 1983, and *ca.* 1,000 at Alkerton Tip in February 1988. The pattern of mid-winter peaks in the Oxfordshire populations is similar to that found at other inland sites where detailed records have been kept. Analyses of counts at refuse tips in London in the winter of 1976/1977 (Standley *et al.* 1981) and at Blithfield Reservoir, Staffordshire

from 1974 to 1984 (Dean 1987) demonstrate this.

Today no more than a few stragglers wander through the county. In mid-summer these are almost invariably non-breeding birds. It seems that in the first part of the twentieth century there may have been a different pattern of visits. Jourdain (1926) describes them as "not infrequently seen, especially at migration times", and Alexander (1947) describes "considerable flocks" in autumn "frequently seen flying over in a south-westerly direction, almost certainly travelling across the country from the Wash to the Severn". Unfortunately Annual Reports provide no substantiation for these descriptions, and we have no information about the exact timing of these movements, or the numbers involved. In the second half of the twentieth century Herring Gulls appeared increasingly at gull roosts in the county. First reports were of a few hundred occasionally staying at Port Meadow in the 1940s thus escaping the long flight back to the London reservoirs. It was not until the late 1960s that they began to stay regularly at Dorchester Gravel Pits, and the mid-1970s at Farmoor Reservoir.

Ringing studies summarised by Lack (1986) show that while the majority of British Herring Gulls tend to winter relatively near their breeding grounds on the coast, significant numbers of the north European race *L.a. argentatus* from Fennoscandia and Russia visit Britain, arriving in November, reaching a peak in January and dispersing in late January and February. The coincidence of timing suggests the flocks visiting Oxfordshire may be composed mostly of these birds. Examples of the Mediterranean race *L.a. michahellis* (the Yellow-legged Herring Gull) were identified increasingly in southern Britain in the 1980s. In the autumn of 1989 adults were noted at Farmoor Reservoir, Stanton Harcourt and Dorchester Gravel Pits, and it can be expected that greater vigilance by observers will produce more records in the future.

ICELAND GULL
Larus glaucoides

A rare visitor. There is a nineteenth century record of one shot on Port Meadow in spring 1836. Following this was a gap of 132 years until the species was next recorded, also in the spring (2 April 1968) and at the same site. Since then there have been three more records: a third-winter bird at Farmoor Reservoir on 19 February 1969, a third-winter bird at Stanton Harcourt Gravel Pit on 12 January 1975, and one (a probable female) at Farmoor Reservoir on 13 February 1990 during a storm. In comparison, the West Midlands had about 70 records during the 1970s (Harrison *et al*. 1982). As interest in searching through gull flocks increases locally more frequent records of this species may be expected in future.

GLAUCOUS GULL
Larus hyperboreus

A rare winter visitor. After one was shot at Stonesfield in 1836 none was encountered again in the county until 1969. From then until 1988 a total of 14 sightings were made at gull roosts or refuse tips. All were in mid-winter between 2 November and 21 February. Presumably not many individuals of this conspicuous species will have been overlooked, so its status in Oxfordshire remains as "a rare winter visitor". This is in contrast to the West Midlands where it has been an annual visitor since 1966 with about 120 birds in the decade 1969–1978. (Harrison *et al*. 1982) The presence of massive rubbish dumps in that area might, in part, explain the difference.

The dates of records are 18 December 1969, 12 January 1975, 12 December 1976, 6 January 1979 and 3–23 January 1983. There were three different birds in February 1986, and one, presumed to be the same individual, remained at Stanton Harcourt from 2 November 1987 until 6 February 1988. These were solitary individuals, but in January 1988 two were together at the Alkerton Tip. Sites at which it has been recorded are Farmoor and Grimsbury Reservoirs, Stanton Harcourt, Dorchester and Wolvercote Gravel Pits, the Alkerton Tip, and one was seen flying over Abingdon.

The majority were young birds; records stating age show two adults, two second- or third-winter, and five first-winter birds.

GREAT BLACK-BACKED GULL
Larus marinus

While Alexander (1947) found the Great Black-backed Gull a "rare visitor, recorded nine times

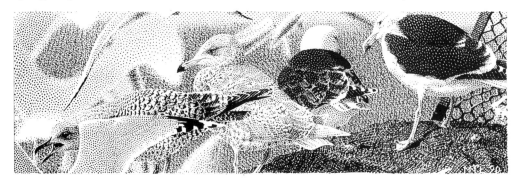

in the last 60 years," Radford (1966) describes its "improved status", for by then it was seen annually. This progress has continued. At first its appearances in the 1950s and 1960s were confined to the mid-winter months of November to February. It is still found most often then, and there have now been seven accounts of larger parties of between ten and 38 in mid-winter. However it has also been seen at other seasons and by 1981 it had been recorded in every month of the year.

Nearly all records are restricted to rubbish tip sites or roosts, and the impression given is of birds passing through rather than remaining in the area.

Confusion with the Lesser Black-backed Gull may mean that this species has been under-recorded. Two observations suggest this. The combined count of gull roosts on 22 January 1983 produced a total of at least 47 at the three main roosts, and there was one exceptionally large flock of 134 at Pixey Mead on 13 February 1977. Gosler (1987, 1988b) estimated that fewer than 1% of the 10,000 gulls visiting the Sutton Courtenay Landfill Site in February 1987 were of this species, and indeed true numbers were often in single figures.

KITTIWAKE
Rissa tridactyla

Formerly an occasional passage migrant and vagrant, it is now a regular passage visitor. Before 1980 these pelagic gulls were regarded as uncommon visitors occasionally blown inland by storms at various times in the year except summer (Aplin 1889, Radford 1966). These were usually found in an exhausted state, and weakened birds rarely survived.

The totals seen in five-year periods from 1960–1989 were typical of the pattern of occurrence noted since the mid-nineteenth century (Table 5.44).

Wind-blown Kittiwakes still appear, but there has been a new development in recent years. There was a hint of this in 1957, not understood at the time, when between 2 and 28 February there were up to six on Port Meadow on several dates, another three at Wallingford, two at Iffley, and singles at Shotover, Dorchester and Nuneham. Two dead birds were found, indicating difficulties in survival inland, but weather for once appeared not to be a factor because it was an unusually mild spring. Possibly this was a first hint of the spring appearances which were to become regular at Farmoor Reservoir during the 1980s. In 1981 more than 60 arrived there on 26 April and although only one remained the following day, another six came in on 3 May. In 1982 ten were there on 13 April, and 35 on the next two days, one or two staying until 26 April. They seemed in no hurry to move on as they fed busily by leaping from the water to snap up rising chironomids (in contrast Black-headed Gulls caught these in the air). Similar visits were made in 1983, 1984 and 1985. Such large groups have not been noticed since although the numbers of birds visiting overall continues to increase annually. The spring visits were not confined to this county, but have been reported at other inland sites. For example there were 40 at Tring Reservoir, Hertfordshire on 28 April 1985, and 115 at Willen, Buckinghamshire on 20 March 1987. In all instances nearly all birds involved were adults. Presumably they were returning to breeding grounds, although April is unusually late for this. The substantial increase of the species as a breeding bird in Britain is probably connected with its more frequent occurrence inland (Lloyd et al. 1991).

Table 5.44. Kittiwake.
Total numbers recorded 1960-1980.

Period	No.
1960-64	2
1965-69	3
1970-74	2
1975-79	8
1980-84	132+
1985-89	186+

Family: Sternidae
Terns

Like the gulls, terns also occur in greater numbers than previously, and one species now breeds in the county. Of the others, two species are regular passage migrants in good numbers, and the rest are less predictable but also occur on passage. The increased frequency of occurrence of many of several species reflects a growth in population during the twentieth century.

Table 5.45. Sandwich Tern.
Total number of birds seen in five-year periods.

Period	No. of birds
1950-54	0
1955-59	5
1960-64	6
1965-69	0
1970-74	13
1975-79	9
1980-84	25
1985-89	50

Figure 5.50. Sandwich Tern.
Monthly distribution of records.

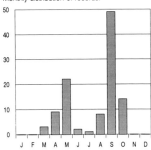

SANDWICH TERN
Sterna sandvicensis

An infrequent passage visitor. Once rare, by the 1980s a few were being recorded in most spring and autumn periods. They are less inclined to linger than other tern species, and are not often seen feeding. Their brief appearances are at a range of sites including some seen moving across open countryside, but more usually records come from the Thames valley or the larger lakes in mid-Oxfordshire. They often join gull roosts at Farmoor Reservoir with a maximum of eight on one occasion.

Prior to 1950 there were only four records. Table 5.45 shows the progress that has been made since then. Almost twice as many appear in autumn as in spring (Figure 5.50). The earliest date they have been seen is 25 March, and the latest 26 October.

There are several possible explanations for the increase in sightings in recent years. There are more competent observers capable of recognizing the calls of these noisy terns which usually give the first indication of their presence. Some birds recorded flying over places away from water in open countryside would probably have been missed had they been silent. The recent availability of safe inland roosts presumably encourages migration over inland Britain. However, it is most likely that this reflects the recent growth in Sandwich Tern populations in Britain. The causes of these changes are unknown (Lloyd *et al.* 1991).

ROSEATE TERN
Sterna dougallii

A very rare passage migrant. There have been only two records. One was seen at Pangbourne on 6 September 1967, and one at Farmoor Reservoir on 12 May 1970.

COMMON TERN
Sterna hirundo

A frequent passage migrant along the Thames and at the larger lakes throughout the county as it was in Aplin's day. A few pairs now breed annually. This tern lives up to its name in being the commonest of the tern visitors to the county. Numbers vary considerably from year to year, but even when the passage is thin at least a few are to be seen every spring and autumn. Records date from 10 April–20 November, with the main passage in May, August and September. Migration appears to occur both by day and night, for parties have been seen moving off at dusk, and early morning watchers have discovered terns which have arrived during the night.

The spring of 1978 produced the greatest influx of white terns during the period 2 May to 6 May, when there were 100–120 at Farmoor, 80 at Kiddington, and 60 at Grimsbury. Although most were described as "Commic Terns" owing to identification problems, the majority were considered to be of this species.

More usually groups number one to ten, and in some years fewer than ten passage birds have been recorded in total.

The Common Tern has persisted in attempts to breed in Oxfordshire. There was an early account of nesting at Otmoor in 1934. The next confirmed breeding in the county was not until 1969. This was on a gravel pit island near Reading where a small colony has existed ever since with a maximum of six pairs in 1979. Breeding colonies were established at other gravel pits in the Reading area on the Berkshire side of the Thames in the 1980s, and in the late 1980s occasional pairs began breeding in Oxfordshire gravel pits at Radley, Abingdon and Stanton Harcourt. Then in 1989 a pair bred at Farmoor Reservoir on a platform provided for the purpose. Three pairs bred successfully there in 1990 and 1991.

Whereas migrating terns mainly feed on flies and midges, the young are fed on small fishes. Observations during 1991 suggested that the parents from Farmoor fished mainly on the River Thames upstream of the reservoir. It appeared that the principle prey fish taken was Bleak. Since 1990, the tern chicks have been ringed each year. The appearances of family parties have become a welcome sight in summer locally, especially along the Thames, with contact and food-begging calls becoming a familiar sound as the young trail around after their parents.

As yet there are probably fewer than ten pairs nesting in mid-Oxfordshire, but if additional platform or island sites could be created there is every indication that flourishing colonies could develop.

ARCTIC TERN
Sterna paradisaea

A frequent passage visitor, in recent years seen every spring and autumn over lakes at gravel pits and reservoirs, or the River Thames. The early history of this species is shrouded by the difficulties in separating it from the similar Common Tern. Until the improvement in identification skills in the 1980s most white terns were described as 'Commic'.

Numbers of terns seen in the county in the first half of the twentieth century were low in comparison with those in recent years. As terns typically spend no more than an hour or so feeding before continuing their journey an unusual record was of a group of up to 19 terns which remained on Port Meadow between 22 April and 7 May 1947 during a period of south-west gales. They spent most of their time sitting in the middle of the meadow, and as they allowed close approach, could be identified positively as Arctic Terns.

In the last two decades, reservoirs and other large areas of water have attracted many more terns of most of the common species, and in most years in the 1980s a marked passage of Arctic Terns has been noted at the end of April. This was matched by observations by members of the Buckinghamshire Bird Club who have witnessed similar inland passages at this time. Some of the maximum numbers during these periods have been as follows: 70 at Farmoor Reservoir on 27 April 1982, 83 at Farmoor Reservoir on 29 April 1985, 30 at Dorchester Gravel Pits on 5 May 1987, 19 at Farmoor Reservoir on 8 May 1988, 125 at Farmoor Reservoir on 29 April 1989, 41 at Grimsbury Reservoir on 23 April 1990, and 100 at Farmoor Reservoir on 24 April 1990.

There have been one or two records of solitary birds in June, but return passage is usually noted from late July, and continues until September. This is of a much more modest nature generally, with only a few birds involved. The latest record for the species locally is 17 October.

LITTLE TERN
Sterna albifrons

An occasional passage migrant through Oxfordshire. The Little Tern has always been regarded as an uncommon visitor on migration, a description which remains true to this day. There has only been a slight increase in the frequency of records (Table 5.46), despite better observer cover and the availability of more attractive sites for passing terns. This compares unfavourably with other tern visitors which are now seen much more often. This gives the strongest evidence we have that the numbers of terns seen in the county is determined more by the actual population size or movements of the birds than by observer bias, since while the number of observers has increased considerably during the last 30 years, the national population of Little Tern has remained fairly stable (at least since 1970) at about 2,000–2,800 pairs (Lloyd et al. 1991).

Although in other parts of the world Little Terns are frequently found at inland waters far from the sea, visits to central England are usually fleeting, with birds rarely staying more than an hour or two. On most occasions they are seen in the company of Common or Arctic Terns.

Little Terns have been reported in 19 of the 30 years between 1960 and 1989, on a total of 31 occasions, with one record of three birds, five of two, and the rest singles. Locations of visits have been as follows: Farmoor 12, Dorchester five, Stanton Harcourt and Port Meadow three, Blenheim two and single visits to Radley Gravel Pit, Minster Lovell, Grimsbury Reservoir, Wolvercote Gravel Pit and Abingdon Sewage Farm.

Slightly more birds have been seen on spring passage (59% of all records), which is almost entirely confined to late April and early May (Figure 5.51). Autumn visits are over a longer period, the latest record being on 27 October.

Table 5.46. Little Tern.
Number of records in five-year periods 1960-1989.

Period	No. of records	No. of birds
1960-64	4	7
1965-69	4	6
1970-74	4	4
1975-79	6	6
1980-84	6	6
1985-89	7	8

Figure 5.51. Little Tern.
Monthly distribution of records 1960-1989.

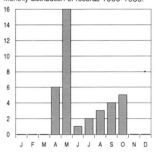

WHISKERED TERN
Chlidonias hybridus

A very rare vagrant. The only record is of one which appeared at Sutton Courtenay Gravel Pits on 2 May 1970 and remained there for five days.

BLACK TERN
Chlidonias niger

A frequent passage migrant in spring and autumn. Aplin (1889) described the species as "an occasional visitor", although Radford (1966) states that it was thought to have bred on Otmoor in the 1850s. However in the second half of the twentieth century it began to appear regularly every migration time, although in extremely variable numbers. Visits are usually brief, typically lasting a few hours.

The annual period of records extends from 14 April to 5 November. For many years the peak of the spring passage was in the second half of May (with several parties of between ten and 30), but in the late 1980s the first week of May produced most records. Weather conditions at migration time have a considerable influence on these timings.

Nearly all are seen over the more extensive waters such as the reservoirs at Farmoor and Grimsbury, and the larger gravel pit lakes, Dix Pit at Stanton Harcourt, and Queenford Pit at Dorchester. At these places opportunities for feeding on flying insects presumably encourage them to drop down more frequently during overland flights.

Over the years there have been some impressive 'falls', but none equal to that of 15 September 1974 when at least 200-300 were present on various waters in the county (Brucker 1974). The day was overcast, and there was intermittent drizzle as low clouds were swept over by winds of up to nine knots, generally in a south-easterly direction. Weather records provided by the RAF Abingdon Meteorological Office show that for most of the day there was complete cloud cover between 1,000 ft and 9,000 ft, and at times clouds were down to 400 ft. Observers saw Black Terns, with some Common Terns, dropping from this cloud to rest and feed, and then continue on their way, heading directly into the cloud. During a two-hour watch at the Queenford Pit, Dorchester, 45-83 were present continually, although groups were arriving and leaving all the time. Maximum counts elsewhere were 63 at Dix Pit, Stanton Harcourt, 18 at Blenheim, 80 at Farmoor, 75 at Didcot Gravel Pit, and 18 at Wolvercote Gravel Pit. Outside the county the passage that day was noted at Wraysbury, Staines and Queen Mary Reservoirs in Middlesex, from which came estimates of 450, and Farnborough to the south where there were at least 100. Emphasising the irregularity of visits to us, in the following autumn period, no more than ten birds were seen. Totally different weather caused the most sustained passage of Black Terns ever recorded in Oxfordshire during the first five days of May 1990. High pressure over Britain and Europe brought a prolonged period of north-easterly winds, which resulted in a westward drift of migrants across Europe. In this period there were 55-116 continually at Farmoor Reservoir, up to 77 at Stanton Harcourt Gravel Pits, 24 at Dorchester Gravel Pits and large numbers at Grimsbury Reservoir. These counts represent only a small portion of the birds which passed through, as flocks were arriving and leaving for much of the time.

There have also been 'falls' in the summer months, often associated with thunderstorms. Highest counts were 25 on 29 July 1978, and 66 on 15 August 1985, but the second week in September remains the most likely to produce high counts (e.g. 70 on 11 September 1981).

WHITE-WINGED BLACK TERN
Chlidonias leucopterus

A very rare vagrant, recorded three times at Farmoor Reservoir. An adult in summer plumage was present for about an hour on the morning of 2 May 1971. One was with Black Terns on 18 October 1976. A juvenile was with Black Terns for a few hours after 36 continuous hours of low cloud and rain on 15 September 1986.

Family: Alcidae
Auks

As with the skuas, four species of auk have occurred in the county as accidentals and their appearance usually coincides with rough weather. It is generally assumed that these originate on the west coast of Britain but there is no conclusive evidence of this. The populations of some of these species have increased dramatically during this century and this might have contributed to the changes in the behaviour of some.

GUILLEMOT
Uria aalge

A very rare vagrant recorded only three times in the county. One was shot at Sandford, October 1840. One was seen flying over Brasenose College playing field then passing down the Thames in July 1927. A postman found one exhausted in the road near Goring on 10 February 1983 and delivered it to a local birdwatcher who released it on the Thames where it swam for a few minutes before flying off strongly.

RAZORBILL
Alca torda

A very rare vagrant with no recent records. One was 'procured' on the River Thames at Oxford in April 1853, and found at Clattercote Reservoir in December 1878, at Wroxton in January 1890, near Swinford in December 1926 and on road south of Burford 4 January 1952. The latter was picked up, but died eight days later.

LITTLE AUK
Alle alle

A rare straggler in winter, the Little Auk has been recorded on 14 occasions between 1950 and 1990 at a variety of sites throughout the county. The period of occurrences is from October to February (Figure 5.52).

Visits nearly always coincide with periods of strong winds from the north and east which cause 'wrecks' of this species along the east coast of Britain. Nine of the 14 records were of dead or dying birds, but two others found in an exhausted state were successfully restored to health and released at sea. Of the three reports of fit and active birds two were of singles, but an unusual sighting was of three together at Hardwick Gravel Pit on 30 October 1983.

Earlier records appear to have been of similar frequency, with an exceptional period in January 1895 when no fewer than five were picked up in various parts of Oxfordshire. There seems to have been no change in status since 1950 although there was only one record between 1962 and 1981 (Table 5.47).

PUFFIN
Fratercula arctica

A rare vagrant, noted fifteen times between 1882 and 1990. After six records in the period 1882–1898 there was a long gap and they were not seen again until 1946. Since then they were seen in 1946, 1952, 1954, 1957, 1961, 1964, 1984 (two occasions) and 1985.

As with other auks the Puffin is a wanderer from the coast at times of exceptionally severe storms. Practically all have been single birds found dead, or exhausted. The only exception was a party of about six flying in a rainstorm

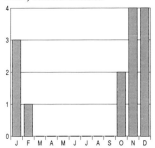

Figure 5.52. Little Auk.
Monthly distribution of records.

Table 5.47. Little Auk.
Number of records per decade.

Decade	No.
1950s	5
1960s	2
1970s	1
1980s	6

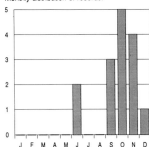

Figure 5.53. Puffin.

Monthly distribution of records.

over Blowing Stone Hill, Uffington on 4 September 1985, identified for certain when one (a juvenile) dropped down and was picked up. It died four days later. This was a typical outcome as efforts to restore exhausted Puffins to health have succeeded on only three occasions.

Figure 5.53 shows that all appearances were in the period from September to December, apart from two in June. The records have generally come from a scattering of sites, although there is some bias towards the north of the county near Banbury from which seven of the observations came.

Family: Columbidae
Doves

Five species of dove breed in Oxfordshire although one, the Rock Dove, occurs as a feral population only. Of the other four, three are abundant residents and the other is a summer visitor in decline.

ROCK DOVE or FERAL PIGEON
Columba livia

As a feral population this is a numerous breeding species. Feral Pigeons are well established throughout the county. The main concentrations are in the larger towns such as Oxford, Henley, Banbury, Abingdon and Witney. In Oxford, for example, several nest around Brasenose College, Gloucester Green, Oxpens and Botley. Some smaller towns also have regular breeding populations. For example, there is a regular flock of 20-30 around Bampton Church where they nest.

Although the species has not been studied the impression is that the Feral Pigeons in the Oxfordshire countryside form separate groups living within defined areas where they can be seen throughout the year. Two such groups of 60-100 which breed in the bridge at Blenheim Palace, and in the Shipton Cement Works quarry fly out in compact groups to favourite fields within a few miles of their nest sites.

The mixed origin of these birds is obvious. The flocks living in the country contain more white or partially white doves than those in the towns. These are presumably derived from the white doves which escaped from dovecotes in the past. Lost racing homers also often join flocks. Few individuals have the appearance of pure Rock Doves.

STOCK DOVE
Columba oenas

A very numerous resident. Although Stock Doves (illustrated here with Woodpigeon) range throughout Oxfordshire in their search for food in winter, their preferred habitat in summer is parkland or the edges of woods. In 1982 M.G. Wilson estimated 20-30 pairs breeding at Blenheim Park, 11 pairs at Shotover Park and Brasenose Wood and six pairs at Nuneham Park. Pairs are also still to be found in Oxford college gardens and in willow trees alongside

tributaries of the Thames. Dense woodland is usually avoided as easy access to open countryside seems to be a requirement. However, Gosler (1990) described it as an abundant breeder in Wytham Woods nesting at high density, sometimes deep in the wood, and flying up to 0.5 km to feed. Here they used medium-sized tree holes, often in Beech, and competed with Jackdaws for nest sites. A reason for the comparative thinness of population in the Chilterns demonstrated in Atlas counts in the 1980s may be that this part of the county is more wooded, has a system of smaller fields and a lower percentage of arable land.

Favoured nest sites are holes and crevices in mature trees. The disappearance of so many of these in recent years as a result of a combination of Dutch Elm Disease, natural decay, severe gales and active woodland management, has created a shortage of nest sites. This is demonstrated by the alacrity with which they accept nestboxes, as shown at Foxcombe Wood where eight pairs used them in 1988. In open

Table 5.48. Woodpigeon.

Largest flocks recorded in OOS Reports in selected years.

Year	Count
1889	<200
1960	900+
1974	1700
1975	2800
1979	5000
1984	5820

countryside areas of extensive corn production, barns, outbuildings, and ruins are used frequently. D.G.C. Harper found them present in 15 out of 29 barns visited in the Brightwell/ Tiddington district of east Oxfordshire in June 1984 and J.W. Brucker found them in 12 out of 19 barns in the Berkshire Downs above Wantage in July 1989.

Oxfordshire has no natural cliffs, but the limestone faces exposed at quarries in the Cotswolds provide additional breeding sites. At Shipton-on-Cherwell Cement Works in 1988 at least 11 pairs nested. At gravel pit sites they also use rabbit holes; 14 were seen in or near burrows at Stanton Harcourt in April 1977.

As with other resident pigeon species the breeding season extends for several months, occasionally even into the winter. For instance one was incubating a clutch on 30 December, and full grown young have been seen at the nest on 9 February.

Although the Stock Dove is generally regarded as a sedentary species (O'Connor and Mead 1984), a record of about 2,000 going south-west over Hartslock Nature Reserve for two hours in parties of about 200 on 24 February 1985, suggests that more than local movements may sometimes occur. However, of 21 recoveries of birds ringed in Oxfordshire, 20 were found still in the county, and 17 were within 9 km of the ringing site. Usually in winter they congregate in flocks in fields near their breeding areas. In the 1970s these typically numbered up to 100 or 200, but there was an increase in the 1980s with, for example, at least 500 on maize stubble at Cothill in 1982 and some 630 at Stanton Harcourt in 1986. This could reflect a genuine increase in the species, but could also be the result of reduced supplies of food causing birds to crowd at fewer sites.

While Stock Doves have been reported feeding on acorns, weed seeds, and in fields containing pea, potato and various brassica crops, the major food is grain. Agricultural developments since the mid-twentieth century leading to extensive tracts of the county being devoted to cereal production have had a considerable impact on Stock Dove populations. In the 1950s reliance on grain was particularly apparent when the species suffered serious losses as a result of the widespread use of dieldrin and other organochlorine seed-dressings. In 1958 B. Campbell reported heavy mortality at Hordley, finding 40 dead at one conifer roost. Since the banning of these poisons recovery has been steady. However, despite the massive switch to cereals, only limited supplies of corn are available to birds. Modern harvesting methods leave the fields comparatively clean, and stubble is usually burnt. Crops are grown at greater densities, leaving few bare patches in which birds can settle. At the same time, weed seeds, which are an important alternative to corn, have declined in abundance due to herbicide use. However, the ban on stubble burning after 1991, and the widespread set-aside of agricultural land, if they encourage weed seed production, are likely to benefit the Stock Dove.

WOODPIGEON
Columba palumbus

Very numerous resident. Woodpigeons are always among the first species encountered on any walk, in any part of the county, at any time of the year. The Oxfordshire Atlas showed them to be the third most widespread breeding bird. Yet, perhaps because of their familiarity, they rarely feature among records submitted to the county recorder. There were only brief mentions in half of the annual reports from 1968 to 1988, and none in the rest.

Woodpigeons are generally sedentary in Britain, as shown by Murton and Redpath (1962) in their study of BTO ringing recoveries. The OOS Report for 1963 includes an analysis of 14 recoveries in January and February of that year of Woodpigeons ringed in Oxfordshire in 1960, 1961 and 1963 (all except one ringed as nestlings). Distances travelled ranged from 8-80 km. Interestingly only three were to the south, and the remaining 11 were in a sector of 90° from north-east to north-west. Since then there have been many more recoveries of birds ringed as nestlings mentioned in annual reports. These show a similar pattern with six recoveries to the north or north-east. Of 97 recoveries of birds ringed in Oxfordshire, 54 were within 9 km of the ringing site, 39 at 10-99 km and four at 100+ km, The most distant being one recovered at Gribbin Head, Cornwall (291 km ESE) in February 1953. There have been no recoveries of continental birds. Woodpigeon movements would seem to be worthy of closer study.

Populations have remained high, and Woodpigeons were able to adapt from their previous staple diet of clover on pastures and leys when there was a change of emphasis to cereal production. They descend in all directions when suitable feeding sources are discovered. Counts of large flocks, mostly on cereal stubbles and later winter cereal sowings, show a steady increase (Table 5.48). A variety of natural foods are also taken. In spring they have been reported feeding on fresh tips and buds of Elm (OOS Report 1970) and Beech (OOS Report 1990). They commonly feed on Ivy berries, acorns and beechmast in the autumn.

They were not slow to discover Oilseed Rape as a potential food when this was increasingly sown in the 1970s and 1980s. The use of this crop in Oxfordshire has been noted since 1977. P. Collier, farming in the Chadlington area, has followed this development (pers. comm.). They first settled on storm damaged crops finding the seeds to their liking. Then by attempting to take seeds from standing crops they flattened the stalks and succeeded in feeding on the ground. After harvesting they take spilt seed. Then in hard winters the emergent shoots in newly sown Oilseed Rape fields provide an important alternative to other brassicas less frequently grown in recent years.

Prolonged cold weather in winter can cause problems. During the unbroken three months of freezing conditions at the beginning of 1963 flocks ranged the countryside in anxious search for food. They came into allotments and gardens stripping Brussels sprouts, kale and any other greens and even turned to eating Crab Apple, Hawthorn and *Cotoneaster* berries. In farmyards they came in to feed among stock in cattle yards. Emaciated corpses of those which failed to survive were a common sight. Farmers reduced their numbers further — more than 3,000 were shot on 20 acres of Brussels sprouts at Hinton Waldrist. Despite this, Woodpigeons showed remarkable powers of recovery and the usual large flocks were found the following winter.

An important factor in sustaining population levels must be the ability to breed in almost every month of the year. This enables them to adapt the timing of nesting to accommodate for changes in agriculture such as the earlier availability of cereals caused by the switch to autumn sowing. It is true that breeding activity is at a height in spring and summer, but even in the intensely cold weather of the 1963 winter a pair was nest building in Oxford in mid-February.

This is one of the few birds which seems to be almost universally disliked and considered a real pest. To farming communities their only redeeming feature is that they make tasty pies. Yet it may be possible to detect a trace of affection in the way older inhabitants of Combe remember the song of the Woodpigeon by the mnemonic "my toes bleed Betty".

COLLARED DOVE
Streptopelia decaocto

A very numerous resident. Local ornithologists eagerly awaited the appearance of the Collared Dove as they observed its dramatic spread through western Europe and its arrival in the east coast of Britain in 1955. The first in Oxfordshire was at Hordley in December 1962. The advance continued and in the following year newly fledged young were discovered on a roof top at Islip, and the year after that at least 18 were present in the same village. Breeding was also proved at Wantage in 1963.

The increase continued at such a pace that most areas were colonised by 1970. By this time Collared Doves were such a familiar sight that few observers bothered to record them, and several subsequent Oxfordshire Bird Reports carried no information about the species. Clearly they had found a vacant niche and exploited it to the full. They were present in most suitable habitats by the mid-1970s and afterwards seem to have maintained a more or less steady level of population.

Table 5.49. Collared Dove.
Largest flocks reported to the County recorder 1967-1984.

Year	No.	
1967	60	Sonning Eye
1973	70	Milton/Farmoor/
		Stanton Harcourt
1977	200+	Warborough
1979	300	Pinkhill Farm
1984	ca 250	East Hendred

Once established, the population seems to be sedentary. They are usually found near places of human habitation although parties sometimes make brief forays into open country at harvest time. In winter they gather in flocks around farm buildings.

An important habitat requirement seems to be the availability of grain. This results in populations being concentrated near farm buildings, chicken runs, pheasant feeding areas, garden bird tables and places where grain is processed. Adequate cover for nest building in the form of large trees, especially evergreens, is appreciated, so parks or large gardens where these can be found are favoured places.

The rapid expansion was undoubtedly aided by the bird's ability to rear several broods in quick succession during a protracted breeding season. In Oxfordshire all stages of nesting have been reported in every month of the year. Table 5.49 lists the largest flocks reported and shows the build-up of numbers.

Mechanised farms in Oxfordshire today are tidy places where wasteful spillage of grain is kept to a minimum. On the other hand there is a far greater amount of cereal production than in the past. It is interesting to speculate how abundant the species might have become had its advance into the county been made in earlier times.

TURTLE DOVE
Streptopelia turtur

A numerous but declining summer visitor. This is our only migrant dove species, arriving in the second half of April and the first half of May and leaving in August and September. First arrival dates mentioned in 32 annual reports show a spread from 4 April to 4 May, with a mean of 24 April. Final autumn dates given in 25 annual reports are from 6-29

September, with a mean of 18 September.

While Sharrock (1976) described them in 40 of the 42 10 km squares in Oxfordshire and Berkshire (former boundaries), the Oxfordshire Atlas (1984–1988) showed them present in only 12% of tetrads. The Atlas illustrates well their preference for the open countryside of the clay vales east and south of Oxford, and the foothills of the chalk downs, and avoidance of the more wooded areas of the county.

The local distribution appears to change rather erratically from year to year. At times they have been discovered nesting almost colonially, as in 1986 when 13 were heard calling near Tetsworth and 12 near Combe. However, in the following year there were none at Combe. Elsewhere nest sites may be widely dispersed, as shown in 1984 when a survey of 21 km of suitable habitat between Sandford, Garsington and Stadhampton revealed a total of 13 pairs.

As in the country as a whole, Turtle Dove populations have clearly been in decline in Oxfordshire during the second half of the twentieth century. This process has been steady rather than abrupt. Report editors in the 1970s and 1980s, while commenting on apparent changes, have complained about the lack of detailed recording. In the 1920s the species was described as "numerous", "abundant" and "plentiful", but counts were not made. They were hardly mentioned in the 1930s, but one record of 300+ in a wheat field at Filkins on 31 August 1937 gives some indication of how common they were then. In 1942 there were even two pairs breeding in the gardens of St. Hugh's College in Oxford. Largest flocks recorded since that time give some impression of the decline: 110 in the 1960s, 50 in the 1970s and 20 in the 1980s.

Reasons for the decline are not well understood. The increase in arable farming which continued during this period should have been to their advantage, but their favourite seeds of plants such as Fumitory have become less available as a consequence of the use of herbicides and the development of intensive mechanized farming. Charlock was mentioned as a food plant for abundant flocks of Turtle Doves in the 1920s. Until the mid-twentieth century the Oxfordshire countryside was painted yellow with this plant in summer, but it is no longer grown. Turtle Doves are found most frequently now in the waste lands between gravel pits and around quarries where weed seeds abound. In late summer Collared Doves now dominate food supplies at grain stores which formerly attracted Turtle Doves, so competition with this closely related species which arrived in Oxfordshire in the 1960s could be another factor.

Of course, explanations may lie outside the county. The Turtle Dove is near the northern and western limit of its European range in this part of Britain, and we may be noting part of a general withdrawal connected with climatic changes. Migratory journeys through the Mediterranean continue to be fraught with danger as the increase of gun ownership exceeds the acceptance of controls over shooting, and doves are popular quarry species. Some evidence of the routes taken by Oxfordshire birds came in 1965 from two recoveries in Spain in September and October of nestlings ringed here. Another was shot in the French Pyrenees on 7 September 1972 and yet another at Sete, France on spring migration on 8 April 1984. Problems do not cease when they reach their winter quarters for British populations apparently winter in the Sahel region of west Africa where droughts have caused the depletion of populations of other species.

There is much speculation about reasons for changes in Turtle Dove numbers, but no certain answers. The only fact of which we are sure is that every year the species is a little more difficult to find. As there are presumably more than 100 pairs still breeding in Oxfordshire it is still considered numerous, but its future is unsure. If the answers lie at home, it is possible that the ban on stubble burning after 1991 and the widespread set-aside of agricultural land (if managed sympathetically without too much 'tidying-up') might sufficiently encourage the return of the food plants that we might also see a revival in the population of this attractive bird. Whether this assessment is correct or not, a ban on the shooting of birds on spring passage (the returning breeding population) in France and Spain is essential.

Family: Psittacidae
Parrots

This large family is best represented in the tropics but many species have been exported to Europe to supply the pet trade. This practice now threatens the survival of several species in the wild. One such introduced species has been able to establish itself as feral populations in several European countries, and this is now becoming established in Oxfordshire.

RING-NECKED PARAKEET
Psittacula krameri

A rare vagrant. In recent years individuals have occasionally wandered into the county. Since this introduced or escaped species began breeding in Kent in 1969, others have bred in some neighbouring counties in south-east Britain, and in Cheshire. It was added to the British List in 1983.

Its early history in Oxfordshire is unclear as records were considered to refer to escaped birds. From 1978 appearances became more regular. Most were seen in 1984 and 1985, and there have been fewer since (Table 5.50). There has been an even spread of records through the year (Figure 5.54).

Until 1990 only single birds were recorded, and none stayed for more than a few hours. The only information about feeding habits have been reports of one eating apples still remaining on a tree in January, and one consuming cherries at Jarn Mound in June.

In 1990 up to seven were present for several weeks in a private estate at Farnborough where they may have bred.

Table 5.50. Ring-necked Parakeet.
Number of sightings per year 1984-1989.

Year	Sightings
1984	5
1985	6
1986	2
1987	1
1988	2
1989	1

Figure 5.54. Ring-necked Parakeet.
Monthly distribution of records 1984-1989.

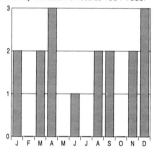

Family: Cuculidae
Cuckoos

Of 139 species of cuckoo world-wide, only two occur in Europe and only one is widespread and found in Britain. Both the European species are brood parasites, the principle hosts of our own species being the Reed Warbler, Dunnock and Meadow Pipit, depending largely on the habitat concerned.

CUCKOO
Cuculus canorus

The Cuckoo is a very numerous summer visitor to Oxfordshire, arriving in the first half of April and departing between July and September.

The distinctive call of the Cuckoo renders it one of our most familiar summer visitors. It is extensively distributed throughout the county and its parasitic behaviour of exploiting small passerines to foster its young is well documented and universally known.

The results of the Oxfordshire Atlas, show the Cuckoo to be widely distributed, with a presence in 79.3% of tetrads. Although probable or confirmed records account for 524 tetrads, there is a danger that some may be records of calling males merely passing through an area. However the known distribution of the primary host species would suggest that there is no shortage of suitable laying opportunities and hence the map should be assumed accurate.

Aplin (1889) cited the Reed Warbler as a

common host but gave little detailed information. More recently, M.J. Bayliss logged some 2,000 hours of fieldwork between 1983 and 1989 in the course of a long-term study of Cuckoos and Reed Warblers in the vicinity of Oxford. Not only has this work provided valuable and detailed information about the inter-relationships between these species locally, it has also yielded valuable data to supplement a number of other important studies of the species (Chance 1922, 1940; Baker 1942; Wyllie 1981; Brooke and Davies 1987; Davies and Brooke 1989a, 1989b). A synopsis, of Bayliss' work is presented in this account.

From a total of 21 known groups or colonies of Reed Warbler along a 24 km stretch of the Thames valley, 18 were investigated. Six of these were the object of Cuckoo nest parasitism (Figure 5.55) on a more or less annual basis, four others were occasionally parasitised while the remaining eight apparently escaped the attentions of Cuckoos altogether. Special attention was paid during the study to those colonies where birds were particularly active and where one could expect to find their eggs. These were conveniently grouped into three workable study sites. Over the seven-year period, a total of 638 Reed Warbler nests were located of which 162 (25.4%) were parasitised — four nests on two occasions by separate females. At the point of discovery, the 166 layings comprised of 141 eggs and 25 nestlings involving a total of at least 17 females.

Success rates fluctuated markedly between sites and from season to season with 81 (48.7%) succeeding to fledging. However, it must be noted that 104 of all Cuckoo eggs laid were deposited by one exceptionally prolific and dominant female (designated Cuckoo-X) who enjoyed total sovereignty over her territory thus precluding the often disruptive effects of intra-specific competition with rival females. Moreover, unlike several of the other Cuckoos, she possessed a highly mimetic egg-type bearing a close resemblance to those of the host and thereby resulting in minimal rejection. These two factors were both significant in maximising her chances of success.

During 1988 and 1989, Cuckoo-X laid 41 eggs and attained a parasitism level of 34.4% of the 119 host nests found. Between 18 May 1988 and 7 July 1988, she laid the remarkable number of 25 eggs — a world record for any Cuckoo under natural conditions. Another milestone was reached in 1990 when this bird returned to breed at the same site for the eighth consecutive year thus establishing a new UK breeding longevity record for this species and equalling the European record.

The high level of parasitism in these colonies should not be regarded as typical of the county-wide or indeed, the national situation. Nest Record Cards held at the BTO suggest that although parasitism of Reed Warblers is possibly increasing, only 5% of nests are currently parasitised by Cuckoos (Davies and Brooke 1989a).

Owing to the belated arrival of their hosts, Reed Warbler Cuckoos do not generally commence laying until late May, as the first nests become available. During the Oxford study, the earliest Cuckoo egg was laid on 14 May, whereas the latest was calculated as having been laid on 12 July.

During 1988 and 1989, the host dependency period of young Cuckoos was closely monitored. On average, nestlings fledged at 18 days old, although one individual remained in a particularly well constructed nest for 25 days. The full dependency period (hatching to full independence) averaged 33.2 days (n=15), and is virtually identical to other studies (Wyllie 1981).

Apart from Reed Warblers, over a dozen other species have been recorded as hosts to Oxfordshire Cuckoos. Nest Record Cards show Dunnock, Reed Bunting, Wren, Robin, Pied Wagtail, Sedge Warbler, Garden Warbler,

Chiffchaff and Whitethroat to be successful hosts but whilst eggs were laid in nests of granivorous species such as Bullfinch, Greenfinch and Linnet, these were unsuccessful.

During the Oxford study, three Sedge Warbler nests were parasitised. Whilst it is known that in the absence of nests of the preferred host (Reed Warbler), Cuckoos will select this species, it seems likely that a totally separate population of Cuckoos, dependent upon Sedge Warblers, also exists.

Cuckoos feed freely on large caterpillars which are coloured so as to warn other insectivorous birds that they are distasteful. At one site in May and June 1989 they were observed avidly consuming the larvae of the Drinker Moth which is a common species in damp riverine habitats. At a second site, up to six individuals were regularly seen to congregate in a small area of low, rough herbage to feed on large numbers of caterpillars belonging to the Five-spot Burnet moth.

The earliest arrival dates for the species are from 3–18 April with a mean of 11 April. The very first birds are probably on passage to destinations further afield. At the Oxford study sites, territory holding males generally did not appear until the third week of April. Departure of birds is well under way by mid-July and through into August, with juveniles following several weeks later. These juveniles probably account for most of the September/October sightings and the average latest departure date is September 26.

During the 1985 and 1986 seasons, a total of 32 nestlings were colour-ringed at Oxford study sites but, to date, there have been no reports of these birds.

There is a single ringing recovery. A bird ringed at Clifton Hampden on 17 June 1964, was recovered in Denmark on 2 August of the same year.

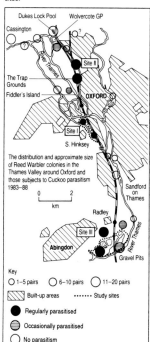

Figure 5.55. Cuckoo.
Location of Cuckoo nest-parasitism study sites.

Family: Tytonidae
Barn Owls

World-wide, the Barn Owl has one of the most extensive distributions of any species. However, in Britain it is declining. Several reasons have been suggested for this and these are discussed below. Important among these was the affect of pesticide use in the 1950s and 1960s. However, whereas the population recovery of raptors such as the Sparrowhawk has been complete, that of the Barn Owl has not and other factors such as road casualties and loss of suitable hunting and nesting sites must be contributory factors.

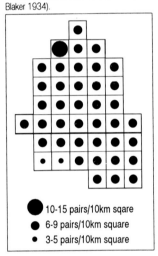

Figure 5.56. Barn Owl.
Breeding distribution and density 1932 (after Blaker 1934).

● 10-15 pairs/10km sqare
● 6-9 pairs/10km square
· 3-5 pairs/10km square

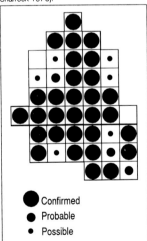

Figure 5.57. Barn Owl.
Breeding distribution 1968-1972 (after Sharrock 1976).

● Confirmed
● Probable
· Possible

BARN OWL
Tyto alba

This silent hunter, graceful, ghostly white as it quarters meadows and rough grassland or patrols roadside verges, creates a beautiful yet eerie spectacle. Its very name comes from the close relationship that it has held with man and his traditional agricultural activities. Thus, given the high percentage of farmland in Oxfordshire, one might assume the resident Barn Owl population to be thriving. Unhappily this is not the case for the species is in decline and has become an uncommon bird in a large part of the county and an estimated 35 pairs now nest.

A review of the previous county avifaunas shows the development of this decline. Aplin (1889) described the Barn Owl as very common and, despite increasing persecution from keepers and collectors, was holding its own. In addition to the association with agricultural buildings, birds were seen to be regular inhabitants of churchyards, nesting in towers and in nearby

trees. In 1932, a national survey was conducted by G. Blaker on behalf of the RSPB. During the course of this work a total of 130 pairs were located in the county (Vice County 23 as it was then) which is equivalent to approximately 170 pairs in the area occupied by the present county. The species was widely distributed, being present in all of the county's 10 km squares (Figure 5.56). Alexander (1947) regarded the species as a "still fairly common resident" but noted that it had become less plentiful than in former years. Radford (1966) wrote of a continued decline in numbers, which was particularly marked in 1963 and 1964, and attributed this to the destruction of nest sites and continued persecution. The use of a range of organochlorine insecticides was another important factor and many dead or dying birds were reported during the late 1950s. Whilst the National Atlas (Sharrock 1976) did not seek to census birds, the work did demonstrate a slight contraction of range in Oxfordshire (Figure 5.57) and, using the estimate given at the time of between two and four pairs per occupied 10 km square, would give a county population in the range 60–120 pairs.

From 1982-1985, a second national survey of breeding Barn Owls was conducted, this time by the Hawk Trust (Shawyer 1987). The census figures are given in Figure 5.58. These results clearly demonstrate the huge decline in the population that had taken place over the previous 50 years, a reduction of over 65% to approximately 50 pairs. Such a degree of reduction was seen throughout much of England and Wales.

The results of the Oxfordshire Atlas give indications of a further decline (Figure 5.59). Whilst birds were noted in 74 tetrads, a large proportion were 'possible' breeding records only and are thought to be of birds known to breed in neighbouring squares or of non-breeders. The distribution and circumstances of these and some 'probable' records were such that it is unlikely that more than 35-40 pairs bred in Oxfordshire. The strongholds were seen to be in the north and west of the county particularly around the Wychwood Forest and Blenheim areas. The overall decline is represented in Table 5.51.

It must be acknowledged that the Barn Owl is not the easiest species to census. They are essentially birds of agricultural land, which is itself difficult to census, and being nocturnal and lacking the territorial calls of the Tawny Owl, they can be difficult to locate. In the two most recent surveys, some effort was made to obtain information from the farming community and this supplemented the data obtained through the ornithological societies to the extent that both surveys were believed to have been completed to a high degree of accuracy. Records of Barn Owls compiled in the county bird reports are sparse in detail. Sightings are few, sometimes as few as 18 per year, breeding records are rare and up to two-thirds of records come from December and January. Population estimates based on figures so derived can be misleading, although through most of the 1980s there is evidence for a decline.

The reasons for the decline are many and varied and all are discussed in depth by Shawyer (1987). Locally, three main factors have been implicated. First, many nest sites, or potential nest sites, have been destroyed. Oxfordshire's Barn Owls nest in trees and in buildings, in roughly equal proportions. Many of the favoured Elm trees were lost in the late 1970s, other tree nest sites were lost as a result of encroaching urbanisation, whilst many of the traditional barns have been replaced by structures lacking the suitable access and nesting ledges. Other farm buildings are subject to conversion into houses or workshops and many of the once favoured church towers have been altered for weather-proofing or to keep out Feral Pigeons or Jackdaws, thus preventing access to owls. One such site, less than 500 m from Oxford railway station had been occupied by breeding Barn Owls for many years when, in 1984, building work on the tower led to the site being deserted. Secondly, the decline is also due to loss of hunting areas. Barn Owls feed almost entirely on mice, voles and rats, small mammals

that are plentiful in grassland habitats and also once a feature of barns and farmyards. Modern farm buildings provide fewer opportunities for these rodents to thrive and the frequent use of pesticides has further reduced prey numbers. Probably of greatest importance is the loss of permanent pasture and grass-edged hedgerows to intensive agriculture such that any suitable habitat that remains in the county is fragmented and isolated. It is interesting to note that many records, particularly during the breeding season, come from river valleys, where a relatively large area of permanent pasture and rough grazing remains. In many parts of the county, roadside verges now provide a substantial part of the available hunting area, which is also of importance in the dispersal of birds across the countryside. A consequence of the dependence upon verges is that Barn Owls suffer high rates of mortality from collisions with vehicles and this provides the third important reason for the decline. Most deaths occur in the winter period and, in the 1988/89 winter, at least five deaths were reported along west Oxfordshire roads alone.

Nationally, initiatives have been undertaken in an attempt to reverse the downward trend in the Barn Owl population and it is vital that locally based schemes are launched. Provision of nestboxes would be a good starting point, but encouraging landowners to leave wide grassy, hedgerow margins, important for the small rodents, is a more urgent requirement. Ideally one would hope to see a network of wildlife corridors across the county which would not only aid the dispersal of birds but also reduce the number of fatalities on our roads.

In the north and east of the county, a group has been attempting to breed Barn Owls in captivity (which, paradoxically is quite easy) and then to release them into the wild. Schemes such as these have variable success rates and while in some circumstances this approach may prove valuable, the provision of appropriate nesting, feeding and dispersal opportunities, for example from the appropriate set-aside of arable land, is the most useful long-term strategy.

Figure 5.58. Barn Owl.
Breeding distribution and density 1982-1985 (after Shawyer 1987).

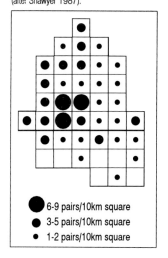

● 6-9 pairs/10km square
● 3-5 pairs/10km square
• 1-2 pairs/10km square

Figure 5.59. Barn Owl.
Breeding distribution 1985-1988, results of the Oxfordshire Atlas.

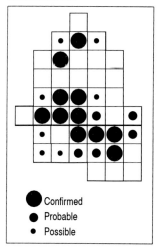

● Confirmed
● Probable
• Possible

Table 5.51. Barn Owl.
Number of breeding pairs in Oxfordshire 1932-1988 adjusted to post-1974 county.

Survey date	Number of pairs
1932	170
1968-72	60-120
1982-85	50
1985-88	35-40

Family: Strigidae
Owls

Five Owl species in this family have been recorded in the county during the twentieth century. However, one of these was recorded only once. Three of the others breed in the county, one in small numbers. The history of Owls in the county shares much in common with that of the raptors already considered. They were heavily persecuted in the past by misguided gamekeepers, apparently ignorant of the fact that small mammals and invertebrates make up by far the greater part of the diet of most owls. Thankfully this is no longer the case, but some species suffered significant losses from pesticide use.

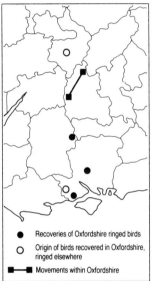

Figure 5.60. Little Owl.
Recoveries of birds ringed in Oxfordshire.

● Recoveries of Oxfordshire ringed birds

○ Origin of birds recovered in Oxfordshire, ringed elsewhere

■——■ Movements within Oxfordshire

LITTLE OWL
Athene noctua

The Little Owl is fairly common in Oxfordshire and is the smallest owl in the county. Its diminutive size, rather rounded profile, dumpy figure and somewhat expressive facial patterning give it an easily recognisable, if rather comical, appearance. Although primarily nocturnal, it is also very active during the daytime and probably makes it the easiest of the owls to observe and in quiet tracts of countryside may be seen at any time of day apparently enjoying the sunshine. It is also a very vocal species, by day or by night. These features make it a relatively easy bird to locate in the course of atlas studies and the Oxfordshire Atlas results show the species to be widespread across the county. The Little Owl is primarily associated with open agricultural land having a good system of hedgerows with mature trees. 70% of records submitted to the BOS indicate birds in this type of habitat, with the bulk of the remainder being associated with

woodlands and woodland edges. This situation is generally true for the rest of the county with an apparent concentration along river valleys, especially the Thame, Thames and Windrush. Open parkland, such as at Blenheim and old orchards are also favoured. The low number of records from the Chilterns reflects the species' dislike for more enclosed woodland habitats although there may be an element of low observer coverage in this area, since there are a number of open grassland sites adjacent to woodland with apparently suitable nesting opportunities where pairs may have been missed. Absences elsewhere in the county are mainly in urban areas or in intensively farmed areas with a lack of suitable nest sites. Although a third of the atlas records are in the 'possible' breeding category, the sedentary habits of the species would indicate that the majority are tetrads occupied by nesting pairs. Although the nesting density of the Little Owl throughout Oxfordshire cannot be assessed, the BOS's Annual Breeding Season Survey in 1978 and 1979, gave an estimate of 20 pairs per 10 km square in the north of the county.

Nests are in holes, usually in pollarded willows or Ash, or less commonly in Oaks. Little Owls will take to nestboxes, holes in buildings, and in burrows excavated by rabbits. There is at least some degree of site fidelity.

Despite being such a well recognised member of our avifauna, the Little Owl is not a native to Britain. It is a continental species that was introduced into the British Isles at the end of the nineteenth century. It was first recorded in Oxfordshire in 1891 and breeding first confirmed at Clanfield in 1916. It has gradually spread throughout the county and by 1943 was well established in Wytham and since then has been a consistent part of the wood's avifauna (Gosler 1990).

The species is susceptible to hard winters with a reduced number of records submitted after prolonged periods of severe weather. In the cold winter of 1982, several starving birds were found and taken into the care of Cliff

Christie. Also, from time to time, there have been, largely unexplained local increases or decreases in population but, in the absence of any county-wide study upon which to base an assessment, the consensus of opinion is that levels are stable.

As previously noted, the Little Owl is mainly sedentary within Oxfordshire. Some movements occur in hard weather and birds may move from a rural into an urban situation. One individual even took up residence in a warehouse in Wallingford during one winter to escape the rigours of the climate. Ringing recoveries, although limited, do indicate quite a widespread dispersal (Figure 5.60), particularly of first-year birds which account for five of the seven distant recoveries. The maximum distance travelled was 175 km.

Over the years, the species has suffered persecution from gamekeepers, and even in the 1980s, some estates were known to shoot all Little Owls. This is both illegal and utterly unnecessary since the diet consists primarily of invertebrates and small mammals, and game-birds, even young ones, are rarely if ever taken.

TAWNY OWL
Strix aluco

A resident, sedentary species, in a variety of wooded habitats, the Tawny Owl is well represented in the county. Mixed and deciduous woods and parks, gardens and cemeteries with plentiful tree cover may all be occupied but since the Tawny Owl is mainly a hole-nester, the presence of mature trees is important.

Since it is a nocturnal species, it is more often heard than seen; the characteristic low hooting of the species travels well on a still night and is probably the best way of locating occupied territories. The peak period for such calling is late in the year since nesting may begin in

February. When nesting has started, calling becomes less frequent but when the young are out of the nest, usually in May but occasionally late April, adults and fledglings can be very vocal with frequent contact calling. Also at this time, mobbing by other woodland species is very prevalent and this is another useful indicator of the presence of Tawny Owls. During the atlas fieldwork, observers were encouraged to make suitably timed visits to capitalise on this behaviour. Overall, the Oxfordshire Atlas confirms the distribution pattern that local birdwatchers had suspected although noticeable gaps in the Chilterns are probably due to a lack of observer coverage since there is apparently no shortage of suitable nesting habitat.

The species will readily take to nestboxes, either a chimney or barrel type, and both have been used to good effect in a number of woods in the county, especially Wytham, where H.N. Southern studied the Tawny Owl population from 1947–1959 (Southern 1954, 1970). With the increased rate of tree loss in recent years as a result of storm damage, the provision of artificial nesting holes may be valuable.

The common status of the species seems to have remained largely unchanged for the last century. There was a decline in the nineteenth century owing to persecution and Alexander (1947) reported "an increase in recent years". Both the BOS and OOS report a relatively stable population although because the species is not always reported to the latter group, numbers may appear artificially low and some form of regular monitoring would be desirable. In Wytham, the population has remained little changed: Southern (1970) recorded 30 pairs in 1958 and 32 pairs in 1959, while Hirons (1985) noted 30 pairs in 1973 and 31 pairs in 1974. Local declines have been reported, with a decrease in the West Hendred area for example being attributed to the loss of Elm trees and old orchards.

The prey of Tawny Owls consists predominantly of a range of small mammals (Table 5.52), species which undergo natural cycles of abundance. Southern (1970) showed that when small mammal numbers were at a peak, Tawny Owl breeding success rate was high. In years when prey species were low in number, no Tawny Owls in Wytham Wood succeeded in rearing any young.

Climate also has a profound effect on breeding success. Cold, wet springs lead to complete failure as birds suffer both from the direct effects of such conditions and also indirectly due to the low availability of food.

LONG-EARED OWL
Asio otus

Long-eared Owls are scarce residents within the county although the resident population may be joined by an influx of winter visitors. Traditionally Long-eared Owls are associated

Table 5.52. Tawny Owl.
Prey taken by Tawny Owls in Wytham Woods; analysis of pellet remains (after Southern 1954).

Prey	
Voles (*Clethrionomys* sp.)	27.7%
Voles (*Microtus* sp.)	12.0%
Mice (*Mus* sp., *Apodemus* sp.)	26.4%
Shrews (Soricidae)	12.9%
Insects	9.7%
Weasel, Mole, Rabbit, Hare, Rats	6.7%
Birds	4.6%

with coniferous woodlands and this has been the case in Oxfordshire. However, some of the recent accounts have been of nests in mixed woodland habitats, in dense scrub or overgrown hedgerow.

As a breeding bird it is apparently not present in large numbers. The Oxfordshire Atlas showed birds present in six tetrads (and six 10 km squares) with confirmed breeding in only two of these. In the National Atlas (Sharrock 1976) birds were noted in seven squares with confirmed breeding in four. Whilst the Long-eared Owl is obviously not a common species, it is easily overlooked with many of the records achieved rather by luck than judgment, in areas where until that time presence had not been suspected. The birds are wholly nocturnal, call infrequently (except early in the season) and are superbly camouflaged. The highly vocal young may offer the best chance of discovery. Hence, without an intensive study there is little chance of establishing the true breeding population.

Since the latter half of the nineteenth century, breeding records of the Long-eared Owl have been sporadic with the majority being reported from areas of woodland in the west of the county, from the Downs and parts of the Chilterns. Between 1965 and 1975, no evidence of confirmed breeding was obtained for the county although summering birds were regularly seen along the Downs and also at Wallingford. In 1975 a pair, using an old crow's nest, bred in a conifer plantation in West Oxfordshire. Breeding continued at this site until the early 1980s. It was well watched and the young birds were ringed. A pullus from the 1976 brood was recovered dead in Suffolk the following summer. Breeding was noted at a second west Oxfordshire site in 1981 and between then and 1986 up to three sites were known to be occupied in any one year. One breeding record from west Oxfordshire is particularly interesting. Villagers were being kept awake by a curious noise from

a clump of trees in the centre of the village. After some concern, and a few disturbed nights, a local ornithologist was called and the noise traced to a family of Long-eared Owls, the young of which betrayed their presence by their calls and which had hitherto remained undetected.

Records of wintering birds are somewhat more frequent with variable numbers being recorded from November to March. These records come from all parts of the county and may be of single birds or of roosts of up to six birds. Again, most records are made by chance: for instance, birds picked out in a roadside hedge or by car headlights. A roost of four birds sunning themselves along a Hawthorn hedge just north of Oxford was only discovered when the observer stopped to answer nature's call! In addition, three birds have been found dead (one killed by a car) and others found exhausted or injured.

The increase in winter records are presumed to involve birds from northern Britain although some individuals may be of continental origin. In the winter of 1975/76 a reduction of vole numbers in parts of the continent led to a huge immigration into Britain and was reflected in more reports of wintering birds in Oxfordshire than normal. A similar influx to Britain occurred in 1986/87 although numbers in Oxfordshire were only slightly higher than usual.

SHORT-EARED OWL
Asio flammeus

The Short-eared Owl is an annual winter visitor to Oxfordshire in small but varying numbers, depending on weather conditions and food availability.

Generally in Oxfordshire the lack of suitable habitat for breeding makes it most unlikely that they have ever attempted to do so in modern times. In southern Britain the breeding population tends to keep mainly to undisturbed coastal marshes. Consequently Short-eared Owls are rarely observed during summer in Oxfordshire although in 1945 they were recorded at Bloxham from June to December.

In some winters the earliest arrivals are recorded in September, but October more regularly sees the first reports of small roosting parties and lone birds passing through. Numbers then generally increase until the year's end and remain high through January to March, followed by a return movement with scattered reports from areas where they are not known to have wintered. Numbers dwindle during April until only the occasional lingerer is noted in May.

Short-eared Owls tend to be rather nomadic in behaviour, hence it is difficult to assess accurately the size of our wintering population, but up to 20 in a normal year seems a reasonable estimate.

During the main part of the winter, Short-eared Owls can regularly be found at a handful of favoured sites, either singly or in parties of up

to six. Occasionally others occur throughout the county in suitable habitat.

In some winters exceptional numbers arrive on the English east coast, which in turn has been reflected in the numbers seen in Oxfordshire. 1978/79 was one such winter when hard weather on the continent caused a major influx of Hen Harriers, Long-eared and Short-eared Owls into Britain (Davenport 1982). Onward movement of Short-eared Owls resulted in around 55 individuals wintering in Oxfordshire in what was described as "a bumper year" by the OOS annual report. Included in this total was an unprecedented gathering of 20 at Broughton Poggs during January and February. A smaller but still notable local influx occurred in the last nine days of October 1982 when a spate of records once again coincided with arrivals at east coast sites.

In low-lying areas such as Otmoor and the Thames valley, rough pasture or extensive rank grassy areas around gravel pits, provide suitable hunting and roosting sites. Roosting usually occurs amongst tussocky grass or in the bottom of a thick hedge.

Regular feeding grounds in Oxfordshire are all located in areas of extensive rough grassland. At places along the downs, Short-eared Owls can be found particularly at dusk, quartering such areas along gallops where suitable prey are most abundant.

Several analyses of pellets found at downland locations have revealed the expected prey items of Field and Bank Vole. However in a comprehensive study on the Berkshire Downs in the winters of 1969/70 and 1970/71, Buckley (1973) found surprisingly that the Wood Mouse formed the main component of the Short-eared Owls' diet. The largest items he found in pellets were young Rabbits. The contents of pellets collected on abandoned farmland at Didcot included Skylark and Brown Rat (I. Lewington, pers. comm.).

Providing that suitable areas of rough grassland continue to exist within the county, Short-eared Owls seem set to remain as one of the highlights of a winter day's local birdwatching.

TENGMALM'S OWL
Aegolius funereus

A very rare vagrant from Scandinavia and parts of central Europe. One was shot near Henley on 5 November 1901. Several were obtained about this time on the east coast, and one in Northamptonshire.

Family: Caprimulgidae
Nightjars

Nightjars are nocturnal, insectivorous summer visitors to Britain. Oxfordshire lies at the centre of its breeding range in Britain. Nationally the species has declined markedly in the last 40 years and, sadly, this is reflected well in our county.

NIGHTJAR
Caprimulgus europaeus

While it once bred regularly in small numbers, since the mid-1960s only single birds have occasionally been recorded. There are encouraging recent accounts of probable breeding on the Berkshire Downs in 1986 and churring near Henley in 1988, on waste ground near Standlake Gravel Pits on 2 July 1989 and for several days in 1991 in a former breeding area in the Chilterns.

Typically a bird of lowland heaths, the Nightjar is also found on chalk downland, commons and open woodland. Its disappearance as a breeding species in the county has coincided with the loss of these habitats, or with changes in their character. Today, almost the only reminder of Oxfordshire's former heaths are place names on Ordnance Survey maps. Although the Nightjar was never common or widespread, and Aplin (1889) rarely encountered it in north Oxfordshire, ornithologists living in Oxford before the Second World War needed only a brief trip to the Gorse and Bracken-clad slopes of Shotover or Boar's Hill to find it. By the 1950s and 1960s more distant journeys were required to the chalk hills of the Chilterns or the Berkshire Downs, or to conifer plantations in woodlands.

The OOS Report for 1934 includes a special survey of the species. On the Berkshire Downs they appeared only in small woods and patches of scrub on the grassland as by then much of the

area was under plough. The eastern end was best populated with five pairs in an area of a little less than two square miles. On the wooded part of the chalk area in the Chilterns they were "much more common", preferring the "more open spurs, partly covered by patches of juniper and mixed scrub". Counts were not made in this year, but presumably they were as numerous then as ten years later when at least 12 were heard churring at Swyncombe Downs. In woodland between Henley and Goring "distribution seemed even" although no estimate of abundance is given. Within six miles of Oxford there were 12 or 13 pairs estimated, and another three at Wychwood Forest.

The following list shows the last date when breeding was suspected or proved at sites where they had bred for many years previously: Hen Wood 1937, Shiplake 1949, Goring and Streatley 1949, Wytham 1950, Wychwood 1955, Christmas Common 1957, Bruern 1958, Swyncombe Downs 1959, Boar's Hill 1959, Woodcote 1962, Cholsey Fairmile 1966, "the Chilterns" 1975, Stonor 1979.

Until the 1940s the Nightjar appeared in the migration tables given in annual reports, and a summary of these by Alexander (OOS Report 1946) showed an average arrival date of 1 May, with exceptionally early ones on 3 March 1867, 16 April 1912, and 19 April 1909. Records in late summer are less frequent, and the latest date mentioned is 25 August.

There have always been records of Nightjars wandering around the county, sometimes

appearing at unlikely places. For example, one heard churring in a garden in Banbury Road, north Oxford in May 1937, was flushed from a flower bed. These surprise visits still occur. A recent instance was when one flew low over the A40 near Wolvercote in busy traffic in 1989.

The decline of Nightjars is not restricted to Oxfordshire, and cannot be attributed simply to habitat loss although this has undoubtedly played a part. Persecution was implied by Aplin (1889) who said that many people believed these birds turned into hawks in the winter. Disturbance by increasing numbers of human visitors can cause problems, as at Shotover and the Cholsey Fairmile. Possibly of more importance are climatic changes and the reduction in insect life, factors which may have affected other insectivorous summer visitors such as the Wryneck and Red-backed Shrike.

Despite some recent promising signs, there can be little cause for optimism. For the foreseeable future Oxford birdwatchers may have to continue their annual journeys, made through the 1970s and 1980s, to see and hear these extraordinary birds, in their nearest regular breeding site at Snelsmore Common in Berkshire.

Family: Apodidae
Swifts

One species of swift breeds in Britain. This is widespread in our county and has been the subject of dteailed research at Oxford University. Another four species have occurred as vagrants to Britain, and one of these has been recorded in Oxfordshire.

Table 5.53. Swift.
Nestlings ringed in University Museum Tower 1961-1990.

Year	No. ringed
1961	8
1962	44
1963	40
1964	60
1965	35
1966	37
1967	49
1968	38
1969	32
1970	22
1971	37
1972	23
1973	40
1974	46
1975	48
1976	64
1977	75
1978	75
1979	79
1980	95
1981	108
1982	132
1983	121
1984	97
1985	105
1986	91
1987	196
1988	97
1989	125
1990	104

SWIFT
Apus apus

An abundant summer visitor, the Swift remains a common breeding bird in urban areas, although modern building methods present fewer suitable nesting sites. The Oxfordshire Atlas results show a high number of "possible" breeding records, but these should be regarded with caution as some refer to Swifts ranging widely in their search for food during the breeding season. In spring and autumn there are considerable gatherings of migrants over larger water bodies, especially at Farmoor Reservoir, sometimes numbering several thousand.

Swifts begin to return at the end of April. Examination of the first dates given in reports from 1935-1958, years when these were regularly listed, show a spread from 20 April to 1 May, with a mean date of 24 April. There is an exceptionally early record of one at Wallingford on 14 April 1949. When weather conditions are favourable they start to nest immediately on arrival, but sometimes breeding may not be fully in progress until the end of May.

Much of our understanding of their breeding behaviour is derived from ringing, and detailed observation at the nest. W.D. Campbell's pioneering work in the late 1930s demonstrated fidelity both to nest sites and to partners for several years. In 1948 a programme of ringing Swifts breeding in the University Museum tower in Oxford commenced. Lack (1956) describes how 16 pairs used nestboxes provided in that first year. Although the research has continued without interruption to this day, conditions in the tower have been made more attractive to Swifts, and more boxes have been provided, with the result that an increasing number of nestlings have been ringed each year (Table 5.53). Throughout this period, more than 2,000 nestlings have been ringed, mostly by R. Overall. One bird returned to the Museum for 16 consecutive years. This also demonstrates the potential longevity of the species. Recent work has shown that most of the adults nesting in the tower had not hatched there so that the exact age of most of the adults is unknown.

The young are independent at fledging, and at the end of the breeding season parents leave, usually about five days after the young, but in wet seasons up to 26 days later (Lack and Lack 1952). Before departure from local nesting areas they form vast assemblies over reservoirs, lakes, or fields from which flies are rising. These are noticed most often in the last weeks of July or the first week in August. Occasional late broods have been recorded at the University Museum. Two nestlings ringed on 8 August 1972 fledged on 21 September. Usually all have left by the end of August, and only a few stragglers are seen in September. 'Last dates' noted in annual reports from 1935-1958 ranged from 27 August until 27 September, with an exceptionally late bird at Cholsey on 21 October 1956. Recoveries of Swifts ringed in Oxfordshire

(mostly in the University Museum tower) have come from Oxfordshire (30), southern England (15), Wales (one), France (two), Denmark (one), Spain (one) and Morocco (one).

Swifts are faced with few natural hazards. They can avoid poor weather by making long flights as Lack observed over the Berkshire Downs (Lack 1956). They can delay some stages of the breeding season as described above when it is cold and insects are in short supply, with chicks becoming torpid for several days if food is very scarce. The period between hatching and fledging can vary from 35–56 days according to weather conditions (Lack 1956). Perrins (1971) described how breeding is not likely to be successful until a bird's fourth year, and adult mortality is only 15–16%. Apart from the Hobby, few predators are likely to catch them. It would seem that the only constraint to population growth is the number of nesting sites. It is interesting to speculate on whether there were Swifts in Oxford before man provided them with suitable nesting sites since every nest recorded in the county has been found in a building (although previously they probably used tree-holes, Cramp and Simmons 1976).

Modern houses are of little use to them, and they are mostly found in the older centres of towns and large villages. The University Museum project has shown the demand for suitable nest sites locally as Swifts have readily taken to additional nestboxes when these are provided. Consideration given to providing more of these in appropriate places, especially when old buildings are renovated, would undoubtedly assist the Swift to maintain its present level of population.

ALPINE SWIFT
Apus melba

There have been four records accepted of this very rare vagrant from the Alps and southern Europe. All were in late summer, when Swifts *Apus apus* were migrating. The first was over Cholsey on 14 July 1975. The others were more recent. There were singles over Old Marston on 18 August 1988, on the following day over East Hendred and over Charney Bassett on 15 July 1989.

Family: Alcedinidae
Kingfishers

Of 92 species of kingfisher found throughout the world, only one occurs in Britain and this is widespread in our county. Most kingfisher species have specific ecological requirements. Our own species is no exception and these requirements constrain both its distribution and abundance as described below.

Table 5.54. Kingfisher.
Records from the BOS area 1963-1970.

Year	No. of occupied banks
1963	1
1964	1
1965	6
1966	8
1967	10
1968	12
1969	12
1970	18

KINGFISHER
Alcedo atthis

A numerous resident, closely associated with water in the county. A shrill piping and a streak of brilliant blue as it flies low and fast over the water is often the most a casual observer is likely to see or hear of the Kingfisher. Whilst nobody can fail to recognise the bird, it is able, despite its colourful nature to remain remarkably well concealed as it perches on overhanging branches ever watchful for Sticklebacks, Bullheads or other suitable prey items in the water below.

Its feeding habits ensure that it is rarely far from water and the findings of the Oxfordshire Atlas reflect this, being noted in 22.6% of tetrads with confirmed or probable breeding in 56% of these. Although there is a good association with both still and flowing waters in the county, there remain a number of gaps in the species' distribution. Inaccessibility of some stretches of river mean that some breeding pairs were missed and a few localities suffered from

poor observer coverage. A general study, such as the Oxfordshire Atlas, is not the best way of assessing the distributional status of this species since a great deal of effort throughout a season needs to be spent to plot breeding territories accurately by locating nesting-holes. The problem can be aggravated by the bird's frequent habit of nesting up to 500 m from the main stream. The rapid dispersal of young birds away from the nest also makes the pinpointing of occupied territories difficult and the concealment of nestholes beneath roots and bankside vegetation adds to the difficulties. However, some of the gaps in distribution are real. Parts of the Thames are rather open, with little cover and few suitable feeding areas, whilst other rivers and streams are shallow and fast-flowing, imposing similar constraints. On balance therefore it is felt that the Atlas findings may be an underestimate of the true population.

In the long-term, the status of the species has probably not altered dramatically. A study by the OOS in 1934 yielded 59 pairs over 114 miles of river in the Oxford district. However, the Kingfisher is highly susceptible to extreme weather conditions and in the short-term, marked fluctuations in numbers occur. In prolonged spells of very cold weather when waters become frozen and feeding becomes difficult or impossible, birds must either seek open water, often involving long-distance movements, or perish. The dramatic effects of such conditions was graphically illustrated in 1963 when, immediately after the cold winters of 1962 and 1963, the OOS organised another Kingfisher survey. No more than five breeding pairs could be found. In the north of the county, the BOS demonstrated a parallel reduction in numbers with, in 1963, only one probable breeding record in eight 10 km squares. The crucial factor, at least in the second hard winter period, was that all waterways were frozen, many of them for three months. In this period the only record of Kingfishers was of one feeding at an emergent spring in the Chilterns which flowed a few metres before freezing.

There have been 20 recoveries of Kingfishers ringed in Oxfordshire. Of these, eight were within 9 km of the ringing site, 11 were between 10 and 99 km and one was more than 100 km. 16 were recovered in Oxfordshire, three in southern England and one in Wales.

A survey by the OOS in 1970, covering the same area as in 1963, revealed only 12 pairs but a repeat survey in 1981 indicated that the population had recovered to the 1934 level. However, in 1982, following another prolonged cold spell during the preceding winter, observers in various parts of the county again noted reductions in breeding numbers of 25-60% since the previous season.

Following such declines, a full recovery may take several years. Surviving pairs, relieved of the restrictions imposed by territory, may raise two or three broods in a season if conditions are favourable, and dispersal of young birds aided by mild winters will ensure rapid re-colonisation. Records from the BOS in the seasons after the 1963 winter (Table 5.54) show the time scale involved in such a recovery.

Weather conditions are not the only problems facing the Kingfisher. Pollution incidents, particularly silage effluent run-off, have caused some local problems, whilst elsewhere, unsympathetic river management has led to difficulties. Direct disturbance of nest sites is quite common and appears to be a critical factor, particularly when young are being fed in the nest although the Kingfisher is afforded protection under Schedule 1 of the Wildlife and Countryside Act (1981). Disturbance around feeding areas is not always so critical and birds can often be seen fishing amongst the anglers and boats in busy centres such as Abingdon and Henley and indeed it nests within the Oxford city boundaries.

The Kingfisher is currently doing well in the county despite the increasing human pressures along rivers and streams. As a species on top of a delicate food chain and so obviously reliant upon overall water quality, the Kingfisher can act as an indicator species in the assessment of this lowland freshwater habitat. With concerns currently being expressed about river management and water quality, the continued regular monitoring of this species is vital.

Family: Meropidae
Bee-eaters

The Bee-eater is generally a vagrant to Britain from southern Europe although it has bred on a few occasions in the country. Nationally, appearances usually occur during the fine weather in the spring.

BEE-EATER
Merops apiaster

A very rare vagrant to Oxfordshire though this does not reflect its national incidence. Alexander (1947) mentions one seen at Henley in October 1927 as "the only definite record". On 3 June 1983 seven appeared near beehives in a garden near Stanton St John. A party of this size was seen a few days earlier on the Scilly Isles, and a few days later at Stoke Mandeville. Many local rumours about this species persisted later that summer including one of a nesting attempt at a gravel pit, but no confirmation was received.

Family: Coraciidae
Rollers

A vagrant to Britain from southern and central Europe, the occurrence here of the Roller is similar in many respects to that of the Bee-eater. Like that species, there is a concentration of records in the spring and early summer.

ROLLER
Coracias garrulus

A very rare vagrant to Oxfordshire. There is one early record at Balscot near Banbury in July 1869. More recently, one was seen and photographed on the Aston Upthorpe Downs between 23 and 27 May 1974. Then in 1977, one was noted in west Oxfordshire at Bruern from 14–16 June.

Family: Upupidae
Hoopoes

The Hoopoe, the only member of its family, breeds across much of continental Europe. In Britain it occurs as a passage migrant only, although it formerly bred here.

HOOPOE
Upupa epops

An occasional vagrant. This easily distinguished species is most likely to be found after prolonged anticyclonic conditions in spring when individuals occasionally overshoot on migration. Of the 36 records between 1964 and 1988, 29 (80%) occurred between 12 April and 8 June, and only six in the autumn between 5 September and 25 November. Visits are normally brief, never lasting more than a few days, and there is no proof of breeding. There is one mid-winter record: a bird at Preston Crowmarsh on 14 January 1977.

As such a conspicuous bird is unlikely to be overlooked, it can be presumed that a reasonable proportion of those passing through the county are noticed. Analysis of records in annual reports show that 61% of all sightings in the period 1965–1990 were by people with little more than a casual interest in birds who were moved to send in a description of such an exotic looking bird. It is a salutary thought that if similar percentages of less distinctive species slip through unnoticed by birdwatchers, our knowledge of these must be far from complete.

Radford (1966) finds references to this species in a number of documents dating back as far as 1395, but it seems never to have been more than an occasional visitor to Oxfordshire although it bred elsewhere in the country.

Family: Picidae
Woodpeckers

The four British woodpecker species have been recorded in Oxfordshire, and the three resident species are common, widespread and sedentary. The Wryneck is now scarce. Woodpeckers have specific habitat requirements and their range in the county indicates well the distributions of those habitats. Generally, they benefit from the presence of dead wood, either in which to feed, or in which to excavate a nest chamber. Hence they have benefited from Dutch Elm Disease, over-grazing by deer, and to a lesser extent from storm damage to our woodlands. Their presence is a key to the ecological quality of woodlands and pasture in an area.

WRYNECK
Jynx torquilla

An occasional passage migrant, the Wryneck was formerly an uncommon summer visitor. A few passage birds are noted in most autumns, but rarely in spring. From 1962–1990 inclusive, 51 single birds were recorded. Of these only two were in spring, although they have frequently been found in neighbouring counties at this time. The autumn appearances were restricted to a brief period from the last week in August until the third week in October. For some reason there are more records from the southern half of the county. On many occasions they are seen on garden lawns. Often their visits coincide with times when stormy conditions have interrupted a spell of settled weather. No local evidence of their origin has been obtained, although one recovered at Reading, just over the Berkshire border, had been ringed as a nestling in Norway.

There have been four years in the period 1962–1989 when Wrynecks have not been seen: 1963, 1965, 1977 and 1985. Two years with high counts were 1968 (six individuals), and 1976 (seven individuals).

The national decline of the Wryneck as a breeding species was traced by Monk (1963). His special interest was stimulated by the presence of the surviving remnant of Oxfordshire's population near his home in the south-east corner of the county. He summarised the past status in Oxfordshire as common in 1855, not plentiful in 1877, not at all common in 1889, scarce generally in 1902 but apparently more common in some places than others, suddenly further declined in 1912, regular and in good numbers in the south-east in 1935, and by 1953 almost ceased breeding. The last breeding record was at Caversham in 1955.

Climatic changes have been proposed as the main factor in its decline nationally (Sharrock 1976), so there seems little likelihood of the return of the Wryneck as a breeding bird to Oxfordshire in the near future. It is difficult now to consider that it was once so common that a local egg collector took a nest close to Magdalen Bridge, Oxford in 1860 (Aplin 1889).

GREEN WOODPECKER
Picus viridis

The largest and most colourful of our woodpeckers, the Green Woodpecker is a widely distributed and numerous resident in Oxfordshire. With its loud, laughing call it is an easily recognised member of the county's avifauna.

In common with other woodpeckers it nests in tree holes which it excavates for itself. However, it has a weaker bill than the other species and therefore tends to nest in dead or dying timber. This contrasts especially with the Great Spotted Woodpecker which will excavate in live Oak. Also related to the difference in strength of the bill, the Green Woodpecker feeds more on the ground than the other species,

and can often be watched at close range as it hops around clumsily on rough grassland or a garden lawn as it forages for insect prey, and particularly for ants. This feeding strategy means that it is found mainly in more open woodland habitats and parkland, or in woods close to suitable grassland and pasture. It is commonest in areas of light, dry soils where food may be plentiful and probing for prey easy. Hence places such as Shotover Country Park, the slopes of the Chilterns and parts of the Cotswolds have strong populations. Indeed in the first-named site, some 10–12 pairs were believed to breed in 1986.

The Oxfordshire Atlas map reveals the widespread distribution of the Green Woodpecker in the county and shows some association with the distribution of calcareous rocks, especially Corallian limestone, and their generally lighter soils. There are some difficulties in locating occupied nests and confirming breeding, for while birds are conspicuous as they range far while foraging, when close to the nest they remain quiet and unobtrusive.

Being so dependent upon ants and other soil-dwelling insects, makes the Green Woodpecker very vulnerable to the rigours of hard winters. Following the cold of 1962 and 1963, the bird was scarce throughout the county and, for the rest of the decade, recovery was slow. During the 1970s there was a continued improvement in the fortunes of the species although, in the Oxford area at least, it was not until the 1980s that a return to the population levels of the fifties was recorded. In the BOS area a similar picture emerged although after the crash of 1962/63, breeding did not definitely re-commence until 1970. The total number of records received by the BOS each year since then reflects its recovery. There were fewer than 20 sightings in 1972, about 50 in 1975 but in 1979 over 300 sightings were reported. High numbers have continued since then with a wider distribution pattern emerging.

It is clear to local observers that differences in density occur within the county but to date, little comparative data have been available and further studies are needed or at least a more consistent recording method employed across the county. The only figure as yet obtained is as a result of the BOS's Annual Breeding Season Survey in 1976 when 17 breeding pairs were located in one 10 km square, SP43, well above the national average proposed by Hudson and Marchant (1984). However, this particular square was shown to have a high proportion of pasture and so is probably not truly representative of the county as a whole.

GREAT SPOTTED WOODPECKER
Dendrocopos major

During the breeding season, the Great Spotted Woodpecker can be found in all types of woodland, deciduous, mixed or coniferous,

and open, well-wooded parkland situations are also occupied. The Oxfordshire Atlas map for the species reflects the distribution of such habitats and, although fewer than half of the records are of confirmed breeding, the distribution map of this sedentary bird can be assumed accurate. As with all woodpecker species, location of nests before hatching is not easy but the characteristic drumming of the species, especially in February and March does allow one to find the territory. Once the chicks have hatched, they can be heard from some distance away and nest holes are readily located.

Although the Great Spotted Woodpecker is a woodland bird, by no means all such habitats are occupied. In a study of 20 Oxfordshire woodlands (Ford 1987), nesting was only found in larger woods (i.e. those over three hectares). The species is also absent from those woodland areas where there is insufficient old and dead timber in which to search for its main prey items such as the larvae of wood-boring insects. Thus woodland management practices have an important part to play in the success of the species. The value of old timber was well illustrated at the time of the Dutch Elm Disease in the early 1970s when, locally, there was an obvious increase in the population and a subsequent, if slight, decrease between 1982 and 1984. This followed the national trend (Marchant et al. 1990). Hence breeding densities vary considerably from site to site and from year to year. A figure derived from six woodland plots in the range 2.9–52 ha gives an average of 18 pairs/km² (Wiggins 1984; Ford 1987; Overall 1988). However a count in Bagley Wood (227 ha) in 1984 located only six pairs and in the whole of SP43, the BOS's Annual Breeding Season Survey in 1975 found only six pairs. It must be noted that this particular square was not well wooded and not representative of the district. At Wytham, the CBC results suggest an increase in recent years and Gosler (1990) gives an

estimate of 20 pairs in 1989. In the following year, an estimate of more than 40 pairs was given (Gosler and Hayward pers. comm.). This increase was attributed to an increase in the quantity of dead timber in the wood, the results of Dutch Elm Disease and over-grazing by deer and squirrels.

As well as timber-borne invertebrates, the Great Spotted Woodpecker will also take larger prey items, and in particular the nestlings of other bird species. The woodpeckers will, for instance, go to great lengths to enter wooden tit nestboxes by drilling through the side in order to reach the young birds.

There is evidence nationally of a long-term increase in numbers brought about by a climatic amelioration early in this century (Sharrock 1976). There is however little local evidence to support this since all the previous accounts of Oxfordshire's birds simply refer to the species as being common.

Although the Great Spotted Woodpecker is very closely associated with woodland during the nesting season, it will leave the woods to feed and once the young have fledged, birds, including family parties, may wander further afield. For example a party of seven birds were feeding on peanuts in a Combe garden from 8 June 1989 and again from 6 June 1990. Throughout the winter, birds continue to wander further afield feeding along more isolated hedgerow trees or, entering gardens, to take artificially provided food. Peanuts presented in hanging feeders are the commonest food utilised, although a wide variety of other items may prove attractive. This garden-feeding habit may enable a larger number of birds to survive hard winters.

LESSER SPOTTED WOODPECKER
Dendrocopos minor

Although a numerous resident, the Lesser Spotted Woodpecker is the least common of our woodpecker species, and only just comes into this category as there are probably little more than 100 breeding pairs in the county. Although very vocal in spring and summer, its tendency to feed in the upper tree canopy leads to it being overlooked. In recent years it has become increasingly difficult to find. While the editor of the 1963 annual report received 52 records of the species, in 1989 there were only 35 records although the number of contributors to the report over all had nearly doubled.

The Oxfordshire Atlas survey shows that the population is mainly concentrated near river and stream systems. Christchurch Meadows and the University Parks beside the willow-lined River Cherwell in Oxford seem to be amongst the most reliable locations for a sighting. Old orchards are also favoured places. In woodland it seems to be restricted to the marginal or more impoverished habitats. In the BOS breeding survey of 1975, four pairs were found

in SP43, one of the least wooded 10 km squares containing an aggregate of only 1 km², of woodland.

Some recent estimates of population density in woodland have been made. In 1984 at Bagley Wood there were two to three pairs giving a density of 0.88–1.32/km², and at Little Wittenham Wood two pairs giving a density of 3.84/km² (Wiggins 1984). In May 1989 there were an estimated four pairs in 100 ha of Wytham Woods giving about 12–15 pairs for the whole estate (Gosler 1990).

Radford (1966) described it as "a not uncommon resident in woods, parks and orchards" whose status "has not altered since the last century". However, since then marked fluctuations have occurred. The most conspicuous change took place in the 1970s. There was a gradual build up through this decade, reaching a peak in 1976–1980, followed by a sudden decline. The numbers of records submitted to the BOS (Easterbrook 1983) and subsequently, illustrate this clearly (Table 5.55). In the Oxford area a similar picture is portrayed by the personal records of several observers (Table 5.56).

There seems to be a connection between these sudden developments and the incidence of Dutch Elm Disease. For two or three years in the mid-1970s bark beetles spread a fungus disease destroying all the Elms in the county. This provided additional food and easily excavated nest sites in decaying wood. However this was a short-lived bonus for when all Elms had died and been cleared by the early 1980s the population of Lesser Spotted Woodpeckers could not be sustained at such a high level, and there were several records of juveniles found dead in the summer months. This pattern reflects closely the change in population nationally during this time (Marchant et al. 1990).

Wiggins (1985), in his studies at Little Wittenham Wood, noted that the species

Table 5.55. Lesser Spotted Woodpecker.
Number of records submitted to BOS 1972-1986.

Year	No. of records
1972	12
1973	14
1974	27
1975	26
1976	57
1977	95
1978	90
1979	114
1980	108
1981	52
1982	35
1983	33
1984	33
1985	29
1986	24

Table 5.56. Lesser Spotted Woodpecker.
The upper table shows number of months each year when the species was recorded by three individual observers in the Oxford area 1970–1983. The lower table shows the actual number of sightings each year by another observer together with the time spent in the field, and both these measures for a fifth observer.

Year	B. Campbell	J. Brucker	R. Scroggs
1970	2	1	1
1971	3	0	8
1972	4	1	0
1973	3	2	1
1974	2	2	1
1975	5	1	5
1976	6	3	8
1977	5	6	6
1978	8	9	5
1979	6	8	10
1980	7	9	8
1981	3	2	3
1982	2	1	1
1983	1	0	0

	M. Bayliss	
Year	Total sightings	Hrs in field
1974	4	195
1975	13	235
1976	11	162
1977	9	376
1978	7	696
1979	2	418
1980	8	395
1981	4	793
1982	0	786
1983	0	810

	I. Walker	
Year	Total sightings	Months seen
1970	0	–
1971	1	Jan
1972	4	Mar
1973	5	Apr
1974	7	May
1975	6	Jun
1976	10	Jun
1977	36	Nov
1978	13	Aug
1979	6	Apr
1980	4	Apr
1981	4	Apr
1982	0	–
1983	1	Jan

"appears to be the victim of inter-specific rivalry with the Great Spotted Woodpecker", with the larger species dominating the prime habitats. This might be a recent development, since the population densities of the two species might now be higher than in the past.

The presence of adequate supplies of decaying wood which can be worked easily is probably important in determining the success of this species. Woodland management involving the clearance of dead timber is becoming increasingly efficient in Oxfordshire and this may continue to restrict Lesser Spotted Woodpecker populations in the future.

Family: Alaudidae
Larks

Larks are birds of open countryside. Two species of lark have occurred in Oxfordshire. Whilst one is common and widespread, the other which formerly bred in the county has not been seen here for many years.

WOODLARK
Lullula arborea

Once resident in small numbers, the only records of Woodlarks since 1972 were two on the north slope of Shotover on 10 November 1985. In the nineteenth century Aplin (1889) knew them as breeding on the tops of the Chilterns where there were "patches of rough, broken ground, partly covered with ling, juniper etc.". This remained the most likely area to find them through the twentieth century until 1966 when the last remaining pair was seen on Watlington Hill from March to June.

Numbers increased from the 1920s, reaching a peak in the 1940s and 1950s. There were one to three pairs at various sites in soft, sandy soils and associated heaths on the Corallian limestone ridges in central Oxfordshire. Shotover, Wytham, Tubney Wood and Boar's Hill all had Woodlarks from time to time. There were one or two pairs on Shotover Plain, for example, from 1949 until 1957, with birds remaining throughout most winters, and at Wytham, six pairs bred and were present throughout 1955. At this time breeding was also proved at Bladon Heath, the Fairmile and near the Thames below Henley.

Larger parties have, on occasions, appeared in the winter as at Wytham, where there were 19 on 11 November 1945, and 9–11 from 19 November 1970 to 15 January 1971, and at Boar's Hill where there were six on December 22 1966. These accounts do not seem to be related to local breeding, and may be associated with immigration from the continent. Until 1985 (see above), the last two records for the county were of single birds at Wytham in September 1971 and at Farmoor in January 1972.

The species in Britain is at the north-western edge of its breeding range and, as in Oxfordshire, has declined significantly elsewhere in the country since the early 1960s. Sitters (1986) considered three possible causes of the change. Cold winters appeared to have an effect, although those in the 1940s did not stem the increase. Climatic changes may be responsible; a series of low spring temperatures in the 1970s was regarded as particularly influential. Another key factor was assumed to be the availability of suitable habitat, with the quality of heathland, limestone grassland and common being particularly important. If so, Woodlarks may find it difficult to return to Oxfordshire even should there be any future advance in their population. However, it is perhaps interesting to consider that the expansion of the species in the 1920s and 1930s coincided with a period of agricultural depression when there were considerable changes in land use.

SKYLARK
Alauda arvensis

The Skylark is well represented in Oxfordshire. It may be found throughout the year and occurs

as a resident breeder, a passage migrant, and as an abundant winter visitor. Nesting occurs in a range of arable crops, permanent pasture, wet meadows and even along roadside verges.

The Oxfordshire Atlas provided breeding records from 93.2% of tetrads. Predictably it was absent from tetrads with a high level of urbanisation and from much of the heavily wooded Chilterns, where fields were often small, enclosed and generally unfavourable to breeding. The use of an aerial song post from which to proclaim its territory, the easily recognised and far-carrying song and the prolonged song period, makes the location of birds very easy, although providing proof of breeding is difficult. Hence 80% of Atlas registrations were of 'probable' breeding records but these can be regarded as reasonable evidence of breeding for this species.

The status of the Skylark as a breeding bird in Oxfordshire has probably remained little changed over the last century although nationally the species declined during the 1980s. There is evidence of slight reductions following hard winters or local reductions due to the encroachment of urbanisation and agricultural changes. The Skylark still seems abundant on the Berkshire Downs although probably at a lower density than in the past since recent work suggests that Skylarks benefit from a diversity of land use in their territory and the trend away from diversification is likely to have affected them.

During the autumn, and especially in October, active migration can be observed as birds move west or south-west, presumably from breeding grounds in upland and northern Britain and continental Europe. Birds tend to fly high, keeping contact by their trilling call-notes and, from vantage points along the Downs or more exposed parts of the Chilterns shortly after dawn, such movements can be observed. Also, as migrant birds cross territories held by resident birds, territorial chases can be seen.

There is a single foreign recovery of an Oxfordshire-ringed bird — an adult ringed in Oxford in early February was recovered three months later, and 920 km ENE, in Jylland, Denmark.

During the winter months Skylarks are usually found in flocks, foraging amongst the emerging autumn-sown crops, fields of brassicas or over bare, ploughed fields. This behaviour is especially noticeable during cold weather and was reported by Radford (1966) but the largest flocks mentioned are ones of 50 birds such as those at Otmoor and at Farmoor in 1961. Since the mid-1960s, flocks of this size have become common in any winter period and in any part of the county, including the high ground of the Downs or Cotswolds, but when severe weather occurs, considerably larger parties may be seen. In 1979 six flocks in excess of 500 birds were reported in January and February, mostly along the low-lying parts of the Thames valley. At Shifford, in the same period a flock of 1,000 birds was seen. February 1986, a time of severe weather both here and on the continent, saw an immense influx into the county. A tightly packed flock estimated at 2,000 birds was present close to Berinsfield, there was another of about 1,000 at Cholsey and flocks of between 150 and 450 birds were recorded at 13 other sites. During a two-week cold spell in February 1991, birds survived by gathering into tight flocks to feed on the green tops of Oilseed Rape where these showed above snow in wind-swept fields. Seven flocks in excess of 100 birds were noted, with a maximum of 700 birds near to the River Cherwell at Kidlington. When severe conditions become more prolonged the Skylark moves out of Oxfordshire altogether with just a scattering of small flocks (20–30 birds) remaining. In these conditions a few may enter gardens or agricultural yards to feed while others, severely weakened, may die or be taken by predators.

Family: Hirundinidae
Swallows and Martins

The three British hirundines are well represented in Oxfordshire. All are insectivorous summer visitors which spend much time on the wing, and large numbers are often seen during migration. Like all migrants, their fortunes are dictated by conditions across a wider domain than in their British breeding quarters alone. Nevertheless, for populations which may suffer 50% adult mortality between years, a successful breeding season is essential. The three species have very specific nesting requirements and as we demonstrate here, the availability of these in the county are strongly influenced by human activities.

SAND MARTIN
Riparia riparia

The Sand Martin is a summer visitor to Oxfordshire and, although numerous, its distribution is limited by the availability of suitable breeding habitat. These include river banks, such as at Cholsey and between Abingdon and Wallingford, the sand quarry at Stanford-in-the-Vale and, in 1975, a drainpipe by the canal in Oxford. However, the most commonly used breeding sites in Oxfordshire today are at gravel pits. The number of these sites has increased considerably since 1945 as the result of the post-war construction boom (see introduction). This in turn resulted in an increase in the Sand Martin population throughout southern Britain during the 1950s and 1960s (Marchant *et al.* 1990). The Sand Martin's liking for this habitat is reflected in the Oxfordshire Atlas map which shows that the majority breed in the gravel-rich areas in the centre of the county. Sand Martins were recorded in a total of 33 tetrads (4.4%) with confirmed or probable breeding in 20 of them.

Sand Martins begin to arrive in Oxfordshire at the end of March with the main influx during April. An early bird was present at Dorchester Gravel Pit on 9 March 1986. Sand Martins often raise two broods and the young fledge between June and August.

Sand Martins are communal nesters with colony sizes ranging from a few pairs to several hundred (Radford 1966). Stanton Harcourt Gravel Pits have, over the years, had the largest colonies with 1,050 pairs throughout the complex estimated in 1981. Significant numbers of Sand Martins are known to return to the same colony each year (Cramp and Simmons 1976) and a ringing study of a colony at Stanton Harcourt from 1979–1983 by Holmes *et al.* (1987) showed that males had a higher return rate to the site in subsequent years than females.

A study of Sand Martin movements was carried out during the 1960s, initiated by the Ringing Committee of the BTO. This led to many data for Oxfordshire which were analysed by Pepler (1966). He found that, after fledging, Oxfordshire's juvenile Sand Martins rapidly dispersed in any direction up to distances of 200 miles before starting their true migration in August and September.

Some birds linger until October or, rarely, November with the latest record being 11 November 1967. When on autumn migration the birds first take a south-easterly route with many of them passing through the Chichester area of Sussex, presumably to take advantage of a relatively short sea crossing. The national data show that, once across the Channel, the birds travel south-west through France to the Biscay coast and then south to Spain. They then cross the Mediterranean into Morocco and then down to the Sahel region where they winter (Cramp and Simmons 1976). The ringing data from Oxfordshire support the national pattern and recoveries involving Oxfordshire are given in Table 5.57.

A more easterly route may be taken by the

Table 5.57. Sand Martin.
Continental recoveries of birds involving Oxfordshire.

| | No. of recoveries | |
| | Oxfordshire | Foreign |
Country	ringed	ringed
France	15	4
Belgium	1	-
Netherlands	-	1
Spain	5	1
Morocco	1	-
Senegal	1	-
Tunisia	1	-

birds in spring (Mead 1983) but no evidence for this has been obtained from Oxfordshire-ringed birds. The bird recovered in Tunisia was ringed 27 June 1981 and recovered 5 July 1982. The circumstances of recovery are unknown but it could have been a bird travelling north during the spring of 1982.

Another interesting result of ringing studies was a bird ringed at Cassington as a juvenile on 19 July 1960 which was controlled at the same site on 16 June 1964 and again on 26 May 1968 at Long Handborough — in its eighth year. This is one of the oldest Sand Martins on record and demonstrates well the site fidelity of the species.

Sand Martins are prone to large population fluctuations and several of these have occurred since the 1960s. Numbers rose steadily through the 1960s to a peak in 1968. Then, in 1968/9, a nationwide collapse in the Sand Martin population was reflected in Oxfordshire's colonies which fell to less than half the size of previous years. This was said to be due to a drought in the Sahel region of Africa in which our Sand Martins winter (Cowley 1979). Numbers then rose again through the 1970s and early 1980s until 1983 and 1984 when the population dropped to less than 10% of its peak in earlier years, again considered to be due to mortality in the Sahel (Mead 1984). An indication of the scale of this crash is given by estimates of breeding pairs at Stanton Harcourt and Dorchester Gravel Pits made during ringing surveys (Table 5.58). Happily numbers increased again during the late 1980s with over 300 nest burrows noted at one site in 1988. Changes in gravel extraction procedures have resulted in pits being dug and filled-in much faster nowadays and may influence the future availability of nest sites and, consequently, population levels.

The tendency for gravel pits to be constantly reworked means that Sand Martins have to re-excavate their nest burrows each year. If a site is rendered unsuitable outside the breeding season the birds move to another in the vicinity on returning in the spring. This happened in 1979 when birds from Sutton Courtenay and Dorchester joined those at Stanton Harcourt (Holmes *et al.* 1987). Unfortunately, some nests are destroyed whilst occupied such as at Abingdon and Radley Gravel Pits in 1987. However, this is exceptional due to the concern shown by local gravel extraction companies for the welfare of the birds. On occasions they have contacted the OOS for advice about excavating at breeding sites. As recently as 1990 a new colony of about 50 pairs at the new Yarnton Gravel Pits was saved by the intervention of a local birdwatcher and the cooperation of the gravel extraction company.

Sand Martins are susceptible to a number of hazards in their winter quarters and suffer drastic population fluctuations. Their survival depends on successful breeding in what can only be described as unstable habitats. It is up to us to ensure that they are given all the help possible to keep their population at a healthy level. This can be done by leaving their nesting colonies undisturbed during the breeding season and keeping the local gravel extraction companies, in whose gravel pits the majority of our Sand Martins breed, aware of the situation.

SWALLOW
Hirundo rustica

The Swallow is a very numerous summer visitor to Oxfordshire. Its favoured nest sites include old open farm buildings with a plentiful supply of airborne insects nearby. As Oxfordshire is a predominantly rural county with many scattered farm buildings, the wide distribution of the Swallow, as shown by the Oxfordshire Atlas map, is not surprising. Also, there are no major environmental factors, such as altitude or large areas of woodland, to discourage its presence. The low number of records from the Downs is likely to be due to a lack of suitable nest sites there.

Swallows start to arrive in Oxfordshire during the last week of March or the first week of April. Earlier arrivals as on 28 February 1846 and 8 March 1977 may possibly relate to over-wintering birds. The main influx into the county occurs during late April and early May.

Annual reports show that Swallows can have a protracted breeding season as in 1980 when young were recorded in nests on both 8 May and 28 September. Late fledging was also noted in 1965 with young still in nests at two sites in Oxfordshire during the first week of October. This long season enables them to raise two broods in most years and sometimes even three as occurred, for example, in 1981. Breeding success is, however, subject to fluctuation with some poor seasons such as in the long, hot, dry summer of 1976 when many broods failed. These changing fortunes are well known, but up to the early 1970s it was thought that, in the

long term, the national population of Swallows was stable (Sharrock 1976). Recent CBC data, however, have indicated that the Swallow declined nationally during the early 1980s with its CBC index down to only 50% of its level in the 1960s (Marchant 1984). No data are available specifically relating to Oxfordshire. A locally important difficulty is the reduction in the number of nest sites available as many old, open farm buildings are replaced with new, less suitable ones or converted into luxury homes. Furthermore, Swallows are said to prefer buildings which contain animals (Campbell and Ferguson-Lees 1972) and the recent local decline in dairy farming may exacerbate the problem.

After breeding, Swallows tend to congregate in the evenings to roost, often in reedbeds. Aplin (1889) mentions one roost of 1,500 birds at Clattercote Reservoir in July 1883. In late August 1966, groups of Swallows were noted at several places along the River Thame coming in during the hour before dusk and leaving between 06.00 and 06.30 hrs. The largest roost known in the county in recent years was near Duke's Lock, Wolvercote which was studied in the late 1960s and early 1970s by a group of Oxfordshire ringers. The size of this roost increased, slowly at first, from a few dozen birds during early autumn often to reach a peak of over a thousand. Over 3,500 birds were present on 10 September 1966 with the roost being vacated soon after.

Autumn migration starts in August and most Swallows have left the county by the middle of October although a few are reported during November in many years. One exceptionally late bird was recorded at Folly Bridge on 2 December 1986. Movements are diurnal and often visible. On September days with low cloud and adverse winds Swallows may be seen streaming south at hedge-top height on a broad front right across the county. Although departure gatherings, usually on telegraph wires, produce large concentrations, migrating birds are more typically thinly spread.

From 1948-1989 some 16,304 Swallows were ringed in the county. Particularly large numbers were ringed at the reedbed roosts in the 1970s and 6,440 were ringed in that decade alone! Swallow recoveries indicate that our birds winter in the Republic of South Africa, particularly in Cape Province, with a few in Natal and Transvaal. The migration route appears to go through Belgium and France to Spain, then over the Mediterranean to Morocco and Algeria. It crosses the Sahara to Nigeria then down through the Congo to the Republic of South Africa. The journey may, however, be taken on a broader front as there is an Oxfordshire recovery of a bird ringed in Malta in April. This pattern reflects that seen on a national scale (Cramp and Simmons 1976). Table 5.58 shows all recoveries of Swallows ringed in Oxfordshire.

It is to be hoped that the recent decline in the number of our Swallows is only temporary.

HOUSE MARTIN
Delichon urbica

A widespread and very numerous summer visitor, House Martins appear to be particularly common during migration times. The Oxfordshire Atlas map suggests that it is slightly less frequently encountered on the higher ground of the Downs, Chilterns, Cotswolds and in the north of the county.

In Oxfordshire House Martins nest on the outside of buildings and do not use natural sites. They are quick to exploit new housing, sometimes moving in before the human occupants. The considerable development in house building in the twentieth century has provided an ample supply of suitable sites. Most are in small colonies spread throughout the towns and villages of the county, although there are some larger concentrations as at the Shipton-on-Cherwell Cement Works (100+ pairs) and Blenheim Bridge (40+). Former large colonies on bridges over the Thames at Clifton Hampden and Swinford showed considerable fluctuations in numbers between years (Table 5.60) which are difficult to explain. The dramatic decline at Clifton Hampden in 1966 and 1967 was particularly surprising as this colony had existed for many years. For example Gibbings (1958) counted 128 nests there in 1939. M. Radford and B. Campbell examining the nests under the bridge from a boat found old nests intact, and no signs of deliberate human interference. Speculation about the causes were summarised by Brucker (1975) and included suggestions that the colony may have been devastated by epidemic disease, or met with disaster on migration. Another idea was that they deserted under pressure from increasing disturbance from river or road traffic to find quieter accommodation on the new houses being built at the time in nearby villages, but this is unlikely given the sudden nature of the

Table 5.59. Swallow.
Recoveries of birds ringed in Oxfordshire.

Country/Region	No. of recoveries
Northern England	3
Southern England	38
Wales	1
Belgium	2
France & Channel Isles	2
Spain	1
Morocco	1
Algeria	1
Nigeria	1
Congo	1
Southern Africa	8

Table 5.60. House Martin.
Census of colonies at two bridges across the River Thames.

Year	Clifton Hampden	Swinford
1951	439	
1952	513	
1953	445	
1954	399	
1955	302	
1956	200	
1957	158	
1958	81	
1959	66	80
1960	91	152
1961	14	170
1962	170	73
1963	223	93
1964	279	134
1965	283	145
1966	192	73
1967	0	100
1968	7	112
1969	29	123
1970	33	no census
1971	41	105
1972	51	no census
1973	71	no census
1974	83	38
1975	103	14

Table 5.61. House Martin.
The distribution of nests by villages surveyed by G.R.M. Peplar in 1966.

No. of villages	No. of nests
5	60+
8	40-60
13	20-40
6	10-20
3	1-9
1	0

Table 5.62. House Martin.
The number of nests in an area of north Oxford monitored at approximately 15-year intervals since 1930.

Year	No. of nests
1930	47
1945	45
1961	41
1975	50
1989	53

decrease. If heavy mortality on migration had been the cause, one would have expected to have seen parallel changes at other colonies such as at Swinford (Table 5.60). Breeding at both sites ceased in the early 1980s. However after an absence of several years, nesting was resumed on the Clifton Hampden Bridge in the mid-1980s, and about 20 pairs were present in 1989.

House Martin populations have been the subject of other studies in Oxfordshire over the years. In 1931 a census of an area of 145 km around Oxford revealed a total of 694 nests, with those in predominantly urban areas at a density of about 7.7 pairs/km^2 and in rural areas at about 3.5 pairs/km^2 (OOS Report 1931).

A survey of nests in 36 villages north and east of Oxford in 1966 by G.R.M. Peplar also showed that healthy populations of House Martins were present in most villages (Table 5.61). A longer-term census of nests concerns an area of north Oxford first defined in the 1930 Report (Brucker 1975). The number of nests in the area was counted at about 15-yearly intervals starting in 1930 (Table 5.62).

The level of population here has been well maintained despite fears of a decline in 1929 which prompted the first count. The problem for House Martins in Oxford was then expressed as "lack of mud on modern roads" which might cause difficulties in nest building. In recent years most nests were on houses closest to the Oxford Canal, suggesting that the proximity of a mud supply is at least of some significance.

House Martins are conspicuous during both migration periods when vast assemblies collect over larger waters throughout the county (e.g. 19,000 estimated at Farmoor Reservoir on 19

September 1983), or when they stream over high places under low cloud cover. In spring the main return is usually in the second half of April, although this may be delayed by adverse weather conditions until mid-May (as in 1989). The earliest-ever record is 20 March 1968.

Autumn migration starts in the second half of August and continues until mid-October. In most years a few stragglers are reported in mid-November. These may be late breeding birds. House Martins regularly raise two or three broods, and young are sometimes still in nests in the first week of October. One family party did not leave a nest in Kidlington until 2 November in 1965. Rev. Gilbert White wrote in 1767 that he "once saw, in Christchurch College quadrangle in Oxford, on a very sunny warm morning, a House Martin flying about, and settling on the parapet, so late as the twentieth of November." The latest House Martin on record is one at Henley on 18 December 1880 (Aplin 1889). More recently one was seen at Duns Tew on 4 December 1981.

A few dozen House Martins are ringed in Oxfordshire in most years but recoveries are rare, with only one from overseas: a bird ringed in Oxford, 31 May 1974 was recovered in Switzerland on 8 October of the same year.

Local knowledge of the House Martin is comparatively good, and should enable us to monitor future developments. Although there seems no need for concern for the well being of this species in Oxfordshire the inexplicable desertions of the bridge colonies causes unease, and there was a considerable reduction in breeding numbers in 1991 after adverse weather conditions during the spring migration.

Family: Motacillidae
Pipits and Wagtails

These slender-bodied, insectivorous birds are well represented in the county with seven species recorded during this century. Of these, the three wagtails breed in good numbers in appropriate habitat, two pipits breed also, but are less widespread, and a further two are vagrants.

RICHARD'S PIPIT
Anthus novaeseelandiae

A very rare vagrant. One was taken alive in Oxford in 1831 (Aplin 1889). A large pipit which was aggressive towards Meadow Pipits at Cholsey Sewage Works on 10 December 1961 was considered to be this by the observer, who had good views.

TREE PIPIT
Anthus trivialis

The Tree Pipit is an uncommon and declining summer visitor to Oxfordshire, arriving in the county during April, with the usual first arrival date falling in the first half of the month. It is a bird of open woodland, particularly plantation areas and areas of open grassland on hillsides or those studded with occasional trees.

The Oxfordshire Atlas provided breeding records from 65 tetrads with over 70% of the records being in the 'probable' breeding category and reflecting the conspicuousness of territory holding birds although this behaviour is not always a guarantee of successful nesting. However, it must be remembered that this represents data from four years of survey and not all sites were occupied in all years. The map shows strongholds to be the wooded slopes of the Chilterns and the more open Downland areas, woodlands such as Waterperry, Wytham and Bagley and also the rifle range at Otmoor.

The history of the Tree Pipit in Oxfordshire is not clear, but the status descriptions of earlier authors suggest fluctuations from time to time. Aplin (1889) considers it fairly abundant, Jourdain (1926) describes it as thinly distributed, and Alexander (1947) calls it widely distributed but not very common. Radford (1966) describes it as a regular summer visitor, but not common, and considers it to be less common than in the nineteenth century.

With the outbreak of *Myxomatosis* in the 1950s and the extensive development of ungrazed grassland and scrub, a striking increase occurred in the recorded numbers of Tree Pipits at Wytham Woods (Gosler 1990). This increase was observed in other parts of Oxfordshire.

Since the 1960s, the overall population trend is of a species in decline. In the BOS's Annual Breeding Season Survey of 1968, 46 singing males were reported from north Oxfordshire. By 1986, only seven records, from five localities were received. The status in the BOS area has now been reconsidered and lowered from "fairly numerous" in 1971 to "not scarce" (Easterbrook 1983). Elsewhere in the county, there were nine named sites known to hold singing males in 1968 and they were also present in "most southern squares". At sites in the county such as Blenheim, Shotover, Wytham and Waterperry, which at their peaks held three, four, 12 and seven singing males respectively, birds are currently absent or very scarce.

The reasons for the decline are not clear but may relate in part to changes in their nesting habitat. The BOS survey in 1968, demonstrated

Figure 5.61. Rock/Water Pipit.
Total numbers of Rock and Water Pipits
reported 1964-1989 (based on first dates
seen). Grey = Rock Pipit, black = Water Pipit.

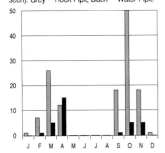

that 65% of Tree Pipits nest in young forestry plantations although that study also pointed out the need for mature trees, at least 6 m tall, from which the characteristic 'parachuting' song-flight could be performed. Birds also nest on open grassland sites, typically on hillsides where they can song-flight from lower perches, such as fence-posts or scrub, down to the valley floor. It is difficult to assess the causes of the their decline, though habitat loss or alteration seems unlikely since many traditional sites do not appear to have altered substantially. Presumably this is more than a local development, and there are other, as yet unknown, reasons for the changes.

MEADOW PIPIT
Anthus pratensis

The Meadow Pipit may be found in the county as a locally distributed resident and very frequent passage migrant and winter visitor.

Although nationally, the Meadow Pipit is regarded as a widespread breeding species (Sharrock 1976), the distribution pattern in lowland Britain, including Oxfordshire, is very local. The findings of the Oxfordshire Atlas confirm this, with confirmed and probable breeding noted in 60 (8%) tetrads. These are mostly along the Chilterns and Downs with the only other stronghold being Otmoor. These sites provide low, tussocky vegetation on undisturbed ground with an open aspect. The majority of the 51 records of possible breeding are presumed to be birds on passage. Comparison with earlier accounts of Oxfordshire's birdlife would indicate that there is no evidence of any change during the twentieth century. Since 1965, breeding has been confirmed at a few other sites scattered throughout the county (e.g. Farmoor, Sutton Courtenay, Port Meadow and Milton) but these developments have been only short-lived.

Substantial movements through the county are noted every spring and autumn. These can be well observed as they are usually at tree top height. Organised migration watches at high vantage points have shown that spring passage usually occurs between the third week of March and the second week of April and the autumn passage over a longer period from the third week of September until the first week in November. At peak times, counts of 90-120

birds/hr are usual. As passage is on a broad front, considerable total numbers must be involved. Morning flights are usually in parties of one to six birds, but evening flights are more typically of 10-20 birds. Evening flights in autumn continue at dusk, suggesting that they carry on into the night. Large flocks sometimes gather when they rest on their journeys, particularly in the spring. For example, 1,500 were counted along a 3.2 km stretch of the River Evenlode on 5 April 1963. The origin of these passage birds is unknown. There are six ringing recoveries of Meadow Pipits ringed in Oxfordshire. Five are local but one involves a nestling ringed on 4 May 1961 on Otmoor. On 15 December 1961 it was at Badajoz, Spain, 1,555 km SSW.

Some Meadow Pipits stay throughout the winter favouring meadows with long grass, although they are less in evidence in extremely cold weather. It seems probable that local breeders remain in the area. A few are always present at breeding haunts, and in spring 1991 pairs were in territories and displaying at Churn on 6 March, and at Otmoor on 14 March while passage birds were not noted until 28 March.

ROCK/WATER PIPIT
Anthus petrosus/A. spinoletta

Infrequent passage migrants. Rock and Water Pipits were once rare, but are now regular visitors in small numbers in spring and autumn.

After a total absence of records in the nineteenth century there were two sightings in the first half of the twentieth. A general lack of interest in unspectacular pipits probably caused them to be overlooked. This was the view of C.J. Cadbury who knew the species well and heard them flying over Wytham on two occasions in the early 1960s.

In the second half of the twentieth century they were identified more frequently. Since 1967 they have occurred annually. Most records are from the concrete banks of Farmoor Reservoir where they usually drop in for a few hours, but occasionally remain for several days. One individual was there from 15 October until 6 November 1968. Usually these are solitary birds, although sometimes there are two or three together.

Most filter through in March, September and October (Figure 5.61) suggesting regular

passage movements rather than a casual straying from breeding habitats. There are few winter records.

Water Pipits are much less frequently claimed, especially in the autumn when there are identification problems. Their spring passage (18 February to 27 April) occurs later than that of the Rock Pipit with most appearing in April. Farmoor Reservoir, Port Meadow, Dorchester Gravel Pit are favoured sites, with other records from Banbury and Abingdon Sewage Farms. Occasionally parties of three or four have been seen together.

YELLOW WAGTAIL
Motacilla flava

The Yellow Wagtail is a common summer migrant to Oxfordshire from its winter quarters south of the Sahara. The first birds usually arrive within a few days of 1 April, gathering in large flocks at favoured wet and grassy sites such as Farmoor, Grimsbury, Port Meadow and Little Wittenham. These flocks sometimes reach three figures at the peak of passage in mid April.

The breeding distribution in the county, as shown by the Oxfordshire Atlas map, suggests a relationship with the underlying geology. In general the clay vales appear to be favoured and the calcareous rocks, particularly the oolites to the north and west of Oxford, less popular. The Windrush valley seemingly (to the human eye) providing ideal habitat has surprisingly few records. In the south there is a noticeable scarcity on the chalk downs although scattered pairs do occur, however to the east of the Goring Gap there are many occupied tetrads on the chalk. Comparison with the distribution map for Reed Bunting shows some interesting similarities.

During the fieldwork for the Oxfordshire Atlas breeding was usually easy to prove since adults are conspicuous when flying back to the nests with beaks full of insect prey. The presence of dung heaps, areas of short grass or hay fields after cutting, near to nest sites are regularly used for foraging.

Aplin (1889) considered the Yellow Wagtail to be "common", but Jordain (1926) found it to be "local, chiefly confined to water meadows and marshes and now rare in north Oxfordshire where many nested formerly in corn lands". In a review of the species by the BOS in 1964

observers thought it to have been "common enough" since the early 1950s. Radford's comment in 1966 that it is "regular and common, local in distribution" accords well with the current view of its status. The *National Atlas* (Sharrock 1976) proved breeding in all of the county's 10 km squares. The Oxfordshire Atlas survey gives a more detailed account with which to compare the progress of the species in the future.

Arable fields often provide suitable nesting habitat. The BOS 1964 study showed that 70% of those pairs found on arable land were in wheat and 15% in barley. More recently, records have come from bean, pea and potato fields in parts of the county where they were once uncommon. Market garden areas are also favoured. The use of arable land is not new, as Aplin (1889) stated, "though often found in the lower grounds, the greater number breed in the dry cornfields".

In September post-breeding flocks form at the same sites as in spring, prior to autumn migration. The last birds have departed by the second half of October. Several locally-ringed birds have been recovered in Dorset pointing to this being the main route into and out of our area when moving to and from their wintering grounds. In addition, three recoveries from abroad, two in Portugal and one in Morocco, indicate a direct route into Africa.

Besides the British subspecies *M.f. flavissima* of the Yellow Wagtail, others have occurred, the most frequent being the continental nominate Blue-headed race *M.f. flava*. One or two *flava* wagtails are recorded in Oxfordshire in most years in the spring flocks of *flavissima*, usually two weeks after the first arrivals. Over 90% of *flava* records appear between mid-April and mid-May after which they move on. Autumn records are extremely scarce.

Breeding by two *flava* females with *flavissima* males were reported in 1945 and another instance of breeding took place during the Oxfordshire Atlas survey when a male *flava* was seen feeding young in a wheat field near Brightwell-cum-Sotwell, Wallingford during June 1988. In the same month an extremely rare vagrant to Britain, a male of the Black-headed race *M.f. feldegg* from south-east Europe held territory at Brightwell-cum-Sotwell, Wallingford. Although breeding was not observed, it behaved aggressively towards the other Yellow Wagtails present in the same

wheat field. Besides the bird's obvious plumage features, it was also noted giving different calls and behaviour than those *flavissima* present (Lewington 1988).

GREY WAGTAIL
Motacilla cinerea

An uncommon resident and winter visitor, the Grey Wagtail is the least abundant Wagtail species in Oxfordshire. During the Oxfordshire Atlas it was found in only 12% of the county's tetrads, compared with 41% for the Yellow and 61% for the Pied Wagtail. Even this gives an inflated idea of their abundance as there is likely only to be one or two pairs in most of the occupied tetrads. Assuming that to be the case, the county breeding population is unlikely to exceed 100 pairs even in a good year following mild winters. Linear water courses form an important habitat feature of breeding territories. This is indicated by the Atlas map, albeit less sharply than for more abundant riparian species such as Mute Swan or Great Crested Grebe. Grey Wagtails will use even quite small streams, particularly those that are fast-flowing and shallow. Man-made waterside structures such as bridges, walls and weirs, frequently in a state of disrepair, often provide sites for nest building, and the availability of these might be limiting their distribution.

A BOS survey in 1988 recorded some interesting features regarding nesting. Riffles and overhanging deciduous trees were noted at a large proportion of the riverine feeding sites used during the breeding season. During the nestling period both parents foraged predominantly within 100 metres of the nest site. There was one noted exception to this. One bird at Sor Brook collected Common Blue Damselflies some 450 m from the nest. This species, which was caught by fly-catching, has not been recorded before as a food (Brownett 1990). After the young left the nest, the parents split the broods and the female with her fledglings foraged considerably further from the nest than the male with his charges. This might indicate the males wish to maintain a strong link with his home territory.

Unfortunately, Oxfordshire ringing recoveries tell us little about their movements. Of four recoveries outside the county, two were summer-ringed birds recovered in Sussex and Hertfordshire. Another ringed in winter was found in the following summer in North Yorkshire whilst one ringed in summer in Essex was recovered in Oxfordshire in autumn.

Recent OOS Reports have noted an increase in the number of records in the last months of the year, indicating a strong autumn immigration and in several winters birds have come into towns, presumably for the extra warmth that such places provide. Since 1984, Grey Wagtails have been seen regularly each winter in central Oxford, sometimes in the Carfax and Cornmarket street area.

In the past, the Grey Wagtail was considered less common and Aplin (1889) believed it to be largely a winter visitor to the county. He cites only two known cases of breeding, but an OOS survey in 1936 cites 16 breeding records at as many sites. Being aware of at least eight pairs around Banbury in 1959, the BOS realised that it was probably more common than previously stated, and conducted breeding season surveys in 1960 and 1961. In 390 km^2 of north-west Oxfordshire they located 23 pairs (or 0.06 pairs/km^2). This followed a period of range expansion in lowland Britain during the 1950s (Parslow 1973).

Grey Wagtails suffer particularly badly in hard winters and those of the early 1960s had a dramatic effect on the local breeding population (Radford 1966). After the long severe winter of 1963 they were completely lost from the River Thame and in the Banbury area their population crashed, not recovering to its previous levels until 1971. By 1974, every mill or former mill-stream on the Rivers Evenlode and Windrush had a breeding pair (J. Brucker pers. comm.).

The general impression from the 1970s onwards is that although their range may have expanded, the local density of breeding pairs has declined. The 1987 OOS annual report suggested that their population was low after a succession of hard winters and this could possibly account for the lower numbers recorded in 1988 in the Banbury area during a repeat of the BOS's earlier survey. On this occasion only 17 pairs were located in a wider area of 1,200 km^2, 13 of which (compared with 23 previously) were found in the earlier 390 km^2 (or 0.03 pairs/km^2).

Other suggestions for this apparent decline were loss of nest sites due to the conversion of a number of water mills, although water quality might play a part.

PIED WAGTAIL
Motacilla alba

The Pied Wagtail is both a numerous resident with a rather patchy breeding distribution and a frequent passage migrant in Oxfordshire. There seems to be a very strong association with human activity. Industrial sites usually attract Pied Wagtails, and most of the trading estates which have developed in the 1970s and 1980s have a few pairs. Also they can be found in the grounds of large country houses (of which Oxfordshire has many) and around farmyards, reservoirs, gravel pits and sewage works.

This species used commonly to be called the Water Wagtail. In a study by the BOS in 1965, 70% of nesting sites were described as being of an aquatic nature. Nests are not only found in natural sites such as ivy-covered trees, but often also in a variety of human artefacts. Pied Wagtails appear to make a habit of using unusual nest sites. The wheel arch of an old fire engine, a window box, the engine compartment of a motor roller and a discarded cardboard box were all sites used at one location in the south of the county. This association with Man is not recent. By the end of the nineteenth century, almost every railway station in the county had a pair of Pied Wagtails (Warde Fowler 1895).

During the breeding season, food is gathered from areas with close-cropped or little ground vegetation near the nest sites. The BOS study showed that food carried to the young consisted exclusively of insects and that the male was invariably the main provider to the fledged young.

If we assume a breeding density of three to six pairs per occupied tetrad (Sharrock 1976), and that the Atlas map does not exaggerate their distribution because of differences between survey years, we would estimate there to be 2,700–5,500 birds in the county at the start of each breeding season.

In the autumn, numbers build up as Pied Wagtails migrate to their winter quarters. Some understanding of the complexity of their movements was achieved as a result of intensive ringing of the birds using a major roost in reedbeds at Wolvercote Gravel Pit in the 1960s and early 1970s. There were several recoveries from south-west Europe, and these tended to be of birds ringed at Wolvercote in the early autumn. At least three were found in Portugal, three in Spain and two in south-west France.

For example, a juvenile ringed at Wolvercote on 23 June 1963 was recovered in Alentejo in Portugal on 5 November 1963. The birds coming in to the roost later in autumn appeared to be mostly from the north of Britain. For example, one ringed in November was recovered in West Lothian, Scotland in May, and another ringed in December was found in Inverness, Scotland in June.

Flemming (1981) studied the roosting behaviour of Pied Wagtails at the Duke's Lock roost in the winter of 1977/78. The number of birds visiting varied from two to 1,200 as might be expected if the birds were on passage. In an attempt to discover the reasons for their communal roosting behaviour, he also looked at the birds' foraging success and noted that it varied considerably between four different habitats, the best being at a pig farm. He concluded that the roost served both physiological and predator-avoidance functions but that when at roost, the wagtails did not share information about the distribution of food in the area, so that this was not the purpose of their social behaviour.

The roost at Wolvercote has existed since at least 1926, but in the late 1970s and 1980s attracted fewer birds. Although reedbeds are still used as roosting places as at Cassington Gravel Pit and along the River Thame, alternative sites are now being adopted. At a site at Stanton Harcourt the birds roosted in the spaces between stacked building blocks. The largest known roost in the 1980s was at the John Radcliffe Hospital in Headington where several hundred birds roost in bushes in enclosed quadrangles. This roost attracted birds throughout the winter.

During daylight in winter Pied Wagtails sometimes congregate in flocks of up to 150 birds when good feeding opportunities present themselves, as when fields are ploughed, or meadows recently swamped by floods leave debris.

In an intensive study of colour-ringed birds at Port Meadow, Davies (1982) noted that Pied Wagtails either join the main feeding flock or defend territories along the river bank depending on the availability of food. Territory defence was strongest during the coldest weather although the territory owner might not even be able to feed on the territory under these conditions. The birds followed a simple strategy. If the conditions were very hard, they would feed with the flock but would still have to defend the

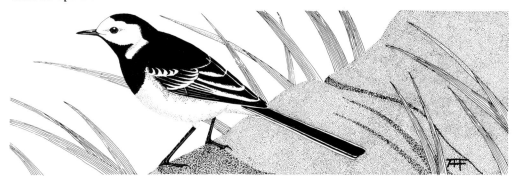

territory against intruders. If food became abundant on the territory, the aggressive behaviour was relaxed, either sufficiently to allow a second bird (or 'satellite') to feed, or even relaxed completely. The reason for this behaviour was that food on the river bank was replaced at a more or less predictable rate by new material washed up by the river. Hence if the bird patrolled its patch at a suitable rate it could exploit this fact efficiently. However, to do this, the wagtail needed to be able to assume that no other bird was exploiting the same resource and so it was defended (Davies and Houston 1983).

The British race M.a. yarrelli appears to have always been common in the county and the Continental nominate race M.a. alba known as the White Wagtail has been noted increasingly of late as a passage migrant. Since the 1960s these have been noted in ones and twos, but occasionally in the spring up to ten or 15 may occur.

White Wagtails are noted from March to May with a main peak in records during the second half of April and also recorded less frequently during the autumn migration from September to November, when they prove more difficult to identify. Aplin (1889) knew of only three sightings in the last century and Alexander (1947) mentioned only 12 records in the previous 60 years, whilst Radford (1966) still considered it to be uncommon. The several hundred records of White Wagtails that have been noted so far in the second half of this century is notable by comparison, but is probably attributable to increased observer awareness. The great majority of these records have come from such well watched sites as Farmoor, Stanton Harcourt Gravel Pits and Port Meadow.

Family: Bombycillidae
Waxwings

One representative from this small family is found in Europe where it breeds in the northern forests. It occurs in Britain only as a winter visitor and passage migrant. Few species are as dependent upon fruit as the Waxwing and the availability of this strongly influences its range outside the breeding season.

WAXWING
Bombycilla garrulus

The Waxwing is typically an 'irruptive' species to Britain. As the county is at the extreme south-western limit of the Waxwing's wanderings, this is an infrequent and erratic visitor which has only been recorded in 23 years during the last century (1890–1989). Table 5.63 lists the number of records each giving numbers present at each visit and shows how irregularly it has been seen.

Two 'invasions' to Britain were marked in Oxfordshire. In the early months of 1944 there were seven reports of a total of 29 birds, and in the winter of 1965/6 there were 18 reports of a total of 46 birds. Other national influxes have not been noted in Oxfordshire.

Flocks are small (mean flock size 3.2) with the largest recorded parties being 20–30 birds. Neighbouring counties to the north and east have occasionally noted much higher numbers.

Visits are usually brief, but many local ornithologists obtained splendid views of nine handsome birds which remained in a *Cotoneaster* hedge in a garden adjacent to the Woodstock Road roundabout in Oxford for 19 days in February and March 1944.

Most Waxwings are seen in November, presumably coming direct from the Continent, and again in January or February when earlier arrivals on the east coast may be moving further inland in search of food (Figure 5.62). The earliest record is of five on Otmoor on 4 October 1975 and the latest was an individual which lingered until 5 May at Hinksey Hill Farm in 1966.

Almost all the records have come from gardens, where food recorded as having been taken includes the fruit of *Cotoneaster*, Hawthorn and Apple. Despite the increase in the number of people watching their garden birds, there has been no corresponding increase in the frequency of reports.

Table 5.63. Waxwing.
All records reported together with flock sizes 1895-1989.

Year	Birds seen
1895	1
1921	1,2
1922	2
1923	1
1924	1
1937	2
1944	2,1,1,9,2,10,4
1948	20
1956	1,1,1
1964	1
1965	2,1,1,2,1,2,1,2,5,4
1966	2,3,1,1,12,3,1,1
1968	1
1970	1,2,1
1971	2,4
1975	1,5
1979	1
1980	12
1986	25
1988	1,1

Figure 5.62. Waxwing.
Monthly distribution of records 1900-1989, based on first dates seen. Grey = number of records, black = number of birds.

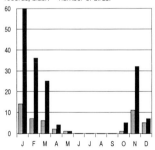

Family: Cinclidae
Dippers

Dippers are birds of fast-flowing streams. They are, therefore, typical of upland regions. Oxfordshire lies on the southern and eastern-most edge of the Dipper's British range, as an extension of the Cotswold population.

Figure 5.63. Dipper.
Breeding distribution 1968-1972 (after Sharrock 1976).

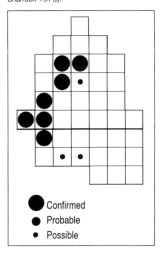

● Confirmed
● Probable
• Possible

Table 5.64. Dipper.
Number of breeding records 1970-1989.

Year	Possible breeding	Confirmed breeding
1970	2	0
1971	2	6
1972	1	3
1973	2	0
1974	1	1
1975	0	0
1976	0	1
1977	0	4
1978	1	5
1979	0	5
1980	1	5
1981	1	4
1982	0	4
1983	0	4
1984	0	4
1985	0	1
1986	0	3
1987	0	1
1988	0	1
1989	0	0

DIPPER
Cinclus cinclus

The Dipper is a rare resident, breeding irregularly in Oxfordshire and also occurring as an occasional visitor. The species' favoured nesting habitat of fast-flowing, well-oxygenated, boulder-strewn streams means that for Oxfordshire, on the eastern-most limit of its range in southern Britain, breeding usually only occurs when the population increases in the strongholds.

There were few breeding records up until the 1960s. Aplin (1889) gives a single occurrence, at Claydon in 1876, whilst Radford (1966) gives nine records of probable or definite breeding between 1939 and 1964, mostly in the north and west of the county. During this period, singles or pairs of birds were recorded in most years and from most months of the year. In 1970 the number of sightings increased and in the following season a total of six pairs bred near north and west Oxfordshire streams giving the results depicted in Figure 5.63. From that time nesting has been noted in each year except 1975 and 1989 (Table 5.64). There have been no breeding records in the north of the county since 1985 but nesting has continued along the western streams. This was demonstrated during the Oxfordshire Atlas when breeding was confirmed in only SP20, with probable breeding in SP21. At one site in west Oxfordshire, Dippers have bred every year, except 1975 and 1989, since at least the early 1960s.

Although the rivers of the county do not appear to be ideal for Dippers, fast-flowing stretches around lashers, mills and waterfalls provide acceptable sites. The River Windrush above Witney has been used most regularly. Birds, assumed to be non-breeders, have been scattered across the county as far south as Letcombe Regis and as far east as the Seacourt Stream, Oxford.

If the Dipper is to remain as a breeding bird in Oxfordshire, and especially if it is to increase as such, then careful monitoring of water quality and abstraction is vital.

Family: Troglodytidae
Wrens

The Wren represents an extension into the Palearctic of an otherwise exclusively New World family. Hence it is the only member of its family in Europe and, as is often the case in such a situation, it is widespread and resident within much of that range since it has no closely related competitors. In southern Europe though, it is often confined to higher altitudes. The secret of its success would seem also to lie in the very wide variety of habitats in which it thrives, and possibly also to its small size which gives it access to a range of niches which are not available to larger birds.

WREN
Troglodytes troglodytes

The Wren is an abundant and ubiquitous resident in the county. It is a very adaptable bird, resident in virtually all habitats — woodlands and hedgerows, parks and gardens, along river banks and in patches of scrubby vegetation. Although small and spending much time skulking in undergrowth, bursts of loud trilling song betray its presence, and this, coupled with a long breeding season, enabled such a good coverage to be achieved in the course of the Oxfordshire Atlas study.

All of the previous authorities on the county's birds describe the Wren as a very common resident and in general this remains true today. However, the Wren population undergoes marked fluctuations from season to season suffering heavy mortality as a result of cold weather. This is shown by the CBC data (Marchant et al. 1990) which reveal just how badly hit the species can be in the severest winters. Locally, this is well illustrated by the census data from Wytham Woods (Overall 1989). The number of Wrens ringed in the county also demonstrates the declines following severe winter weather (Table 5.66). However, numbers are rapidly restored during the next breeding season and Wrens do have strategies to overcome these difficult times in the winter. Communal roosting is common and parties of up to 20 birds have been watched entering roofing thatch, nestboxes or other suitable holes in which birds can huddle together.

In winter, birds will also undertake local movements in search of food and shelter and will freely enter gardens to feed and have been known to become regular visitors to the garden feeding station. Despite this, Wrens are amongst the most sedentary of birds in the county and there are no recoveries of birds ringed in Oxfordshire, greater than 9 km from the ringing site.

Although a large number of habitats are occupied, population densities vary considerably in different habitats. The Wren is primarily a bird of woodland and woodland edge since it requires dense low vegetation in which to feed. Nests are built in thick vegetation so that these tend also to be in low cover. Hence, densities are greatest in these habitats and data from four woodland sites in 1984 gave the figures shown in Table 5.65. Garson (1978) recorded a density of 2.6 pairs per hectare in an 8.5 ha block of woodland at Wytham. Similarly, Ford (1987) showed the ubiquity of the Wren in 20 isolated woods in Oxfordshire (ranging from 0.14–18 ha in size). He found it breeding in 19 of these woodlands and demonstrated densities ranging from 0.6–7 pairs per hectare. He also found Wrens breeding on all of eight control census plots. These consisted of areas of similar size to the isolated woodlands which he studied but they were within larger blocks of woodland such as within Wytham. Although Wrens bred on average at a slightly higher density in the isolated woods this was not statistically significant.

Table 5.65. Wren.
Breeding density in four Oxfordshire woodlands in 1984.

Site	Area (ha)	Density (pairs/ha)
Boarstall Decoy CBC	6.6	4.5
Wytham Woods CBC	6.7	1.9
Little Wittenham Wood	52	1.0
Bagley Wood	227	1.0

Table 5.66. Wren.
OOS ringing totals showing the influence of the cold winters of 1962 and 1963.

Year	No. of birds ringed
1961	110
1962	37
1963	18
1964	28
1965	44
1966	73
1967	90

Family: Prunellidae
Accentors

Like the Wren, the Dunnock is the major European representative (though not the sole one) of a family whose centre of diversity is outside the region although in this case it is in the eastern Palearctic. Also like the Wren, it is widespread in Britain, possibly because it lacks closely related competitors.

DUNNOCK
Prunella modularis

The Dunnock is a ubiquitous (though rarely reported) resident in Oxfordshire. A visitor wishing to learn about a county's avifauna is more than likely to browse the pages of the local ornithological societies' bird reports. Anybody coming to Oxfordshire would be forgiven for believing that the Barn Owl or the Stone Curlew was more abundant than the Dunnock, so seldom is anything about its status ever reported. However, a brief walk along a hedgerow, through a park or in a garden would soon give a more accurate picture, showing that it to be an abundant resident. The Dunnock, occasionally still called the Hedge Sparrow, is the archetypal 'little brown job' characteristically skulking in scrub and hedgerow or hopping around a quiet corner of the garden, and rarely seen far from such habitats. It cannot really be classed as a woodland species, indeed census work from Bagley Wood (227 ha) and Little Wittenham

Wood (52 ha) in 1984 recorded nine and ten pairs respectively as compared to Wren for example which in both woods yielded one pair per hectare. At Wytham, it is also relatively scarce (Gosler 1990).

In a study of bird density and diversity in woods of different size in Oxfordshire, Ford (1987) found Dunnocks at 15 times the density in small woods (mean of 1.08 birds/ha) than in woodland plots of similar size within large woods (0.07 birds/ha). This was probably due to the greater density of shrub and ground cover at the edges of the smaller woods.

The Oxfordshire Atlas data are testament to the widespread distribution of the Dunnock. It is even found in relatively high and exposed parts of the county where even a small, scrubby portion of hedge can provide shelter for a pair of nesting Dunnocks. The tetrads in which it was not recorded may represent intensively farmed areas with little suitable hedgerow habitat available, although under-recording in some areas is possible. Like the Wren, the ecology of this species makes it difficult to believe that an area of four square kilometres does not have some potential nesting habitat to support at least one pair. Similarly, the BOS have recorded the species in 93% of the 1 km squares in its area in the course of its Random Square Survey.

The Dunnock is a highly sedentary species. Of 166 recoveries of Dunnocks ringed in the county, only four birds had travelled further than 10 km with the longest movement being only 20 km.

Territories appear to be occupied throughout the year and, especially if a mild period is enjoyed, bursts of full song may be heard throughout the winter. If cold weather ensues, it is possible to find small parties of up to 20 feeding together as a loose flock. In prolonged cold spells local declines in numbers may occur although with so many able to utilise the garden environment, it is unlikely to be as severely affected as a number of other species. There are no data to suggest that Oxfordshire maintains anything other than a stable population.

Family: Turdidae
Thrushes

This diverse family is well represented in Oxfordshire with 15 species recorded during the twentieth century. These display as great a range of status as any family with common residents, summer visitors, winter visitors, passage migrants and vagrants although several species fall into more than one of these categories since they are partial migrants. In general the larger species which typically take a range of foods are more abundant than the small insectivorous species. This is especially true of the insectivorous summer visitors, several of which have declined terribly in the county during the last 100 years.

ROBIN
Erithacus rubecula

Probably the most familiar of our resident birds, the Robin has adapted to the man-made habitats of hedgerows with trees, scrub, parks and gardens. It is no surprise that during the Oxfordshire Atlas survey it was found in 97.5% of tetrads. The breeding density of Robins is higher in woodland than farmland (Marchant et al. 1990). Farmland where the hedges are severely trimmed or fields enlarged and surrounded with wire fences are particularly unsuitable. Parks and gardens, which effectively simulate woodland from the Robin's point of view also support a high density in both summer and winter. Ford (1987) found 1.56 pairs/ha in small, isolated woodlands in Oxfordshire and 0.85 pairs/ha in larger woods. Harper found 0.64 pairs/ha in Bagley Wood and Wiggins found 0.79 pairs/ha at Little Wittenham (Wiggins 1984). The density in Wytham Woods has varied between 0.45 and 2.2 pairs/ha on a 6.7 ha plot (Overall 1988).

Pairs are formed between mid-December and mid-February (Lack 1943). The main nesting period is from April to June with two, or sometimes three, broods being raised. A particularly early record was of a nest with four eggs on 24 February 1980 at Dean Court. Song continues up until mid-June. For about a month there is very little song, the only quiet period during the year.

Most Oxfordshire Robins are sedentary; of 253 recoveries, 91% were recovered less than 9 km from the place of ringing. Only two were recovered further than 100 km away within Britain. One ringed at Newington on 1 September 1965 was controlled at Beachy Head, Sussex 18 days later and one ringed on Otmoor in August 1988 was found dead at Tiverton, Devon after a month. Very few Robins spend the winter abroad and almost all of those are females (Lack 1986). The only foreign recovery from Oxfordshire was of a female ringed at Cassington in August 1959 and found dead in

January 1960 in the Vendée, France 583 km S. Two Robins, ringed in northern England have been recovered in Oxfordshire, one from Lincolnshire and one from Northumberland.

Autumn song is subtly different from that in the spring. About half the females also sing, a unique situation among British birds. Singing after dark is also heard quite often, especially near to street lights. For example, in Oxford city up to 02.00 hr in February 1980, regularly two hours before dawn at the John Radcliffe Hospital in December 1987 and throughout the night at a market garden in Sutton Courtenay during the winter of 1990/91.

Robins are mainly ground feeders and invertebrates comprise more than 90% of their diet. Studies around Oxford show that abundant ground cover up to six feet high is an important feature of winter habitat. Gardens are of course, also included in this category and the added support of supplementary feeding by the public in winter must be significant.

On the whole the Robin population has

Table 5.67. Nightingale.

The relationship between altitude and breeding distribution in Oxfordshire in 1976 (Knight 1976) and 1985/86 Oxfordshire Atlas.

Altitude (m)	Breeding pairs 1976	All records 1985-86
50-75	17	16
76-100	17	5
101-125	0	0
126-150	3	1
151+	3	1

remained stable over the past hundred years (Sharrock 1976, Marchant *et al.* 1990). They are susceptible to hard winter weather, but recover in a couple of years. In view of this there seems no reason to doubt that our most popular and familiar bird will remain so in the years to come.

NIGHTINGALE
Luscinia megarhynchos

A scarce and declining but regularly breeding summer visitor. Nightingales arrive in the third or fourth weeks of April, showing up not only at potential breeding sites, but also in such unlikely places as the edge of a housing estate in Kidlington and a hedge bordering a school at Woodstock. The few which do find suitable breeding places slip away quietly at the end of the breeding season, and there have been very few records after singing has ceased.

Their apparent preference for a lowland habitat is illustrated in Table 5.67. The species is traditionally less common on higher ground in the north, south and east of the county.

By the early 1990s the population had declined considerably even in more favoured areas. The only place in the county to which they were returning annually was the BBONT Nature Reserve at Otmoor where about nine pairs bred in the ancient hedgerows. Each spring a few pairs breed in suitable woodland and hedgerow sites scattered throughout the county, but rarely reappear the following season.

In the early years of bird recording in the county, Nightingales were undoubtedly more common than at present, although numbers fluctuated from year to year. In 1886, Warde Fowler even writes of hearing their song in Holywell Meadows and elsewhere in Oxford.

Their progress in the first half of the twentieth century is not well documented, but the general

impression is of a gradual decline (OOS Report 1930). Since then there has been a continued reduction. A count of singing males in 1965 in an area around Oxford, organized by the OOS as part of a programme to revive interest in field studies, achieved a total of 42 singing males. In the same year a BOS survey produced 17 singing males (most in Oxfordshire). The 1976 BTO survey attracted more support, but despite its more comprehensive nature the county could only produce a total of 55 singing males, which was 1.7% of the national total. A repeat survey in 1980 (Davis 1982) showed an improvement with 79 singing males noted. This was again 1.7% of the national figure showing how local changes were representative of the national trend. However this was only a temporary respite as the downward pattern was resumed in the 1980s. The BOS found them present in eight 10 km squares in 1965, but only one in 1985–1987. Despite considerable fieldwork effort for the Oxfordshire Atlas survey, breeding was confirmed in only 0.9% of tetrads, and probable breeding in 4.8%.

One local reason for the decline is habitat change. In the mid-1950s the OOS organised annual summer visits to the B4027 between the Woodeaton and Beckley turns alongside which an assart hedge about 25 m wide and 1 km long was the regular home for at least 12 pairs. In the early 1960s this hedge was grubbed up to enable arable fields to be extended and the Nightingales were lost. Several other formerly popular sites were destroyed in a similar manner.

Changes in woodland management practice such as the ending of coppicing have also caused problems. A critical requirement for breeding is a dense ground and shrub layer which is only achieved in well managed (and especially coppiced) woodland. For example, in a conifer plantation in Holton Wood in the 1970s the population of breeding Nightingales peaked at six pairs, but declined when the trees exceeded 5 m in height and their shade reduced the ground cover.

Gosler (1990) has traced the fortunes of this species at Wytham Wood. He considers it was present at low densities until the outbreak of *Myxomatosis* in the 1950s. The virtual disappearance of Rabbits led to the growth of extensive scrub and thicket formation producing suitable conditions for Nightingales. Thus in 1958–1962 there were about 20–30 singing males present annually. In 1978, 13 pairs were still present, but since then there has been a steady decline, with no breeding reported in 1985–1990. Gosler suggests that the probable reason for the latter change is the increase in the Fallow and Muntjac Deer populations in Wytham which have severely damaged the shrub layer of the wood.

If serious measures are taken to control deer and to reverse the pattern of habitat destruction that has become so widespread in Oxfordshire, there is some prospect that Nightingales could return to their former strength in our county.

BLUETHROAT
Luscinia svecica

A very rare vagrant. An adult male was seen in the Cherwell valley in north Oxfordshire on 21 September 1980. A male of the red-spotted race was killed by a cat in a garden in Hamilton Road, north Oxford on the surprising date of 11 February 1986.

BLACK REDSTART
Phoenicurus ochruros

A passage visitor in small numbers, and an occasional wintering bird. The Black Redstart has appeared at a wide range of sites, but is mostly seen near industrial sites or in gardens.

Little is known about its migration, but it is assumed that these are drift migrants from northern and central Europe moving to and from winter quarters in the Mediterranean (Langslow 1977). Their susceptibility to changing weather patterns is presumably responsible for the erratic nature of their visits to us. The main movements through the county are March to April and October to November, although the exact timing varies (Figure 5.64).

Radford (1966) called the Black Redstart "a rare visitor" for it had been found no more than about ten times before 1950. In the 1950s a few began to appear in most years, and there were even records in May, such as the male singing on the Bodleian Library in 1958, which raised hopes of the species joining our list of breeding birds. The number of sightings has continued to increase. In the period 1964–1988 it was noted annually except in 1986.

Most records are of single birds, but small parties of up to three have been noted at Cote in April, Cholsey in March, and Farmoor in April and October. On three occasions individuals stayed for periods in the winter: at Didcot from late December 1968 until February 1969, at Crowmarsh in January and February 1983, and at Thame from January to March 1984. Breeding in the county remains unproven, although the sound of one singing at Didcot Power Station on 18 May 1985 raised expectations again. Such a place, or the buildings in some gravel pit or quarry, might offer a suitable habitat should the British breeding population ever extend from its present mainly coastal distribution.

REDSTART
Phoenicurus phoenicurus

A passage migrant in small numbers, today the Redstart rarely breeds in the county's mature Oak woodlands.

The spring passage is brief, usually confined to a few days in mid-April. Most records are of males, a few of which may stay for a while in potential breeding areas. Autumn migration is a more leisurely affair. From August to October usually singles, but sometimes small parties of up to four birds, appear in hedgerow and woodland edge habitats in a wide range of locations. These include exposed hedgerows on the Berkshire Downs or in the centre of Otmoor. There have also been a few records from gardens.

The local population has probably never been at such a low level as at present, although the Redstart has always had an uncertain place in the county. Few species have shown such obvious fluctuations. Warde Fowler (1886) notes this, commenting: "Four or five years ago they were getting quite rare: but this year the flicker of the red tail is to be seen all along the Cherwell, in the Broad Walk, where they build in holes in elms, in Port Meadow, where I have heard the gentle warbling song from telegraph wires, and doubtless in most gardens". Writing again in 1913 he suggested that, "When as in recent years, the numbers are below average, they go on to those breeding grounds which really suit them best — the woods and hills of Wales and the North".

In 1930 and 1935 when Redstarts were the subjects of a 'special investigation' by the OOS they were considered to be decreasing. Most were found near rivers around Oxford, at Otmoor and Wytham, but they were "far from common" in Wychwood.

Attention was next paid to the Redstart in 1963 when the OOS and the BOS combined to survey its breeding distribution. The results showed clearly that breeding was confined to two distinct habitats — streams and rivers where they nested in pollarded willows and woods and parks where they nested in old timber, drystone walls and occasionally in nestboxes. Although some counters thought numbers were down a little compared with previous years, the final tally was of what today would be an impressive total of 73 breeding pairs. Of these, 40 were near streams and the rest in woodland. The survey was fairly comprehensive, but not all

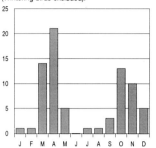

Figure 5.64. Black Redstart.
Monthly distribution of records 1964-1988 (Wintering birds excluded).

likely places were searched. For this reason, and as others were probably missed because of the elusive nature of the species for much of the breeding season, the count must be regarded as a minimum, and the real number may have been much higher.

Since then there has been a steady withdrawal from the county and it is now a scarce breeder. It was evident that the pollard willow nesters left first, suggesting that this was the less favoured of the two main habitat types. In his study area of the Thame valley from Shabbington to Cuddesdon Brook, Brucker found a reduction from 11 pairs in 1963 to three pairs in 1969, one pair in 1975 and none since. Meanwhile at his CBC plot in Wytham Woods, Overall found the final disappearance of the species was not until the late 1980s. In 1980 there were six to nine singing males in the wood, and 13 juveniles were ringed. The last confirmed breeding in the BOS area was in 1983. In the four years of the Oxfordshire Atlas survey there was only one record of confirmed breeding and that for one year only.

The BOS surveyed this species again in 1989. All good Redstart habitat was searched, but no breeding pairs were located and there were only a few records of passage birds and unattached males.

Reasons for the decline in our Redstart population seem more likely to be connected with problems experienced in the winter or on migration for there have been no obvious changes in the availability of breeding opportunities in Oxfordshire. Many woodlands and parks where they formerly bred remain much as they were 25 years ago, and there are relatively undisturbed stretches of the former riparian habitat. The 1963 BOS survey showed that in all nest sites in river valleys the immediate general habitat was grazed pasture, but although there has been a reduction in this habitat type, it is by no means absent. Thus it is not impossible that the species might re-establish itself here if its fortunes elsewhere improved.

WHINCHAT
Saxicola rubetra

The Whinchat is a summer visitor to Britain and occurs in Oxfordshire as a passage migrant and scarce summer visitor. The first sighting in spring in the county will usually be of three or four birds, sometimes more making sallies from a fence post or wire to pick up an insect from the ground or in mid-air. Rough grassy areas with low bushes, tall weeds or fences to provide feeding and song perches are the preferred habitat for Whinchats. Various marginal areas such as commons, wet meadows, railway banks, parts of the Downs and gravel pits can provide suitable habitats. However, the overall extent of these areas has been reduced considerably in Oxfordshire during the last 40 years as a consequence of agricultural intensification. This

has been linked with the decline of Whinchats in the south-east (Parslow 1973, Sharrock 1976), although it may not be the only cause. In many upland areas of Britain the population has, in fact, increased due to the extensive planting of conifers since four- and five-year-old plantations have proved particularly attractive to Whinchats (Phillips 1973).

Small parties pass through, mostly between mid-April and mid-May although there are variations from year to year (e.g. in 1983 the passage period was from 16 April to 6 May, while in 1965 it was from 2 May to 20 May). Whinchats often associate with Wheatears on migration through the county and will be gone by the next day. The birds apparently move through very quickly; for example, arrival dates in breeding areas in Ayrshire are between 25 April and 10 May (Gray 1974). In autumn, the passage is more extended – from the last week of July until mid-October.

Spring totals between 1960 and 1980 (where quoted in the reports) averaged 15 birds/year, ranging from 5–37 with a maximum of nine in one party. Autumn numbers over the same period averaged 33 per year (range, 5–64), with a maximum party of 15. Presumably, autumn passage is augmented by birds of the year; some groups appear to be family parties.

Although the Whinchat is typically a northern and western breeding species in Britain a few pairs do stay to nest in southern and eastern England. While Aplin (1889) regarded its breeding status as "very common in some seasons" a gradual decline reduced it in the mid-twentieth century to Radford's (1966) description as, "a former regular summer visitor now becoming rare". The reduction has continued with fewer pairs nesting annually from 1961 to 1975, and then a total of about ten pairs nesting from 1976–1989. In the *National Atlas* survey breeding was proved in three 10 km squares, while, in contrast, the Oxfordshire Atlas survey produced only one confirmed record.

Like the Stonechat and Wheatear, the Whinchat has been decreasing in Oxfordshire over much of the twentieth century at least partly as a result of the loss of suitable rough and wild areas in which to breed. Maybe the policy of 'set-aside' land introduced by the European Community to reduce the present agricultural over-production will aid this species. If so, with informed management, suitable marginal land could be re-created which might entice more of these attractive birds back into Oxfordshire.

STONECHAT
Saxicola torquata

The Stonechat is an occasional passage migrant and winter visitor to Oxfordshire and although it has bred in the past, these occasions have been infrequent. Indeed, the species has probably bred fewer than ten times since 1960. The last proved breeding was in 1978 with a possible record in 1979. Stonechats were not recorded at all during the Oxfordshire Atlas survey.

In the nineteenth century the Stonechat (illustrated below) was described as a scarce resident or winter visitor (Clark-Kennedy 1868, Aplin 1892–1915). Radford (1966) classified it as a "former resident, now a scarce winter visitor and passage migrant", indeed as it is today.

During the 1960s, records of winter and passage (late September to early May) birds in Oxfordshire were few. However, from 1968 when, perhaps, the Stonechat population had recovered from the severe winters of 1961/62 and 1962/63, there followed a period of relative abundance up to 1980. For instance, records reached 25–30 in 1972 and 47 'bird-days' in November 1976. Following the severe weather of the 1981/82 winter, Stonechat records fell again to between four and 11 per year with none at all in 1984.

Stonechats are primarily birds of coastal and near-coastal distribution in Britain with local concentrations inland on southern heaths and other areas where gorse or heather are present (Sharrock 1976). When they do occur in Oxfordshire they may appear in areas with scrub, rough grass and weeds such as Otmoor, the surroundings of Farmoor Reservoir, sewage works and the Downs.

Nationally the summer and winter distributions are broadly similar, the main difference being the desertion of nesting areas on high ground. It may be that these are the birds that are found widely scattered inland as far as Oxfordshire during the winter (Lack 1986). These may also be augmented by any surplus individuals produced after a series of good breeding seasons.

Two main factors affect Stonechat populations in Britain, as a whole (Magee 1965). The first, short-term one is severe winter weather, to which they are very sensitive since they feed on the ground, mainly on insects. However, Stonechats are often triple-brooded and have been shown to recover their numbers within three years after a severe winter (Phillips and Greig-Smith 1980). The second, and more serious threat in the long-term is the destruction of heathland and other suitable habitat. Aplin (1889) stated that "rather high ground, more or less covered with gorse or juniper bushes seems essential to it in the nesting season". Such places are practically non-existent in Oxfordshire

now. Thus, it may be that instead of the expected revival of occurrences after a series of mild winters the Stonechat will remain a rare and occasional visitor to Oxfordshire.

WHEATEAR
Oenanthe oenanthe

The Wheatear occurs in Oxfordshire as a very frequent passage migrant but a rare breeding bird. In the nineteenth century, small numbers were reported to have bred (Clark-Kennedy 1868, Aplin 1889), mainly on the Chilterns and the Downs and occasionally in the Cotswolds. A survey of the species by the OOS in 1931 found them still breeding on the western slopes of the Chilterns and along the Downs. Breeding ceased to be annual in the early 1950s, there being only three records between 1953 and 1966 (Radford 1966) and one in 1967. The National Atlas (Sharrock 1976) shows proven breeding in four 10 km squares, probable in three and possible breeding in six (Figure 5.65). The Oxfordshire Atlas obtained evidence of confirmed breeding in one tetrad, probable in two and possible in ten (Figure 5.66). Although both of the probable records were of birds prospecting likely nest holes and which remained in the area for more than a week, no further sightings were made. It is believed that these, along with the eight other records, were of passage birds.

The decline has been due to a combination of factors. The reduction of grazing on the hills during the agricultural depression of the 1920s and 1930s allowed scrub formation across large areas. Increased ploughing on the Downs has led to the loss of typical grassland habitat and a reduction in the number of Rabbits (by *myxomatosis*) to keep the remaining turf close-cropped has also been instrumental. Rabbits are additionally important since old burrows are a favoured nest site, particularly in the absence of natural rock crevices or drystone walls (Marchant *et al.* 1990).

The Wheatear is most evident in Oxfordshire as a passage migrant and is one of the first summer visitors to arrive. The first arrivals are usually in the third week of March which makes the arrival date for 1977 of 4 March extremely early. Passage may be a protracted affair with scattered occurrences usually continuing until the second or third week of May. Birds passing

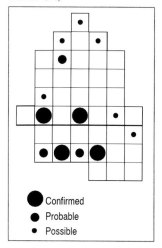

Figure 5.65. Wheatear.
Breeding distribution 1968-1972 (after Sharrock 1976).

● Confirmed
● Probable
• Possible

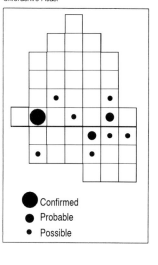

Figure 5.66. Wheatear.
Breeding distribution 1985-1988, results of Oxfordshire Atlas.

● Confirmed
● Probable
• Possible

Table 5.68. Ring Ouzel.
Distribution of Spring records by five-day periods 1960-1989.

Five-day period commencing	No. of records
16 March	1
21 March	1
26 March	3
31 March	4
5 April	9
10 April	9
15 April	14
20 April	13
25 April	4
30 April	8
5 May	1
10 May	0
15 May	0
20 May	0
25 May	1

Table 5.69. Ring Ouzel.
Distribution of Autumn records by five-day periods 1960-1989.

Five-day period commencing	No. of records
25 September	1
30 September	2
5 October	3
10 October	7
15 October	6
20 October	2
25 October	2
30 October	0
4 November	2

through the county in March and April are usually of the nominate race *O.o. oenanthe*, whereas many of the May arrivals are now recognised as belonging to the larger and brighter plumaged Greenland race, *O.o. leucorrhoa*. From mid-April, Wheatears are frequently accompanied by Whinchats, apparently migrating with them. Wheatears are regular at certain sites in both spring and autumn. For example, they can be expected with certainty on the concrete banks of Farmoor Reservoir, the disused runways of Oxford Airport and on the Downs near Harwell.

Return migration is usually first noted in mid-July and consists of singles, or small groups of up to five birds. Occasionally larger parties are noted (e.g. 50+ at Stanton Harcourt on 17 August 1982). Passage usually continues until October but a particularly late record was of a bird seen on 28 November 1970 at Wootton, Woodstock. Both the spring and autumn passages normally produce reports of a total number of 40-100 birds.

There is one ringing recovery: a bird ringed on 30 August 1970 at Gibraltar Point, Lincolnshire, was found (dead) at Wantage on 26 March 1972.

The Wheatear in Oxfordshire appears likely to remain as a passage migrant since it is primarily a nesting species in western and northern Britain. It would need major changes in farming practice to make more suitable habitat available once more although the dramatic expansion in the Rabbit population in the early 1990s could encourage their return.

BLACK-EARED WHEATEAR
Oenanthe hispanica

A very rare vagrant to Britain. One was seen at King's Lock on the Thames above Oxford on 16 April 1953.

RING OUZEL
Turdus torquatus

The Ring Ouzel is a summer visitor to Britain breeding in upland situations and does not nest south-east of a line from the Severn to the Humber (Sharrock 1976). In Oxfordshire it is therefore only a passage migrant. Numbers reported annually since 1960 have varied from 0-14, with a mean of three per year. In the 60 years before 1945, only 14 had been recorded, fewer than one in four years (Alexander, 1947). The improvement is almost certainly due to the increase in the number of observers, especially at favoured sites. For example, a series of records from the Aston Rowant National Nature Reserve between 1974 and 1979 were from a single resident observer.

Ring Ouzels like short grass where they can feed during migration. Toynton (1975), stated that for Aston Rowant National Nature Reserve, "In spring and autumn, Ring Ouzels and Wheatears use the open grassland on passage, sometimes stopping for several days... ". Hence the Chilterns and the Downs are favourite locations (50% of records) although such habitat is now much rarer as a result of the reduction in the number of sheep and Rabbits. The escarpment of the Chilterns and Downs is used by some species as a migration flight-path, which may also account for the concentration of records. It certainly provides suitable feeding habitat where the steep slopes cannot be cultivated and the thin soil keeps the grass naturally short. Ring Ouzels may also appear almost anywhere in the county, and the frequency of records in the Oxford and Banbury areas presumably reflects the distribution of observers.

The first arrivals in spring are from the second half of March and birds are seen up to mid-May, but the peak passage is in the second half of April (Table 5.68). Autumn migration is less protracted, peaking in mid-October (Table 5.69). Since 1960, 80% of records have been in spring, although the difficulty of identification of females and juveniles in autumn no doubt accounts for much of this difference.

BLACKBIRD
Turdus merula

Although familiar as an abundant resident in the county, the Blackbird occurs as a passage migrant and winter visitor. Its extensive distribution was highlighted during the Oxfordshire Atlas when, as might be expected, Blackbirds were found in virtually all tetrads, with breeding proved or probable in 99.5% of them.

Although the Blackbird was originally a woodland, and especially a woodland-edge species, it has proved adaptable and has extended into its range all types of habitats found in Oxfordshire. This includes the centres of towns, wherever a little green area and some cover are

Table 5.70. Blackbird.
Foreign recoveries of birds ringed in Oxfordshire.

Country	No. of recoveries
Ireland	1
France	3
Sweden	5
Finland	3
Denmark	2
Netherlands	4
Germany	7

present. Dependence on earthworms as a major food source and a readiness to take food provided directly or indirectly by man are major factors. This adaptation has been so extensive that Blackbirds often nest at higher density in suburban gardens than in woodland (Simms 1971, Sharrock 1976).

Snow (1958), in his detailed studies of 59 pairs of Blackbirds in the Oxford Botanic Gardens between 1953 and 1956 showed that the population density there was 5.0–7.3 pairs/ha (500–730/km²). This population level was at saturation and remained stable from year to year. The excess of young birds did not disperse before trying to settle into territories. His parallel studies in the University Parks showed a similar stability at a lower level of 1.2 pairs/ha. The population at Wytham Woods which Snow also studied was much more variable with only about a tenth of the population density of the Botanic Gardens. Gosler (1990) suggests a figure of about 0.3–1.0 pairs/ha in Wytham which would indicate an increase since Snow's study, possibly due to habitat change caused by deer browsing.

Snow (1958) and Snow and Mayer-Gross (1967) also showed that the highest nesting success (percentage of nests producing at least one young) occurs in gardens: 50% compared with only 12–14% in woodland and 28% in farmland. One of the suggested reasons for this was the effect of rodent predation in woodland. The main predator of nests in the Botanic Gardens was the Carrion Crow with Jackdaw, Magpie and Jay also suspected. Tawny Owls were thought to be the main predators of adults. Conversely, fledging success (young fledged as a percentage of eggs laid, excluding total failures) was highest in woodland compared with urban gardens. This was attributed to the increased difficulty of finding earthworms in dry conditions whilst trees provide an abundance of defoliating caterpillars when food demand is at its maximum. The ground also remains moister in the shade of a wood.

Most British Blackbirds are sedentary. Werth showed that 93% of ringing recoveries of British bred Blackbirds were recovered within 8 km of their birth place and 72% "where ringed" (Snow 1966). Those individuals which do move mostly go west or south-west within Britain or south to France. (There have been three recoveries in France from Oxfordshire since 1960 but all were ringed in late autumn so could have been continental birds.)

In late September the Oxfordshire population of Blackbirds is swollen by the arrival of birds from the Continent as in other parts of England (Snow 1966). The number of arrivals builds up to a peak in mid-October; other influxes may occur up to the end of the year. Many remain but a few move on into northern France. These probably originate in the Netherlands, Denmark and northern Germany (Spencer 1975). Those arrivals which stay with us originate in the Low Countries, north-west Germany, Denmark, Sweden and, increasingly, Finland (Spencer 1975, Goodacre 1959). Until the 1940s the Blackbird was a rare breeding species in Finland and the first ringing recovery of a Finnish bird was in 1958. The first Oxfordshire-ringed bird to be recovered in Finland was ringed on New Year's Day 1969 and recovered three months later; other records were in 1979 and 1980 (Table 5.70).

During his studies at the Botanic Gardens Snow (1958) observed the feeding habits of Blackbirds at Christchurch Meadows through autumn and winter. These gave a clear indication of how they moved between four major habitats (leaf litter, haws, lawns and rough grass). As haws, contributing 60% of records in October gradually declined to the end of the year, rough grass increased in importance through to February. Leaf litter, at 35% decreased more steadily to about 10% importance in February while lawns, from being insignificant in October passed through a peak in January to being of little importance by February. The Botanic Garden birds managed to survive throughout the year in the neighbourhood. The only time there was any movement away was during exceptionally cold weather, when some moved into local back gardens for scraps.

Such an adaptable and successful bird as the Blackbird should have no difficulty in holding its own, even with all the pressures of modern development and agriculture.

FIELDFARE
Turdus pilaris

Fieldfares are very frequent winter visitors to Oxfordshire and are, perhaps, most familiar to us when they first arrive in the autumn, flying over in loose flocks. Their 'chack-chack' call often draws our attention to them.

The Fieldfare (illustrated below with Redwing) has never been shown to nest in Oxfordshire but it was first proved in Britain in 1967 in Orkney, reaching as far south as Derbyshire in 1969 (Sharrock 1976). However, this expansion was not maintained (Spencer 1989). A number of summer records have occurred in Oxfordshire: one in Cholsey, ringed by W.D. Campbell in June 1969 was still present in July and 13 August, a moulting bird was present at Steeple Aston 12-14 June 1973, one at Eynsham 8 July 1978; one at Ewelme 29 May and two at Shilton Down Farm 4 July 1988.

The main arrival is usually during the second half of October and early November although this depends on the Rowan berry crop in Scandinavia (Lack 1986, Tyrvainen 1975). A few may arrive in September or even earlier, but some very early reports may arise from confusion with flocks of Mistle Thrushes. Some must pass southwards, as Fieldfares occur throughout southern Europe (Lack 1986). One bird, ringed in Oxfordshire, was recovered in Italy during the winter.

Return migration often starts at the beginning of February but birds are usually passing through up to the end of April or occasionally even into early May. That our Fieldfares are from the Scandinavian breeding population is confirmed by ringing recoveries. Of six birds ringed in Oxfordshire and recovered during the breeding season two were found in each of Norway, Sweden and Finland (five in June, one at the end of April).

Those Fieldfares which stay in Oxfordshire descend on the hedgerows in noisy flocks, stripping the berries. They will also feed on the ground, on invertebrates, for example in pastures and on stubble fields. They are nervous, especially compared with Redwings with which they often associate and will often fly up into neighbouring hedges and trees, gradually dropping down again to resume feeding. These flocks can number up to several thousands, for example 3,000 in the Thame valley on 11 November 1970, 10,000 at Somerton on 27 February 1978, three-quarters of a flock of 2,500 (the rest were Redwings) at Grove Park on 24 January 1988. Aplin (1889) noted the same pattern of occurrence but also that in late winter in those days, many hundreds were shot for game-dealers.

Large numbers of Fieldfares also occur at roosts in woods, hedgerows or even on open ground. A notable concentration was of 10,000 roosting at Waterperry Wood during December 1977.

As the berry supply is exhausted, the birds move on westwards and southwards. The timing will depend on the heaviness of the berry crop and the weather. Consequently, numbers and locations of birds will be variable from year to year — they are essentially nomadic. In very hard weather, when the berries are finished and the ground is frozen most will leave. It is only at this time that Fieldfares will venture into towns and gardens, especially if apples are put out for them. Here, an individual may dominate a food supply, driving off all other species. They will also feed on windfalls in orchards. They were found in gardens almost exclusively in January 1982, February 1986 (including feeding stations in central Oxford as well as over 2,000 on fallen apples in Kingston Bagpuize orchards) and early 1987.

The reversal of the trend towards the colonisation of Britain may mean that we are unlikely to witness the nesting of the Fieldfare in Oxfordshire in the foreseeable future. So, it will be as autumn arrivals and winter visitors that Fieldfares will remain most familiar to us and be a characteristic reminder of the winter to come.

SONG THRUSH
Turdus philomelos

The Song Thrush is a familiar resident in Oxfordshire, but is also a very frequent passage migrant and winter visitor. Like the Blackbird, the Song Thrush is a woodland and woodland-edge species which has adapted to hedgerows, any areas with trees and bushes and, especially, gardens where it is a common and familiar bird. Song Thrushes nest in a wide variety of situations but are particularly noticeable in gardens. The species is not now as common as the Blackbird but it might still be expected that all Oxfordshire tetrads should hold some. However, Song Thrushes were recorded in less than 90% of Oxfordshire tetrads placing them twentieth in the list of most widely distributed species.

Ford (1987) found that Song Thrushes bred at higher densities in small woodlands in Oxfordshire (mean of 0.14 birds/ha) as in woodland plots of similar size within larger woods (0.04 birds/ha). This probably reflects

an edge-effect in that there might be more nest sites for Song Thrushes near the edge of woods. It might also reflect the fact that birds in small woods can include pasture in the territory in which to feed.

Although Song Thrushes are present throughout the year, the composition of the winter population is more complex than it might appear. The proportion of our breeding population which is migratory is higher than that of the Blackbird. Many move to south-west England or Wales but some continue on to north and west France (Lack 1986). Of 12 Oxfordshire-ringed birds recovered in France and the Channel Islands at least four were of locally-bred birds. The local birds which do migrate appear to move away in September (e.g. OOS Reports 1979, 1985), with more juveniles than adults leaving (Lack 1986).

After the local juveniles have left in September there are influxes from the Continent, especially from mid-October to November, often associated with other thrush species. Song is resumed, if the weather is suitable – this is often a reaction by the residents, intent on holding their territories. The immigrants, from Belgium and the Netherlands are racially the same as our own, and some stay with us for the winter (Lack 1986, Goodacre 1960).

Song Thrushes are also subject to hard-weather movements, especially when berries are in short supply, and freezing conditions make their main winter diet of earthworms and snails inaccessible. A large proportion of the population may then leave as shown by ringing recoveries (Radford 1966). Only garden birds remain, surviving on food put out for them. They eat more animal matter (75%) than Blackbirds and rely heavily on snails, both in winter and high summer when earthworms are less available (Crowley 1976). For this reason they are more susceptible than Blackbirds to both cold winters and summer droughts.

Although the breeding season lasts from March to August, during which up to four broods may be reared, Oxfordshire CBC plots (e.g. Wytham, Table 5.71) show that Song Thrushes have declined significantly during recent years. CBC results show that this is part of a national trend which began in the mid-1970s. Reasons for this are not clear, but cold winters, a reduction in the number of snails and an increase in the autumn sowing of cereals (reducing the extent of spring tillage, an important source of food at that time) have all been suggested. (Marchant et al. 1990). The answer could well be a combination of these, or other factors.

Because of its adaptability and its adoption of our gardens as a habitat, the Song Thrush should remain a familiar part of our bird-life. Apart from late summer and early autumn the male's song is an integral part of our environment. On many winter's days, unless the weather is particularly bad he can be heard, free from competition from other songsters, bringing a breath of spring to come.

REDWING
Turdus iliacus

The Redwing (illustrated with Fieldfare) is a common winter visitor and very frequent passage migrant. The first birds usually arrive in Oxfordshire at the end of September or early October, occasionally earlier in September. The main arrivals occur during the latter half of October and into early November, when they may come in their thousands. They can often be heard flying over at night, when their continual high 'seep' contact call can often be heard.

Many must pass over but hundreds come down to feed on haws in the hedgerows with Fieldfares and other thrushes. When haws are in short supply they will turn to other berries. For example, in 1962 thousands were feeding on Yews at Watlington Hill and in 1987 on Whitebeam on the Chilterns. Later, when the berries are finished they move to the fields to feed on earthworms and other invertebrates, again often with other thrushes.

Prolonged severe weather will cause the Redwings to move out of Oxfordshire altogether and high mortality can occur. A bird ringed at Cholsey in December of the exceptionally severe winter of 1962/63 was found dead six weeks later in Plymouth, Devon. Similarly, another, ringed at Horton-cum-Studley in November 1985 was found dead at Paignton, Devon, the following March, after an extremely cold February.

Foreign ringing recoveries are widely scattered (Table 5.72). Records from Murmansk in Russian Lapland, near Minsk in Byelorussia and in Finland were in the breeding season. The rest are winter recoveries: six to south-west France and one just over the border into Spain (Santander). The last was ringed at Wykham,

Table 5.71. Song Thrush.
Mean population density in Wytham Woods by four-year periods, calculated as pairs/km² from a 6.7 ha CBC plot on the hilltop (after Overall 1988).

Period	Mean per year
1971-74	67.2
1975-78	44.8
1979-82	22.4
1983-86	29.8
1987-90	14.9

Table 5.72. Redwing.
Foreign recoveries of birds ringed in Oxfordshire.

Country	No. of recoveries
Finland	1
USSR	3
Belgium	1
France	7
Spain	1

Banbury in December 1979 and recovered two winters later. Redwings may change wintering areas from year to year, as in the above example (Lack 1986). An extreme example of this behaviour was of a Redwing ringed at Wytham in December 1962 being recovered two years later in Georgia, USSR. These two wintering areas are 3,440 km apart. Of the 13 foreign ringing recoveries, at least ten were reported "shot, or killed by man" which includes all those from the notorious south of France (and the one from Spain).

Redwings are more nomadic than Fieldfares and wander according to the available food supply. They are also more susceptible to hard weather. Under these conditions they will readily come into gardens and even into the centre of Oxford, where tame individuals were found in February 1986. Piles of rotting apples in orchards are also an attraction, as in January 1985 when over 500 were feeding at Kingston Bagpuize. Some of the birds also move into woodland and feed in the leaf litter in the manner of Blackbirds (Lack 1986).

Redwings roost communally, sometimes in company with Fieldfares and roosts can reach very high numbers, for example 10,000 with Fieldfares at Wytham in 1962, over 1,000 at Little Wittenham and Woodcote in 1979 and several sites with over 1,000 in 1983.

Return migration begins in March and most Redwings are gone by mid-April although a few may linger on until May in some years. They often gather in pre-migratory flocks and at this time one is sometimes privileged to hear them singing their sweet, twittering song, in chorus.

MISTLE THRUSH
Turdus viscivorus

An abundant resident, what we now know as the Mistle Thrush, Aplin (1889) called the Mistletoe-thrush. He also quoted the local Oxfordshire name of 'Norman Gizer' which, he suggested could come from the French 'Gui' — Mistletoe. Although Mistletoe is not sufficiently common in most areas of Britain to be a significant food-source today, the bird's name suggests that it may have been in the past. Alternatively, the name may have been a direct import from France where mistletoe is certainly very common in many parts.

Earlier authors described the Mistle Thrush as a common resident (Aplin 1889, Radford 1966) but it has not always been so. Before the nineteenth century it had been strictly a woodland species and rarely came near human habitation. From the early 1900s it began a widespread expansion, both in habitat and range, colonising parks and gardens and expanding northwards into Scotland and Ireland. A parallel expansion occurred on the Continent. No explanation has been found for this expansion, but the Mistle Thrush seems to have filled a vacant niche.

The Mistle Thrush's habit of nesting in the main forks of bare trees, even in the centre of Oxford, makes it easily observed in early spring. It is a large, aggressive thrush and will defend its nest vigorously against predators such as Magpies and cats; its rattling calls make it conspicuous, even later in the breeding season. Although two broods are common it is the first nest which is most noticed, as the species is an early nester, usually sitting on eggs well before the end of March. These details made it readily recorded by Atlas fieldworkers.

The Oxfordshire Atlas recorded the Mistle Thrush in 80% of tetrads. Nevertheless, the gaps in the north-east and south-west of the county could reflect less thorough coverage. Ford (1987) found that the occurrence of Mistle Thrushes breeding in woodland in Oxfordshire did not depend on the size of that wood. This is because they feed mostly in pasture outside the wood and may fly considerable distances to do so when feeding young (e.g. Wytham, Gosler 1990).

By late summer, flocks begin to form. Those in June and July are probably feeding flocks made up of family parties, for example 50+ feeding on Cherries at Boar's Hill on 20 July 1978. An unusually large flock was of 96 at Wychwood on 1 September 1988, after a particularly good breeding season.

Ringing recoveries elsewhere in Britain have shown that Mistle Thrushes which do migrate are all juveniles and those recovered abroad move between more or less southwards into France (Snow 1969). This presumably applies to Oxfordshire, but of 29 recoveries of Oxfordshire-ringed birds 25 were still within the county and 25 (not necessarily the same) were less than 9 km from their ringing site. The other four had moved less than 99 km. There have been no recoveries abroad. Although many authors have suggested that our winter population is augmented by immigrants from

the Continent (Aplin 1889, Alexander 1952, Radford 1966), there is no evidence from ringing that this is the case, not only in Oxfordshire, but in Britain as a whole.

By November the flocks break up or move away and individuals or pairs begin defending fruiting trees and shrubs, especially Holly, Hawthorn and Buckthorn (Snow and Snow 1984). These food sources are usually isolated trees near to open feeding areas where the Mistle Thrushes will feed when the weather allows. The berry supplies will be defended, without necessarily being eaten straight away. In some years, the Holly and Yew trees in the University Parks have rung in winter to the rattling calls of Mistle Thrushes! When ground feeding is impossible during frost or snow or is less productive in late winter the birds will have a supply of berries to exploit. In very hard winters recently, when berry stocks elsewhere were depleted Mistle Thrushes have moved into quite small gardens to take control of *Pyracantha* or *Cotoneaster* bushes.

The Mistle Thrush may be one of our birds which, far from decreasing, as we have to report for many species, has an assured future with us as long as we have parks and gardens with their accompanying playing fields, lawns, and berry-bearing shrubs and trees. The 'Stormcock' singing from the top of a large tree during a gale should remain a familiar sight and sound to us in the foreseeable future.

Family: Sylviidae
Warblers

This large family of chiefly insectivorous birds is well represented in Oxfordshire with 18 species recorded this century. Furthermore, 17 of these have occurred since 1980. Of these, ten are principally regular summer visitors to the county although one occurs occasionally in winter and another is also a regular winter visitor. Three others are resident, of which one is abundant and also occurs as a winter visitor. Three others have occurred as vagrants to the county. The different warbler species have specific habitat requirements and many are important indicators of habitat quality in the county.

CETTI'S WARBLER
Cettia cetti

A very rare resident. The appearance of this species was anticipated as its population spread from southern Britain. It reached Berkshire in 1971. The first Oxfordshire record came on 12 March 1989 when one was heard singing in a reedbed in the south-east of the county. On the following days a second silent bird was observed and the possibility of breeding arose, but the birds were not seen after 25 March. In October a female was ringed at another site about 2 km away, then a male was ringed at the original site. The latter bird stayed in the area until early February 1990. In the spring of 1990 singing males were heard at two more sites near the Thames in mid-Oxfordshire, and breeding proved at one. A singing bird was heard at one of these sites again in March 1991.

Although Oxfordshire possesses a limited amount of suitable habitat, there is hope that the Cetti's Warbler may become a regular breeding bird in the future. Winter weather conditions appear to influence its progress and it is worth noting that the winters of 1988/89 and 1989/90 were exceptionally mild, but it is encouraging that at least one pair in the county survived the extremely cold period of January/February 1991. Although the drab colouration and skulking behaviour of the Cetti's Warbler make it inconspicuous at certain times of the year, its explosive song should ensure that any range expansion will not be missed.

GRASSHOPPER WARBLER
Locustella naevia

A summer visitor, the distribution of the Grasshopper Warbler (illustrated below) in Oxfordshire is very local. Traditionally, the species was thought to inhabit low, marshy sites with a ground cover of rank grasses and sedges and dotted with small bushes which serve as song-posts. Otmoor is typical of this type of habitat and remains one of the major strongholds for the species in the county with more than ten reeling males in some years. Other suitable habitats include gorse-clad commons, downland scrub, overgrown hedgerows and disused railway lines. Perhaps the most significant development has been the bird's willingness to occupy young forestry plantations. The coarse grasses growing between the trees (mostly conifers) offer ideal nesting sites. A survey by the BOS in 1969, illustrated this point and demonstrated the value of these plantations, especially in largely agricultural districts where there may otherwise be little alternative terrain. In a study of ten 10 km squares, eight of them either wholly or partly in Oxfordshire, 74 pairs were located in four distinct habitat types (Table 5.73).

The BOS survey also showed that there is an optimum period when plantations are most suitable. Of the 24 territories where the age of the trees were specified, it was discovered that 75% were in plantations of between five and eight years old and where the trees had attained a height of 1.5–2.5 m. However, the practice of

felling trees in blocks means that as they are replanted they offer a succession of suitable sites.

The Oxfordshire Atlas obtained evidence for confirmed or probable breeding in 62 (8.2%) tetrads, with a presence noted in a further 11 squares. It is likely that a number of pairs occupy plantations on private estates and farmland not easily open to census so the picture may be understated. The Oxford district, with its numerous waterways, the more traditional type of nesting habitat described above, probably holds more pairs than the habitats utilised in the north of the county.

Assessing the Grasshopper Warbler's status in Oxfordshire, Aplin (1889) described it as of very local distribution. Jourdain (1926) reiterated this, although Radford (1966) suggested that there were indications of an increase in the 1960s. Further evidence for an increase in the 1960s was given by Gosler (1990) who suggested that on the Wytham Estate the species might have benefited from the reduction in Rabbit grazing caused by the introduction of Myxomatosis in the 1950s. A. Brownett noted 13 singing males there in 1965. National CBC data also peaked at that time (Marchant et al. 1990).

Grasshopper Warblers arrive in the county in April. First arrival dates are generally in the range 11–28 April, with a mean of 19 April. A record of a bird on 27 March 1989 is therefore exceptionally early. In every year, there are many April/May records of males singing in territories which are not adopted for breeding. Sometimes these are at improbable sites suggesting birds passing through. Others remain for several days or even weeks in suitable breeding habitat but are not seen after May and presumably have not bred. Departure dates for such a skulking species are much more difficult to assess but the majority of birds are thought to have left by mid-September.

This furtive little bird has captivated generations of ornithologists, not least on account of its distinctive 'reeling' song. On a quiet, still day the strange, metallic whirring sound, which can be heard up to 1 km away, has a certain ventriloquial quality, as, with body shivering, the bird turns its head from side to side. Occasionally, a bird has been heard to break off reeling momentarily and intersperse a brief individual variance of other notes. At Osney in 1981, a bird suddenly paused after a long spell of reeling and then issued a staggered, almost laboured stuttering sound delivered at less than half the tempo of the more normal song. This peculiarity was timed and persisted for just five seconds before orthodox song was resumed (Bayliss 1981). This observation adds to a number of similar instances recorded in the literature (Milblad 1978, Norris 1977).

The Grasshopper Warbler population on Otmoor has been studied by R. Louch and D. Thompson (in Glue 1990) who returned 46 Nest Record Cards for the site. In common with

a national picture, the protracted breeding season of the species was demonstrated with eggs laid as early as the fourth week in April and young birds fledging as late as 24 August. Two broods are the norm.

Given the species' habitat preferences, it will be interesting to see whether future agricultural changes, such as if suitable land is set-aside, prove beneficial. Equally, increased afforestation could also lead to the provision of additional habitat for the species to colonise.

AQUATIC WARBLER
Acrocephalus paludicola

A very rare vagrant. One was ringed amongst sedges and reedmace at the Appleford end of Sutton Courtenay Gravel Pits on 19 August 1976. It was particularly unusual because it was an adult, whereas most found in Britain are juveniles.

SEDGE WARBLER
Acrocephalus schoenobaenus

A common summer visitor in suitable habitat, the Sedge Warbler is by far the most numerous and widely distributed of our wetland warblers. Its garrulous and lively song adds a special dimension to the riverside scene during late spring and summer. Although commonly found in herbaceous, waterside tangles, many now breed away from damp sites in much drier situations including lowland scrub and fields of Oilseed Rape. In Oxford city, pairs often colonise redundant and overgrown allotments, especially if there is a ditch or stream nearby.

The Oxfordshire Atlas survey located Sedge Warblers in 203 tetrads (27%). 90% of these were probable or confirmed breeding records which reflect the relative ease with which birds

Table 5.73. Grasshopper Warbler.
Breeding habitat preference demonstrated by the BOS survey of 1969.

Habitat type	No. pairs	(%)
Coniferous Plantation	48	(65)
Disused Railway	12	(16)
Riparian	8	(11)
Miscellaneous Scrub	6	(8)
TOTAL	74	(100)

can be located. A comparison of the Oxfordshire Atlas map for this species with the closely related Reed Warbler shows a superficial resemblance with a distinct concentration along the major waterways. The greater number of tetrads occupied by Sedge Warblers reflects the species' ability accept a wider variety of habitats.

Despite its local distribution, in optimal habitats Sedge Warblers are often present in high numbers. For example, in May and June 1987 along a 3.2 km stretch of canal, stream and drainage ditches between Wolvercote and Medley, an estimated 40-50 territories were counted.

The somewhat bulky nest is generally lodged or loosely attached among supporting stems close to the ground in thick herbage. There are also a few instances of nests being suspended from vertical stems in Reed Warbler-fashion. Indeed one such nest so closely resembled that of a Reed Warbler that it was not until the first eggs had been laid and adult birds seen in the vicinity, that the true identity could be confirmed.

Sedge Warblers may occasionally be parasitised by Cuckoos. Sometimes this may be exclusively so, as at Osney in the late 1970s, or as alternatives for Reed Warbler-Cuckoos unable to find a suitable nest of the preferred host.

Arrival of the first birds in the county averages 16 April and the average latest departure date is 23 September. Many individuals demonstrate a marked site fidelity, For example, an adult female ringed at Holywell Meadow in May 1976 was retrapped on the same site in 1977, 1978, 1981 and 1982. Similarly a male ringed on the same site in 1976 was retrapped there in 1977 and 1981. Oxfordshire recoveries show that our reedbeds are important sites for passage birds also with one ringed at Whitekirk, Lothian on 5 July 1981 trapped in Wantage on 4 August the same year (501 km S). Recoveries of Oxfordshire-ringed birds within Britain suggest a south or south-easterly route out of the country via Dorset or Kent in autumn.

Whilst British Sedge Warblers are known to winter in Africa, south of the Sahara, there have been no recoveries of Oxfordshire-ringed birds that far south, and the only foreign recoveries are three from France and the Channel Islands, presumed to be birds on passage.

MARSH WARBLER
Acrocephalus palustris

Today the Marsh Warbler is a very rare vagrant to Oxfordshire with only three records between 1965 and 1991. Singing birds were heard between 28 May and 15 July in south Oxfordshire, Radley Gravel Pits, and Somerton, in 1973, 1981 and 1987. None remained more than a day or two.

William Warde Fowler was the first to prove that this species bred in Oxfordshire, although there was one earlier possible record in the nineteenth century. It is with delight that he describes the progress of a small colony of up to three or four pairs in an Osier bed near his home in Kingham from 1890 until 1904 when the habitat was destroyed. One of the interesting discoveries he made was of a Cuckoo's egg in one nest in 1898; the first time the Marsh Warbler had been recorded as a host species in Britain.

Breeding was not noted again in the county until 1920, but from then until 1947 single nests were found in 11 summers along the Thames and Kennet valleys and at Sandford Sewage Farm. Except in the brief period at the end of May and beginning of June when its remarkable song can be heard, its similarity in appearance to the Reed Warbler makes it difficult to identify. Thus there may have been even more in those years of plenty when there were comparatively few ornithologists in the field.

There has been only one record of breeding since then, in 1960, when a pair nested at "an Oxfordshire site" and successfully reared one juvenile. The origin of a juvenile ringed at Sonning Gravel Pit in 1964 is not known.

Its withdrawal from Oxfordshire fits in with the decline of the species nationally.

REED WARBLER
Acrocephalus scirpaceus

The Reed Warbler is a numerous but locally distributed summer visitor to Oxfordshire. The results of the Oxfordshire Atlas indicate that the species is virtually absent from the Chiltern escarpment and Cotswolds with, as might be expected, colonies established principally along the numerous rivers and waterways that bisect the Oxfordshire Plain. Further pairs occupy sites north to Banbury in the Oxford Canal/River Cherwell corridor. Probable and confirmed breeding were found in only 10% of tetrads during the Atlas survey. However, where it occurs it is often at high densities.

During the 1980s, this species was the subject of two, independent, breeding season surveys in the county. The BOS in 1983 paid particular attention to the Reed Warbler as part of its cycle of annual breeding season surveys, and there was a long-term study by M.J. Bayliss, currently extending from 1983-1989. The latter investigation was more especially concerned with the degree and effect of Cuckoo parasitism on Reed Warbler colonies in the Oxford area (See also Cuckoo). These two studies, combined with the Oxfordshire Atlas, are particularly interesting when compared with the descriptions given by authors of the previous accounts of Oxfordshire's avifauna. Aplin (1889) describes the Reed Warbler as locally common and a frequent Cuckoo host. In the vicinity of Oxford, where nowadays the species is common, Warde Fowler (1886), regards it as extremely local in it's distribution stating "Now in the whole length of the Isis between Kennington and Godstow, and of the Cherwell between its mouth and Parson's Pleasure, there is no reedbed which answers all the requirements of this little bird". Jourdain (1926) thought it "not uncommon but very local", while Radford (1966) described it as "locally common". Today, its status agrees most closely with those given by Jourdain and Radford, although the huge increase in gravel extraction since the 1960s has benefited this species as many of the older workings develop a shoreline vegetation.

From the results of the two single species surveys, it appears that the Reed Warbler is far more common around Oxford than Banbury. At Oxford (between Sandford and Wolvercote), more than 100 pairs annually occupy about a dozen sites, mostly along waterways other than the Thames. In addition, further colonies in the Radley Gravel Pit - River Thames complex hold at least 50 pairs. By contrast, in the BOS area only 80 pairs were located.

An interesting finding of the surveys by the BOS and Bayliss, related to the choice of nest site. In the former, nine (22.5%) of the 40 nests where the precise situation was known, were in herbaceous plants other than *Phragmites* and a similar number were found nesting in a mixture of reeds and other plants. Of the 511 nests located in the Oxford survey in the period 1983-1987, a total of 75 (14.7%) were in plants other than *Phragmites*. Among the list of plants used, Great Willowherb was favourite, with 26 (34.6%) of nests found here but a further 16 plants used as a nesting site were also identified. Similarly, in a study beside the River Trent, Catchpole (1974) found 46% of nests in non-*Phragmites* situations, with willowherbs again featuring prominently. Each of these studies indicate that Reed Warblers will readily adopt plant species other than the traditional stands of *Phragmites* in which to nest. However, the density at which nesting occurs is usually much lower in these habitats when compared with pure stands of reed.

Reed Warblers arrive in the county from mid-May, with the earliest recorded arrival date being 14 April, the latest 9 May giving a mean arrival date of 28 April. However, immigration into breeding areas is a very protracted affair. At the Oxford study sites, the first birds arrive during late April or early May with a flow of birds arriving throughout June (Table 5.74). It can be seen that, even by late May, only half the territories are occupied. Also, it is interesting to note that the pattern of occupation is similar from year to year, except for the initial stages when the arrival of birds varied by as much as eight days.

As remarked upon by Aplin, this species is a frequent Cuckoo host. The number of parasitised Reed Warbler nests recorded on Nest Record Cards for Oxfordshire and submitted to the BTO stands at 94 and comprises 48% of all instances for any host species of cuckoldry on these cards for the county. In addition, a total of 162 parasitised Reed Warbler nests were found during the Oxford survey. It must be noted that this high number reflects a certain observer bias and might not accurately reflect the true rate of parasitism.

Nevertheless, where Cuckoos are especially active, parasitism has a significant effect on host colonies. At the Oxford study sites where 638 Reed Warbler nests were monitored, 162 (25.4%) were parasitised, 326 (51.1%) failed, many due to the activities of Cuckoos and only 150 (23.5%) reared young Reed Warblers. Of course, many of the parasitised nests also failed for various reasons and if the season was not too advanced, pairs re-nested and often succeeded in eventually rearing young of their own. One must note that the majority of Reed Warbler colonies escape the attention of Cuckoos so that success rates are usually rather higher. Interestingly, during the BOS survey, there was only one recorded instance of parasitism of Reed Warblers by Cuckoos. This possibly reflects the greater abundance of this particular potential host in the south of the county.

Reed Warblers display remarkable site fidelity. A bird ringed at South Stoke in 1982 was retrapped there in 1984, 1986 and 1987. Also at South Stoke, three individuals ringed in 1986 and a fourth in 1987, were all retrapped in 1989. At Dorchester, a bird ringed in July 1977 was retrapped in July 1979 and again in the same month in 1982. Ringing at reedbed sites also indicates their importance as stop-over sites for birds on passage with one ringed at Wytham on 9 May 1979 recovered at Attenborough, Nottinghamshire on 13 May (four days later) and another adult ringed at Abingdon on 24 June 1978 was at Barnsley, South Yorkshire on 22 August 1978.

There have been 81 recoveries of Reed Warblers ringed in Oxfordshire. Seven were within 9 km of the ringing site, 63 between 10 and 99 km and 11 at more than 100 km. Of foreign movements of Reed Warblers ringed in Oxfordshire, there are three from Morocco,

Table 5.74. Reed Warbler.

Arrival of males at Oxford study site, given as % of total number of territories occupied in each season.

Seven-day period commencing	% of occupied territories			
	1986	1987	1988	1989
17 April	0	0	0	0
24 April	0	5	0	0
1 May	3	10	9	20
8 May	9	25	23	43
15 May	29	37	35	57
22 May	51	50	51	71
29 May	71	68	58	77
5 June	77	82	63	85
12 June	83	88	84	91
19 June	91	93	93	100
26 June	100	100	100	100

three from Portugal and one each from Spain and Belgium. An interesting capture history was recorded by a bird ringed at South Stoke on 27 August 1989. Is was retrapped there on 3 September, controlled at Icklesham, Surrey on 18 September and then captured alive at El Jadida, Morocco on 14 October of the same year.

ICTERINE WARBLER
Hippolais icterina

The only record of this vagrant in Oxfordshire is of two at Sutton Courtenay Gravel Pit on 17 August 1975. A few appear regularly on the coasts of Britain each spring and autumn, but inland sightings are rare. It is also unusual to see two together.

DARTFORD WARBLER
Sylvia undata

The Dartford Warbler formerly bred in Oxfordshire but has been absent for many years. Aplin (1889) mentions nesting at Beckley in 1834 and at Shotover in 1878 or 1879, and a probable sighting at Sibford Heath in September 1909. Since then heathland habitat has almost disappeared, and Dartford Warblers have completely.

LESSER WHITETHROAT
Sylvia curruca

A numerous summer visitor with a widespread distribution, the Lesser Whitethroat is primarily a bird of scrub and hedgerow often particularly favouring large and neglected hedges. Scrub along railways and at woodland edges also provide the dense thickets inhabited by the species. The bird is rather skulking in habit and hence inconspicuous although its characteristically rattling song, deep inside the undergrowth will betray its presence.

Birds arrive in the county in April with first recorded dates ranging from the third to the thirtieth of the month. The third week of April is the median period for the first arrivals. By the first few days of May most birds have taken up residence and eggs have been found in the nest as early as 9 May.

County-wide, the Oxfordshire Atlas found Lesser Whitethroats in 55.5% of tetrads, (Cf. Whitethroat 77%). However as it is easily overlooked there may be a degree of under-recording. Knowledge of its penetrating song is an essential aid to finding this species, although it tends not to be recognised by inexperienced observers. The distribution in Oxfordshire today appears to correspond with the Clay Vales and the lower slopes of the Chilterns and Downs, indicating the species' preference for low ground. These results can therefore probably be regarded

as an accurate reflection of the species' distribution. The Lesser Whitethroat needs an extensive hedgerow/scrub system so that the reduction in the quantity and quality of hedgerows in the county has been deleterious.

In the Banbury area, Easterbrook (1983) classified it as "fairly numerous" (3–30 pairs per 10 km square) and implied a more widespread distribution than the Whitethroat. In 1984, and in the light of the results of an Annual Breeding Season Survey carried out by the BOS, the species' status was reassessed and upgraded to 'numerous'(i.e. 30–300 pairs per 10 km square). This survey reinforced the previously described habitat preferences of the Lesser Whitethroat showing a strong association with Bramble and Hawthorn and also provided another useful association, namely that 70% of nesting pairs were adjacent to permanent pasture. This resulted from the association between hedge quality and the occurrence of pasture.

The fortunes of the bird are not easy to gauge with any accuracy. Warde Fowler (1886) recorded that in the vicinity of Oxford it "makes his presence felt in almost every lane and meadow" while Aplin (1889), noted it as being generally distributed and locally abundant. Alexander (1945) called it generally distributed but not very common and Radford (1965) commented that although well distributed it was less abundant than the Whitethroat.

Once the breeding season is over, birds may travel more widely, frequently entering gardens in both urban and rural situations and occasionally pausing to bathe in ponds thus providing a fine opportunity to observe this handsome but often overlooked bird. Most Lesser Whitethroats leave Oxfordshire in September although in two years, birds have been recorded as late as the end of October or into November.

Foreign ringing recoveries of Oxfordshire Lesser Whitethroats (Figure 5.67) have helped

to establish the pattern of a movement to more easterly wintering grounds than the Whitethroat. This explains why the species did not suffer the same declines as the Whitethroat. However, passage through the eastern Mediterranean is not without its own perils, since these birds run a greater risk from bird-catchers and shooters. Factors connected with its migratory journey may account for its apparent fluctuations in numbers from season to season. When one then adds to this the problems of pressure upon the bird's nesting habitat in Oxfordshire, it may be that some regular local monitoring of the species would be desirable.

WHITETHROAT
Sylvia communis

As shown by the Oxfordshire Atlas map the Whitethroat is currently a common and widely distributed member of our avifauna. Previous accounts of the birds of Oxfordshire describe the bird as a regular, common, or very common, summer visitor. It is a bird of scrub, hedgerow and woodland-edge, nesting in apparently impenetrable thorn bushes and clumps of bramble or in stands of nettle, willowherb or Meadowsweet. It will occasionally be found within woodlands, typically in open clearings or in young plantations with a dense undergrowth. Closed woodland is generally avoided.

The Whitethroat is probably the most conspicuous of all the breeding warblers for, in addition to the song-flights, birds will become very vocal at the approach of an intruder. With birds in 77.3% of tetrads, the Oxfordshire Atlas map probably gives an accurate indication of our breeding population, since few tetrads are likely to have been missed. The blank squares in the south-east represent the heavily wooded Chilterns, whilst elsewhere the impact of

agriculture has reduced nesting opportunities.

Whitethroats arrive in Oxfordshire in April with first dates ranging from the fifth to the twenty-eighth of the month. Departure dates vary from 1 September to 6 October. There have been some very late reports; in 1984 a bird was seen on 25 November and in 1988, a bird believed to be injured, was recorded in November and December.

In 1969, there was a drastic and dramatic crash in the Whitethroat population in the British Isles with the national CBC index for the species falling to less than one-third of its 1968 level and the number of Whitethroats ringed by the OOS reflected this picture (Table 5.75). Before 1968, the mean number of birds ringed each year was 109, whilst it has been only 21 since then. Further reductions followed in the early 1970s. Locally, this decline was very clear and from 1969–1974 the bird was very scarce in Oxfordshire although some sites in the west of the county still retained a moderate although reduced population. Since that decline, there appear to have been good years and bad. Overall, the trend has been upwards, although the pre-1969 figures have not yet been attained. The reason for the losses have been attributed to a succession of droughts in the Sahel zone of west Africa, the species' wintering region (Winstanley *et al.* 1974). Its inability to return to the population density of the late 1960s may be connected with the loss of hedgerows in the county.

Although British birds winter in west Africa, no Oxfordshire-ringed birds have been recovered so far south. There have been just eight recoveries of Whitethroats ringed in Oxfordshire. Passage birds have been recovered in France and Spain (Figure 5.68), one of which was known to have been in at least its seventh year. All other recoveries are local and mostly represent post-natal dispersal.

Migratory species such as the Whitethroat seem beset with problems. Conditions in the wintering grounds can have a profound effect, and on route to and from those areas, sportsmen and bird-catchers take their toll in the Mediterranean. In addition, there remains the problem closer to home of hedgerow loss and mismanagement which do nothing to improve the situation for this most delightful of warblers.

GARDEN WARBLER
Sylvia borin

Carrying the inauspicious reputation of being the dullest and drabbest of our warblers, relatively little is known about the Garden Warbler in Oxfordshire. A summer visitor, all previous accounts give the impression of it being a common species in the county and, judging by the results of the Oxfordshire Atlas, this remains true today. However, because of its rather unobtrusive nature, mentions of the species in the county bird reports are few, with only very

Table 5.75. Whitethroat.
Number of birds ringed annually in Oxfordshire. Note the drop after 1967.

Year	No.
1960	67
1961	86
1962	106
1963	110
1964	40
1965	147
1966	139
1967	176
1968	41
1969	41
1970	24
1971	26
1972	30
1973	19
1974	10
1975	23
1976	42
1977	55
1978	41
1979	23
1980	14
1981	32
1982	28
1983	10
1984	14
1985	5
1986	22

Figure 5.68. Whitethroat.
Ringing recoveries.

● Foreign recoveries of birds ringed in Oxfordshire

Table 5.76. Garden Warbler.
Comparison of Garden Warbler and Blackcap densities (Pairs/ha) in two Oxfordshire woodlands.

	Little Wittenham	Bagley Wood
Area (ha)	52	227
Garden Warbler	17.2	9.2
Blackcap	19.0	25.0
Combined	36.2	34.2

Figure 5.69. Garden Warbler.
Ringing recoveries.

Single recovery of a bird at Beni Mellal, Morocco (2198kms)

○ Origin of birds recovered in Oxfordshire
● Recoveries of birds ringed in Oxfordshire

local assessments or very high numbers ever reported. The song is often the only clue to the presence of the Garden Warbler and even this can be misleading since it is easily confused with that of the Blackcap.

These factors may have some bearing upon the interpretation of the results of the Oxfordshire Atlas where it was recorded in 49.8% of tetrads – significantly fewer than the closely related Blackcap. The findings of the National Atlas (Sharrock 1976) describe how both these species occupy similar habitats although the Garden Warbler is more likely to be noted away from mature woods and may be found in scrub and conifers, an observation which would perhaps make for a wider distribution. However, Ford (1987) found Garden Warblers breeding in only two of twenty woodlands studied in west Oxfordshire whereas Blackcaps were thought to breed in 15 of those sites. Also, looking at a number of CBC and other study sites across the county one consistently notes greater numbers of Blackcaps than Garden Warblers which in itself might give a relative bias, making the former easier to record in a tetrad.

Another factor which might affect its rate of being reported might be that Garden Warblers and Blackcaps show inter-specific territoriality, that is, they defend mutually exclusive territories against each other. Garcia (1981) gave good evidence for this in a study of the two species in Wytham Woods and although densities of 0.3-0.5 pairs/ha are similar to those of the Blackcap, their territories were smaller. Wiggins (1984) compared the densities of breeding bird species in two woodlands and provided the data in Table 5.76. The combined densities are similar for both woodlands. However, this is not the case for smaller woodlands such as those studied by Ford (1987). The status of the species in the county would seem to warrant further research.

Garden Warblers usually arrive in Oxfordshire in April or very early May and the dates of first arrivals fall between 3 April and 1 May. Departure dates for the species have a much wider spread with last dates for sightings given as 6 July to 8 December, but most final dates fall in the period 29 August to 11 October.

There are eight distant ringing recoveries of Garden Warblers relating to the county. Of these, seven were recovered within the UK. Six recoveries are of birds ringed in Britain in the season of hatching and recovered in the same season and one is of an adult ringed and recovered in the same season (Figure 5.69). There is a single foreign recovery, that of a Wytham bird ringed as a nestling in 1978 and controlled in Morocco, (2,198 km S) in 1981.

BLACKCAP
Sylvia atricapilla

The Blackcap is primarily a summer visitor to Oxfordshire, nesting in mature, mixed or deciduous woodland, where a good shrub layer, especially of Bramble, is present. Extensive hedgerows, thickets of dense scrub, and larger gardens blessed with plentiful shrubs are also used. It is well distributed in the county with most vacant tetrads found in areas of intensive agriculture where there is a scarcity of suitable nesting habitat. The rich, fluent song allows for rapid location of the species by Atlas fieldworkers and hence there are few 'possible' records, two-thirds of submitted records being in the 'probable' category. It may be that some of these relate to birds on passage and one must also acknowledge that some confusion with the Garden Warbler's song is possible.

The Blackcap may also be seen in the county during the winter. Aplin (1889), Alexander (1947) and Radford (1966) all note that individual birds will over-winter in Oxfordshire

with up to seven records in each winter (October–March) period. From the mid-1970s very many more wintering birds have been recorded and reports have numbered between 15 and 81 annually. These have come from all parts of the county with the majority seen in gardens where they will readily take fruit, seeds and berries of such plants as *Cotoneaster*, Holly, Honeysuckle and Ivy. Peanuts and other artificially provided food is also accepted. It is noticeable that more records come during the second half of the winter period (Figure 5.70) and this is probably a result of either cold weather or a shortage of natural food. The provision of garden feeding stations has been a vital factor in enabling the Blackcap to over-winter in the county. Whilst Leach (1981) showed a preponderance of male over female birds over-wintering in Britain there appears to be no clear distinction in Oxfordshire although the sex of individuals has not always been reported.

A further insight into wintering birds comes from a study made in a woodland site in the south of the county in 1979. Here, ten birds were noted in January and February with the males departing before the females. A pair were noted in November with 13 others in the vicinity but these did not remain. By late November and for all of December two males and two females took up residence. Numbers such as this lead one to question how many are being overlooked in woodlands, which are not always well watched during the winter months.

The birds that over-winter in Britain are known to be a separate population of birds to the breeding individuals (Berthold and Terrill 1988). There are few records in late-October or early November but a rapid increase is seen in late November, implying that breeding birds leave before wintering ones arrive. At the other end of the breeding season, the distinction is not always clear cut. Birds may be noted in late winter (i.e. February/March) apparently paired and often in song and it is therefore difficult to know if these are summer visitors, especially since the quoted summer arrival dates for the species range from 25 March to 27 April.

To date there have been no ringing recoveries relating to Oxfordshire's wintering Blackcaps. There is some information regarding the summer birds however and Figure 5.71 gives the details. The recoveries on the Iberian Peninsula and in north Africa fit the national picture as the majority of British birds are thought to winter here (Mead 1983). The bird controlled in Belgium, on 19 September 1988 had been ringed on Otmoor as an adult one month earlier.

The Blackcap's status as a common summer visitor is not thought to have changed markedly in the long-term. Short-term fluctuations have occurred and the CBC plot at Wytham Woods (6.7 ha) between 1971 and 1987 yielded between two and ten occupied territories with a mean of 4.1 pairs (0.6 pairs/ha). In the same wood, Garcia (1981) found 0.5 pairs/ha (see also Garden Warbler for further density estimates). There have also been local fluctuations due to alterations in the management of woodlands. For example, when a large area of conifers were thinned in a part of Foxcombe Wood on Boar's Hill, scrub rapidly spread into what had been a bare woodland floor. As a result, the population of Blackcaps on the CBC plot in a wood more than doubled (R. Edwards, pers. comm.).

YELLOW-BROWED WARBLER
Phylloscopus inornatus

A very rare vagrant. One flitting around the gardens of a road in Didcot on 22 and 23 October 1989 is Oxfordshire's only record. It was a highly vocal individual, located by its call, but was also seen well for brief periods.

WOOD WARBLER
Phylloscopus sibilatrix

The largest and most colourful of the *Phylloscopus* warblers in Oxfordshire, the Wood Warbler is eagerly searched for by spring-time birdwatchers in the county. It occurs primarily as a passage migrant with most records from the spring period from the second half of April to the first week of May. Although the Oxfordshire Atlas located birds in 28 tetrads, opinion is that the vast majority were passage birds. The only confirmed breeding record from the Atlas period actually falls outside of the county boundary and thus the last confirmed breeding for Oxfordshire was in 1981.

In the nineteenth century the Wood Warbler was regarded as a regular summer visitor although locally distributed. In the 1930s there is some mention of a decline in the county

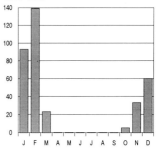

Figure 5.70. Blackcap.
Monthly distribution of winter records 1975-1987.

Figure 5.71. Blackcap.
Ringing recoveries.

● Recoveries of birds ringed in Oxfordshire
○ Origin of birds recovered in Oxfordshire

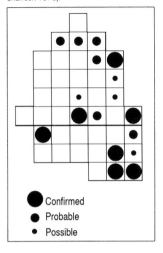

● Confirmed
● Probable
• Possible

Table 5.77. Chiffchaff.
Breeding densities in Oxfordshire woodlands.

Site and reference	Area (ha)	Density (Pairs/km²)
Bagley Wood Wiggins (1984)	227	16.7
Little Wittenham Wiggins (1984)	52	34.8
Wytham Woods Overall (1988)	6.7	30-150
Woodland islands Ford (1987)	–	20.5
Woodland controls Ford (1987)	–	13

although up to four pairs were present in Wychwood. Alexander (1947) describes it as a regular visitor especially to the Chiltern and Cotswold Beechwoods. From that time, a further decrease took place. In 1952, the only county breeding record reported was from along the Chilterns and through the 1950s and 1960s the only definite records of breeding were in Bagley and Wytham woods. Even so, breeding at these sites was sporadic with a maximum of two pairs in any year although up to seven singing birds could be heard at either site in any year.

In the 1970s the pattern of occasional breeding continued. A nest was found at Stoke Row in 1970 and the *National Atlas* (Sharrock 1976) shows a scattered distribution from the results of five years fieldwork (Figure 5.72). In 1975 successful breeding occurred at Blenheim and at the Henry Stephen/C. S. Lewis Nature Reserve on the slopes of Shotover. It may also have bred at the latter site in later years but this was not confirmed. A peak in the breeding population was reached in the last three years of the 1970s with between three and six records of definite or probable breeding in these years. A single record of confirmed breeding in 1980 was followed in 1981 by reports of four territories located in the Chilterns, three pairs in Wytham Wood and a nest found at one other site. Since then, only two seasons have produced probable breeding records, and although between two and six records of Wood Warbler are received every year, all are thought to be passage migrants. A national census of the species conducted by the BTO in 1984 and 1985 could locate no breeding pairs in Oxfordshire (Bibby 1989). The reason for the decline in Oxfordshire is unclear although similar patterns have been noted in a number of other English counties.

There is a single ringing recovery of a Wood Warbler involving Oxfordshire. A bird ringed as a nestling in the New Forest in 1980 was trapped at Goring Heath the following May.

CHIFFCHAFF
Phylloscopus collybita

The Chiffchaff is chiefly a numerous summer visitor to Oxfordshire although some may winter. The far-carrying, if rather monotonous bi-syllabic notes of the Chiffchaff's song are very much a feature of the Oxfordshire countryside in spring and summer.

The species is well represented in the county where it nests mainly in mixed and deciduous woodland, parks and large gardens with an abundance of low vegetation, along hedgerows with a scattering of standard trees or in plantations with occasional mature trees. The Oxfordshire Atlas data bear this out with records obtained from 76.2% of tetrads. This figure is much less than the Willow Warbler and can be explained by the latter's preference for more open habitats. Ford (1987) found that Chiffchaff density is not significantly influenced by the size of woodland area although like most species studied, it tended to be relatively more abundant in smaller woods (Table 5.77). Since the species is easily located and identified by song, under-recording or mis-identification is unlikely to have been a problem in the Atlas fieldwork. If anything, the Chiffchaff map is likely to over-estimate their number due to birds singing while on passage, although it is felt that any such error is likely to be small. The high proportion of 'probable' records reflects not only the ease of finding birds but the problems of proving that breeding has occurred in often dense undergrowth.

The Chiffchaff is among the first of our summer visitors to return. Arrival dates range from 2 March to 3 April although early/mid-March is the norm, with the main influx occurring in late March. During their first few weeks in the county, quite large parties of birds can often be seen and areas of coppice or woodland edge may seem alive with foraging, calling birds before dispersing to take up territories. The majority of birds have departed by mid-October. However, the setting of precise arrival and departure dates is not easy since small numbers of birds over-winter in the county. This habit has been noted since Aplin's time with individuals recorded in every winter period. Numbers are, in the main small (i.e. two to six records per winter period), and most are from town gardens and from gravel pit complexes. Changes in weather conditions would appear to be the most likely cause of these fluctuations especially when one considers that the Chiffchaff is chiefly insectivorous.

The origin of the over-wintering birds is not known. It is known however that the majority of British birds migrate to southern Europe and north and west Africa for the winter. There are four foreign recoveries of birds ringed in Oxfordshire. Two were recovered in France (presumed to be on passage) and a third, in

Portugal in November, may have been over-wintering. Probably the most interesting was a first-year bird ringed at Dorchester-on-Thames on 27 September 1980, which was caught ten weeks later in Senegal. This African recovery is one of the furthest movements of a British Chiffchaff, some 4,118 km.

WILLOW WARBLER
Phylloscopus trochilus

A summer visitor, the Willow Warbler is the most widespread of the county's breeding warblers. Willow Warblers nest in a wide range of habitats from woodlands and hedgerows to areas of sparse scrub. Such habitats at the edges of wetland are particularly favoured and vegetation along river valleys seems important to birds on passage. It is not however a bird of dense woodland but of more open sites or at the edges of woods and hence population densities are higher in small woodlands than in large ones since they have relatively more edge habitat (Ford 1987).

This catholic choice of nesting habitat accounts, in part at least, for the species' widespread distribution. Its easily recognisable song aided location of birds by Atlas workers. The familiar song is uttered by passage birds as well as territory-holders so that there is a tendency to over-record it. However, the high levels of confirmed breeding records coupled with the Willow Warbler's known habitat preferences lead one to regard the Atlas distribution map as accurate.

The first birds typically arrive in the last week of March or the first week of April, thus an arrival on 4 March 1982 is an extremely early record. Radford (1966) gives the arrival period for the species as the second week of April and although this is the start of the main influx, 12 of the first arrival dates between 1974 and 1988

are earlier than this. When the bulk of the population arrive it can be quite dramatic, with falls of birds congregating at sites of abundant food or shelter (e.g. 50 birds at Wolvercote Gravel Pit on 16 April 1984). Arrival coincides with the willows coming into leaf and the combined effect is a real herald of spring. Breeding may commence soon after arrival particularly if a fine spring ensues and it is not uncommon to find clutches before the end of April and fledged young by late May.

The numbers of birds present at a site fluctuate widely from season to season. The CBC plots at Boarstall Decoy (1968-1987) and Wytham Wood (1971-1987), and of 6.7 and 6.6 ha, have ranges of between seven and 15 and seven and 21 territories respectively. It is worth noting that the Oxfordshire Atlas was researched at a time of high population levels as indicated by CBC data.

Departures begin in August and continue until October, with the latest record made in 1979 when a bird was seen on October 28.

Ringing data for Willow Warblers show birds originating and recovered from a wide area of Britain and apart from one Channel Islands record there have been no foreign recoveries of birds ringed in Oxfordshire (Figure 5.73). This is a selective picture since local recoveries (less than 25 km) are not included although a number of these are of interest. A male ringed as an adult at Little Wittenham Nature Reserve in 1977 was retrapped at the site in each of the next two years. At the same reserve, a bird ringed as a juvenile in 1976 was similarly retrapped in 1978 and 1979.

GOLDCREST
Regulus regulus

In Oxfordshire, the Goldcrest is a common resident whose numbers are considerably augmented in winter by immigration. This was clearly recognised by earlier writers on the county's birds (Clark-Kennedy 1868, Aplin 1889). The Goldcrest is essentially a bird of coniferous woodland, but it expands its range into other woodland and garden habitats when the population density is high. The Atlas map shows that in Oxfordshire, Goldcrests are found particularly in tetrads containing all or part of a substantial woodland block (>12.5 ha). This association for larger woodlands is statistically significant (see Appendix 5).

In a study of isolated and predominantly broadleaved woodlands in Oxfordshire, Ford (1987) also found that Goldcrests preferred larger blocks of woodland although their distribution there was not continuous and densities ranged from 0.06-0.85 pairs/ha when they occurred at all. He found them in five out of 20 isolated woods and three out of eight similarly sized plots within larger woods. He suggested that larger blocks of woodland were

Figure 5.73. Willow Warbler.
Ringing recoveries.

Single recovery of bird at Vale Marais, Guernsey, Channel Islands

● Recoveries of birds ringed in Oxfordshire
○ Origin of birds recovered in Oxfordshire

Table 5.78. Firecrest.
Annual number of records 1976-1989.

Year	No. of records
1976	1
1977	0
1978	3
1979	5
1980	5
1981	4
1982	1
1983	5
1984	5
1985	4
1986	5
1987	3
1988	2
1989	7

Figure 5.74. Firecrest.
Monthly distribution of records 1976-1989.

more likely to contain scattered conifers and that these were the essential component of the habitat.

In winter, the population may be swollen by continental immigrants. Large autumn influxes were noted in October 1980 and in October and November 1988 they were described as 'abundant everywhere'. The origin of these winter visitors is, according to national ringing data, northern Britain and north-west Europe, especially Scandinavia. The few ringing recoveries which concern Oxfordshire, (excluding local recoveries) also suggest such a source, with one from Merseyside, one from Humberside, and one from Norfolk although one ringed on Bardsey Isle on 28 September 1988 was at Bletchingdon on 18 October the same year. All recoveries occurred during the winter period (October to February).

In winter, Goldcrests usually band together with other small woodland birds. Morse (1978) found that in mid-winter, 89.1% of mixed-species flocks in Wytham Woods contained Goldcrests and also 89% of Goldcrests that he encountered were in such flocks. Each flock contained on average 2.6 Goldcrests. A mid-winter census suggested a density at Wytham of 1.2 Goldcrests per ha. Despite this tendency to join flocks of other species, large single-species flocks have also been noted, such as a flock of 50 in Christchurch Meadows on 16 January 1982. This would seem to be too late (or too early) to represent on-going passage.

Radford (1966) noted that the Goldcrest is one of the species which is hardest hit by severe winter weather. Alexander (1940) found that the population dropped from ten to six pairs in a 17 ha census plot in Bagley Woods (or from 0.60-0.36 pairs/ha) after the cold winter of 1939/40. A considerable drop in numbers was noted in the OOS report for 1963 following a hard winter but a recovery was reported in 1964 and the following figures for a Banbury census plot were given in the report for 1965: one pair in 1963, eight in 1964 and 17 in 1965. In 1966 it was estimated that the population was back at its pre-1963 level (OOS 1966) whereupon further population expansion may have led birds to occupy new habitats since in 1970 it was recorded breeding in gardens in the Oxford area 'for the first time'. A further drop in numbers was noted in the OOS reports after the hard winters of 1979 and 1986 but in 1987 it bred in gardens again. Other recorded breeding densities for

Oxfordshire are 181 pairs or 0.79 pairs/ha in Bagley Woods in 1984 (Wiggins 1984) and 0.54 pairs/ha in Little Wittenham Wood in the same year. Gosler (1990) estimated the breeding population of Wytham at 60-120 pairs based on Overall's census data giving 0.15-0.31 pairs/ha in a broadleaved plot (Overall 1988).

The association between this species and coniferous woodland is clear in Oxfordshire as elsewhere. For example it is commonly met in forestry plantations such as at Bernwood. It is unfortunate that we have no data on breeding density for such areas with which to compare the figures above. Given the abundance of forestry plantation in the county the future of the Goldcrest would seem assured in Oxfordshire.

FIRECREST
Regulus ignicapillus

The Firecrest occurs in Oxfordshire as a passage migrant and also as a rare resident of woodland. However, before the late 1970s, it could only be regarded as a very rare winter visitor and passage migrant to Oxfordshire, with only 13 recorded between 1881 and 1975. All occurred in the period from September to March and in no single year was there more than one record. Since 1975 there has only been one year without a record (Table 5.78). The pattern of occurrence has shifted somewhat with, in each year, birds having been recorded in the summer months as well as the usual winter records (Figure 5.74). Breeding is known to have taken place in at least five years and singing males have been reported in an additional seven seasons. Whilst there were no reports of confirmed breeding during the course of the Oxfordshire Atlas, three probable and three possible records were obtained, three of these six were from the Chilterns.

What then is the reason for this trend? One might argue that the increase in sightings has resulted from greater observer coverage. The bird is certainly unobtrusive and could easily have been overlooked. However when one notes that many records since 1975 have come from some intensively studied areas (e.g. Wytham), this is unlikely to be the full story and, in fact, the establishment of an Oxfordshire breeding population ties in with much wider trends. The main colonisation of Britain occurred in the

1960s and 1970s as part of a northwards spread through continental Europe. A number of southern counties saw Firecrests become established at this time but, notably, in 1971 a population was discovered in a Buckinghamshire woodland which by 1975 included 43 singing males and, it is estimated, held half of the British population (Sharrock 1976). The relatively close proximity of this site, coupled with the fact that the majority of Oxfordshire records are from the central and south-east portion of the county, makes this the most likely centre from which birds could colonise Oxfordshire.

Norway Spruce is said to be the preferred nesting habitat for Firecrests (Sharrock 1976), but records from the county are of birds in a wide range of coniferous, deciduous and mixed woodland, and passage and wintering birds have been seen in hedgerows, scrub and garden situations. Outside the breeding season, association with Goldcrests or tits may be seen.

The general impression from birdwatchers in Oxfordshire and indeed elsewhere in Britain is that the species is under-recorded. Its small size and habit of remaining high in the leafy canopy, its short song period and possible confusion of song with the Goldcrest's may cause it to be overlooked. Familiarisation with the song is probably the best way of locating birds, and searches from the last week in April when birds return to nesting areas (four of the nine April records in Figure 5.74, are of birds in this week all of which were in song) through to mid-June in larger areas of mixed woodland would appear to be the most profitable. Since the Firecrest is a protected species, it would be of some practical conservation value to know more about the status of the species in the county.

Family: Muscicapidae
Flycatchers

Flycatchers are summer visitors to Britain. Two species occur in Oxfordshire. One is a regular breeding species, the other is chiefly a passage migrant which has bred on a few occasions.

SPOTTED FLYCATCHER
Muscicapa striata

The Spotted Flycatcher is one of the latest of the county's summer visitors to arrive in the spring. Whilst first recorded dates for the species range from 29 March to 18 May, with late-April/early May being usual, the bulk of the arrivals are in the second half of May. In Oxfordshire it is very much a bird of parks and gardens and to a lesser extent woodlands. When found in woodland, it is invariably in clearings or at the woodland edge. Churchyards seem to be particularly favoured as too are farm and stable-yards. Birds also often nest close to ponds and rivers. This distribution pattern is linked to the species' mode of feeding. Spotted Flycatchers are insect feeders making frequent sallies from well situated perches to take insects in flight. This dependence upon aerial prey also explains why the Spotted Flycatcher is such a late arrival, coinciding with a peak in aerial insects and why, in cool years, its breeding success is reduced (O'Connor and Morgan 1982). Birds may lay repeat clutches if the first fails and in seasons of high insect abundance, two broods may be raised.

Nests are built on ledges, typically in creepers and climbing plants which entwine themselves over trees and buildings. Open-fronted nestboxes are readily accepted. On at least two occasions eggs have been laid in old nests of Blackbird and Chaffinch. In the latter case, the clutch of young Chaffinch were ringed on 26 May and after fledging the nest was taken over by the

flycatchers with those young being ringed on 7 July.

As they are very active birds, especially around the time of fledging, their chances of being overlooked in any Atlas field-work is small. In the Oxfordshire Atlas, observers were reminded of the late arrival and breeding season of the species and requested to time visits accordingly. It may be that some garden nesting pairs were missed, but in the main, the map probably gives a realistic picture. It is actually quite a patchy distribution with birds avoiding much of the high ground and showing a poor association with woodlands. A figure of 8.4 pairs/km^2 based on a census of Bagley Wood is the best density estimate available for woodland in the county (Wiggins 1984). Birds were found in 58.4% of tetrads, a low figure compared to other county surveys. This may reflect a genuine lack of suitable habitat but it is most likely to be as a result of a run of poor years for Spotted Flycatchers in the county, with a number of observers noting local declines or absences over the Atlas period. This reduction is mirrored by national CBC data and the accepted explanation is one of problems of drought conditions in the Sahel zone where the species over-winters.

Most birds leave the county in September although a steady and, if it has been a good season, strong passage can be observed from late August. Parties of 12–20 birds may be seen in suitable feeding areas. Departure is usually complete by the fourth week of September making a bird on 22 October 1981 an

exceptionally late record, although this was a good season for the species.

As noted previously, Spotted Flycatchers winter in Africa, in a zone south of the Sahel. Oxfordshire ringing records, although limited, bear this out with autumn passage taking birds through Spain (four recoveries) and a single record of a bird ringed at Charlbury on 7 July 1983 which was in the Congo on 1 October 1984 (6,214 km SSE).

Despite its rather dull plumage its nesting in close proximity to Man coupled with a very active nature makes it a most delightful and endearing species. The main concern for its future in the county seems to lie with the difficulties being encountered in the winter quarters.

PIED FLYCATCHER
Ficedula hypoleuca

An infrequent passage migrant, and very rare breeding species. Alexander (1947) describes the Pied Flycatcher as a rare visitor on spring migration, with only one autumn record, at Port Meadow in September 1934. It has been seen more regularly in the second half of the twentieth century. A review of all the 95 records of passage birds in the years from 1960–1989 shows that it has failed to appear in only three years. There is also evidence of a pronounced increase during this period (Table 5.79), probably in excess of what might be attributed to improved observer cover alone. Most of these birds were solitary, but there have been four instances of two, and there were two males with one or two females together at Steventon in April 1975.

Nearly twice as many records occur in spring (61) as in autumn (34) as they rush through in the brief period between 16 April and 8 May (22 days). The apparent discrepancy may be exaggerated as most of the spring sightings are

of males in breeding plumage, and the less conspicuous autumn birds are more likely to be missed. On the other hand, after the breeding season they are in less of a hurry, sometimes remaining at the same site for a few days as they filter through during the longer period of 25 July to 26 September, (88 days), with one individual as late as 18 October (Figure 5.75).

In both periods there seems to be no regular pattern to these brief visits, with birds dropping in at a wide variety of sites, although most frequently in parkland or woodland edges. It is presumed they are on their way to and from their main breeding areas in deciduous woodland in upland valleys in west and north Britain. The only supportive evidence is the capture of a male at Cholsey in 1965 bearing a red colour ring indicating its origin to have been the Forest of Dean.

Although it was considered a rare bird here in the nineteenth century writers then gave two unsubstantiated, and second or third-hand accounts of possible breeding. Although there are areas of Oakwood habitat in the county which appear suitable for this species, there must be a missing component for breeding was not proved until the 1980s. One of the many tit boxes used for research programmes by the Edward Grey Institute in Wytham Woods eventually proved an attraction. In 1982 a female nested in one, incubating for five weeks. No male was seen, and the eggs were presumed infertile. Then, in 1989, the species could at last be safely added to Oxfordshire's list of breeding birds when a pair nested in a box, and successfully fledged five young, all of which were ringed. Of additional interest is the fact that the male had been ringed as a nestling in Staffordshire in 1988. This development, combined with the apparent increase in birds passing through, might be the first indications of a permanent change in status.

Table 5.79. Pied Flycatcher.
Number of birds seen on passage in each decade 1960-1989.

Decade	No. of birds
1960-1969	18
1970-1979	28
1980-1989	48

Figure 5.75. Pied Flycatcher.
Monthly distribution of records 1960-1989 (excluding breeding birds).

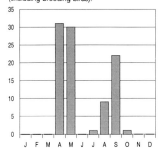

Family: Panuridae
Parrotbills

The Bearded Reedling is the only representative in Europe of this small family whose centre of diversity lies in the eastern Palearctic and Oriental regions. It was formerly known by the inaccurate title of Bearded Tit but, like the Long-tailed Tit, it shares few features in common with the true tits. Chief amongst these differences is its total dependence on reedbeds in which it nests.

BEARDED REEDLING
Panurus biarmicus

The Bearded Reedling is a very rare visitor to Oxfordshire. Its status in the county before this century has been much debated in the past.

Radford (1966) pointed out that while Yarrell (1838) had considered them resident on the banks of the Thames as far as Oxford, Summers-Smith had shown that this was based on a single observation and was almost certainly in error. Aplin (1889) mentions a bird in a ditch by Christchurch Meadows in February 1883.

Most of the records reported by Radford come from present-day Berkshire and do not concern us here. Other records are a pair at Wytham, 18 April 1924, and one near Bloxham, June 1933. From 1950-1989 it was recorded in eight winters (all 30 October to 3 April). Ringing recoveries from Berkshire show that Bearded Reedlings in this part of Britain come especially from East Anglia (see OOS Reports for 1967 and 1968). Furthermore, they have usually occurred when the breeding population there was high.

Records published by the OOS are three at Cassington Gravel Pit, 29 November 1959 and one until 3 April 1960, five at Duke's Lock, Wolvercote, 4-19 November 1961, two at Moulsford/Cholsey, first week of January 1965, four by the River Cherwell north of Bletchingdon, 21-23 January 1972, 13 at Cassington Gravel Pit, 9-30 November 1972 and two until 22 March 1973, eight at Henley Road Gravel Pit, 6 January 1973, one at Cassington Gravel Pit, 20 November 1977 and one at Banbury Sewage Farm, 30 October 1985.

Family: Aegithalidae
Long-tailed Tits

Like the Bearded Reedling, the Long-tailed Tit is the sole European member of a small, mostly Oriental and eastern Palearctic family. Unlike that species though, it retains the inaccurate name of tit. It shares little in common with the true tits apart from its food and the habitats which it frequents. In terms of its morphological structure, its social and territorial behaviour, nest construction and breeding biology, it is quite different.

LONG-TAILED TIT
Aegithalos caudatus

The Long-tailed Tit is a common resident found in a range of Oxfordshire habitats including woodland, scrub, mature hedgerows, churchyards and gardens with large trees. It is a highly social and engaging little bird which seems to have captured the hearts of earlier Oxonians who knew it variously as the 'Bumbarrel', the 'Bottle-Tit' (after its nest) or the 'French Magpie' (Aplin 1889). Aplin himself was unable to resist the temptation to give a lyrical description of the birds' foraging behaviour and also noted that they roosted together in a tight "ball-like cluster".

Radford (1966) describes how family parties are to be seen in autumn wandering through woods and along hedgerows in the county. In fact it is an important constituent of mixed-species flocks in winter. Morse (1978) found that 55.5% of such flocks in Wytham contained Long-tailed Tits, and 85% of his observations of the species were in mixed-species flocks. They feed largely on small insects in the shrub and tree canopies and avoid competition with other flock members partly by being able to reach the outer twigs where few other species can feed.

The Oxfordshire Atlas map shows that the Long-tailed Tit is widespread in the county, indeed wherever there is scrub, mature woodland or hedgerows. Aplin (1889) suggested that winter numbers in Oxfordshire might be augmented by immigration. We now know that this is incorrect as ringing in the county has shown that they are extremely sedentary (although one ringed at Wytham was recovered at Thame!). There have been only 13 recoveries of Long-tailed Tits ringed in Oxfordshire. Of these, 70% moved less than 9 km. In hard winters their wanderings can lead them into towns and away from their usual habitats. For example, one January a party was seen flying through Cornmarket, Oxford, and feeding in trees in St. Mary Magdalene churchyard.

Radford (1966) pointed out that

Oxfordshire's Long-tailed Tit population tends to suffer in severe winters as reported in the county reports for 1917, 1946, 1956, 1962 and 1963, though Alexander (1940) found only a small drop in numbers (from 0.53–0.44 pairs/ha) in Bagley Wood after the severe winter of 1939/40.

The Long-tailed Tit has been well studied in Wytham Woods by Gaston (1976) and Glen (1985). Gaston estimated the Wytham population in October 1970 to be about 223 birds — a density of 0.61 birds/ha which was reduced to about 114 or 0.31 birds/ha by February 1971. Glen estimated the population of the whole wood to be about 159 in the severe winter of 1981/82 (0.43 birds/ha) and 186 in the milder winter of 1982/83 (0.51 birds/ha). At Wytham, breeding success was very low due to nest predation by corvids and Grey Squirrels. In 1981 only 13 (of 79) nests fledged young and only 20 (of 100) did in 1982. Ford (1987) found them to be transient visitors to most isolated woodlands but found them breeding in only

two (of 20 surveyed). Overall (1988) recorded breeding densities of 0.15–0.61 pairs/ha on his Wytham CBC plot and Morse (1978) estimated the winter population there to be 1.6 birds/ha. Harper found 25–30 pairs in Bagley Woods in 1984 (Wiggins 1984).

Despite the high predation rates suffered by eggs and young, the Long-tailed Tit clearly survives well in the county. Unless corvid or squirrel numbers increase dramatically, we expect that it should continue to do so.

Family: Paridae
Tits

Tits regularly associate in mixed-species flocks outside the breeding season. These flocks sometimes contain more than 100 individuals. Most of these species take a wide range of foods, being chiefly insectivorous in the breeding season but taking an increasing proportion of seed in the diet as winter approaches. Between them the winter flocks divide up the woodland feeding sites with Great Tits feeding most on the ground, the acrobatic Blue Tits in the tree canopy and Marsh and Willow Tits in the shrub layers. They are readily attracted to garden bird tables in winter and most of them readily accept nestboxes.

MARSH TIT
Parus palustris

The Marsh Tit is a locally abundant resident found in a variety of woodland habitats in Oxfordshire, but chiefly in broadleaved and especially coppiced woods.

Aplin (1889) described it as "tolerably abundant" and noted that it was found in a more diverse range of habitats than its name implied. However, it must be remembered that since the Willow Tit was not then known to occur in Britain, it would have been included under the present species, so giving the Marsh Tit the habitat diversity today ascribed to the two species separately. Aplin also notes that the Marsh Tit bands with other tits in winter and especially when feeding on beechmast. With the benefit of hindsight, this description probably refers correctly to the behaviour of the Marsh Tit since Willow Tits rarely join winter flocks (Lack 1986) and Morse (1978) found Marsh Tits in 59% of tit flocks in Wytham.

The Marsh Tit has probably always been the more abundant of the two species in Oxfordshire (see Willow Tit) and there are references in the County Bird Report to its abundance in the past in particular woodlands (e.g. Wychwood Forest, OOS Report 1926; Stonor Park, OOS Report 1932). However, its specific habitat requirements, and especially its relation to the Willow Tit do not seem to be straight forward in the county. The Oxfordshire Atlas map shows a very strong association between the two species across tetrads. That is, they occur together in tetrads more often than would be expected by chance alone (see Appendix 5). If the species differ markedly in their habitat requirements we should expect such a result only if the habitats themselves which are preferred by the two species tended to occur together within tetrads. The map also shows a much stronger association between Marsh Tits and large woodlands than was seen in the Willow Tit (Appendix 5). Similar associations between Marsh and Willow Tits across tetrads are found in Buckinghamshire (A.G. Knox pers. comm.), Greater London (Montier 1977), and Kent (KOS 1981), although in Hertfordshire the species show an equally strong dissociation (Appendix 5). It is likely that this tells us more about the distribution of habitats in these counties than about a real association between the species although several observers in the county have reported birds that they believed to be hybrids (e.g. at Stonor Park, OOS Report 1932 and at Holly Wood in 1984, D.G.C. Harper pers. comm.). Like the Willow Tit, the Marsh Tit is extremely sedentary in Oxfordshire. There have been only 11 recoveries of birds ringed in the county of which none moved more than 9 km.

Alexander (1940) noted that after the severe winter of 1939/40, the density of Marsh Tit in Bagley Wood (227 ha) dropped from 0.53 pairs/ha to 0.44 pairs/ha and Harper found 34 pairs (0.15 pairs/ha) there in 1984 (Wiggins 1984). Ford (1987) found that in Oxfordshire, the species' density was influenced by the size of

Table 5.80. Willow Tit.

The distribution of 34 breeding pairs by habitat, based on the BOS survey of 1964.

Habitat	No. pairs	No. tetrads
Coniferous plantation	5	4
Deciduous coppice	24	21
Mixed	1	1
Other	4	4
TOTAL	34	30

Table 5.81. Willow Tit.

The number of birds recorded by one observer in central Oxfordshire.

Year	Marsh Tit	Willow Tit
1985	37	7
1986	30	8
1987	43	8
1988	44	11
1989	43	12

the wood. He found that isolated woods had on average 1.17 birds/ha compared with only 0.46 birds/ha in control plots of similar size within larger woods. Gosler (1990) found 50–60 pairs of Marsh Tit in 100 ha of mixed woodland on Wytham Hill. He also reported that the proportion of juveniles in the winter population was far higher when there was a good Beech crop, suggesting that like the Great Tit (*cf*), their survival was better at this time.

While they are near the bottom of the tit dominance hierarchy, Marsh Tits avoid competition to some extent by hoarding food, most of which they reclaim within 24 hours. This behaviour does not always escape the notice of other birds. One Marsh Tit busied itself for most of the morning by hoarding sunflower seeds around an east Oxford garden while a Great Tit followed behind at a discreet distance and removed them all!

The apparent association observed between the Marsh Tit and coppiced woodland in the county suggests that any threat to that habitat would threaten the Marsh Tit also. Nationally the Marsh Tit population seems to have declined at a slow but steady rate over many years (Marchant *et al.* 1990). While there is little evidence for such a decline in Oxfordshire, further research into the ecology of this bird, especially comparing it with the Willow Tit would be valuable.

WILLOW TIT
Parus montanus

The Willow Tit is a localised resident whose distribution strongly reflects the availability of suitable habitat. Its unusual behaviour of excavating a nest hole limits it to damp woodland or carr, scrub and hedgerow habitats with standing dead timber. Its status in Oxfordshire has been a source of considerable interest since its initial recognition in Britain in 1897. Before then it was not distinguished from the Marsh Tit and therefore was not included by Aplin in his county avifauna. However, in a detailed assessment of its status in the 1923-24 OOS report and after re-examining existing specimens, he concluded that "it will be seen that it has been found nearly all over the county". He also noted, taking this and the Marsh Tit together that "they (Willow Tits) are far less numerous than they used to be, and are now scarce birds", and that they were at one time commoner in his garden in Bloxham than either the Great, Blue or Coal Tits. He considered the Willow Tit to be common in the Chiltern woods in 1904 and 1906 although it was probably scarcer than the Marsh Tit.

Aplin's assessment stimulated speculation on the relative status of the two species almost annually for many years in the County Bird Report. W.B. Alexander noted that the Willow Tit had disappeared in Bagley Wood in 1940 after a severe winter where it had bred at 0.09

pairs/ha in 1939. In 1941 it was reported from 12 localities around Oxford, and in 1942 it was noted that the Marsh Tit was much commoner in Eastern Quarry Woods. An intensive survey of the species' distribution in 1964 by the BOS found 34 pairs in 30 tetrads. Their distribution by habitats are shown in Table 5.80.

These results, together with those for 1965 which showed that 80% of records came from deciduous coppice led Brownett (BOS Report 1965) to conclude that this was the single most important habitat for the species in the county. The other records came from Norway Spruce, brashed Larch and Pine plantations. A repeat survey in 1982 found 24 pairs in the same area. Although there are local exceptions reported in the OOS Report (e.g. nine Willow to one Marsh Tit ringed at Charlbury in 1971), most reports indicate that this is the rarer species in the county. For example, J. Brucker recorded all of the sightings that he made of the two species in central Oxfordshire over a five-year period. Since approximately equal amounts of time were spent in the field each year, and similar amounts of time in the appropriate habitats, these figures give a useful comparison. They are shown in Table 5.81.

The Oxfordshire Atlas map shows a statistically significant association between the distribution of Willow Tits and that of tetrads containing all or part of a sizable wood (>12.5 ha) although this is a weaker relationship than for the Marsh Tit (see Appendix 5).

In Oxfordshire, the Willow Tit is extremely sedentary. There have been only seven recoveries of birds ringed in the county, of which the longest three movements were 2 km, 6 km and 13 km.

Although Marsh Tits are reported four to five times more often than Willow Tits, the Oxfordshire Atlas revealed Marsh Tits in fewer than twice as many tetrads as the Willow Tit. Hence the latter species must occur at much

lower densities. Harper (Wiggins 1984) found nine pairs of Willow to 34 of Marsh Tit in Bagley Woods in 1984. Ford (1987) found Willow Tit breeding in only one isolated woodland out of 20 that he surveyed although it was a transient visitor to another five suggesting that woodland alone was not the only habitat necessary for the species. Gosler (1990) reported that in most years, about ten pairs bred on the Wytham estate where it occupied the damper ancient woodland areas at the base of the hill (see also Marsh Tit).

The association of this species with deciduous coppice and especially with damp woodland gives some cause for concern for its future. Nationally the CBC has shown a decline in the Willow Tit over the last 15 years although this has taken it back to the level of the mid-1960s (Marchant *et al.* 1990). Further research is necessary to look in detail at the ecology of this bird, especially in comparison with the Marsh Tit.

COAL TIT
Parus ater

The Coal Tit is a locally common resident in Oxfordshire. Although it is closely associated with coniferous woodland (Radford 1966), where it breeds at its highest density and with greatest success, it can also be found in a variety of other wooded or semi-wooded habitats in the county such as mature hedgerows and gardens. For example, in a study of bird densities in predominantly broadleaved woodland habitat 'islands' in Oxfordshire, Ford (1987) found that the occurrence of Coal Tits in an isolated wood depended strongly on the size of that woodland. In fact in such woodlands he found them holding territory in only the two largest (of 20) and at densities of 0.3 and 0.05 pairs/ha. However they were frequent in census plots of

similar size within larger woodland areas and occurred on average at 0.44 birds/ha. In winter, Coal Tits are frequent members of mixed-species flocks. Morse (1978) found that they occurred in 52% of mixed-species flocks in Wytham in winter, but 96% of Coal Tits that he encountered at this time were in such flocks.

The status of the Coal Tit has probably changed little since 1889 when Aplin described it as "tolerably abundant" although it has undoubtedly benefited from conifer planting during the present century. They are, for example, together with the Goldcrest, the most frequent species encountered in the forestry plantations of Bernwood Forest.

Ford's results are supported by the Oxfordshire Atlas map which shows that tetrads containing all or part of a wood greater than 12.5 ha were significantly more likely to contain breeding Coal Tits (see Appendix 5). It is possible that such woods are more likely to contain conifers than smaller woodland.

Coal Tits are remarkably sedentary in our area with only 18% of ringing recoveries showing movements greater than 10 km (Table 5.82). Longer movements tend to occur when there is a poor beechmast crop in the woods. For example, Coal Tits are more frequent in gardens in Oxford at such times as has been noted in the country as a whole (Glue 1982).

Breeding densities of this species can be misleading if habitat, weather conditions and the tree seed crop are not taken into account since although there is a preference for conifers, after mild winters and/or winters with a good beechmast crop, the population may expand dramatically so that Coal Tits are found increasingly in less favoured habitat. Gosler (1990) estimated that there were some 70 pairs in a 100 ha area of broadleaved woodland in Wytham Woods in 1988 – a breeding density of 0.7 pairs/ha. Ford (1987) found a density of 0.44 pairs/ha in the same area in 1983 and Overall (1989) reported densities of 0.14–0.60 pairs/ha in his Wytham CBC plot. Alexander (1940) found that densities in Bagley Woods dropped from 0.09 pairs/ha to none after the cold winter of 1939/40, and Harper (Wiggins 1984) found 53 pairs there in 1984 (a density of 0.23 pairs/ha). Unfortunately, because in most years fewer than four pairs use nestboxes in Wytham, rather little is known about their ecology there compared to that of the Great or Blue Tits (see Great Tit).

BLUE TIT
Parus caeruleus

The Blue Tit is the fourth most widespread resident species breeding in the county, and as in Aplin's day is still "the most abundant of the genus". Its ubiquity results from the very wide range of habitats which it frequents in the county.

Although principally a bird of broadleaved

Table 5.82. Coal Tit.
Recovery distances of Coal Tits ringed in Oxfordshire

Month	Distance in km			
	0-9	10-99	100+	TOTAL
January	4	0	0	4
February	3	0	0	3
March	4	1	0	5
April	4	2	0	6
May	4	0	0	4
June	0	0	0	0
July	1	0	0	1
August	1	1	0	2
September	1	0	0	1
October	3	1	0	4
November	2	1	0	3
December	4	0	0	4
Other	1	1	0	2
TOTAL	32	7	0	39

Table 5.83. Blue Tit.
Recovery distances of Blue Tits ringed in Oxfordshire.

Month	Distance in km			
	0-9	10-99	100+	TOTAL
January	78	13	2	93
February	101	13	0	114
March	100	32	3	135
April	95	14	1	110
May	99	14	0	113
June	52	2	0	54
July	28	2	1	31
August	27	4	0	31
September	14	6	1	21
October	25	14	1	40
November	54	12	1	67
December	66	15	0	81
Other	8	1	0	9
TOTAL	747	142	10	899

woodland in which (like the Great Tit) it breeds most successfully, it also occurs in most woodland and scrub habitats, in mature hedgerow, park and garden habitats and, as the Oxfordshire Atlas map indicates, nests throughout the city of Oxford. Although present in these habitats throughout the year, it is more abundant in gardens in winter when shortage of food forces many individuals out of the woods to feed. Indeed the availability of food in gardens (see Great Tit) may account for the fact that few Oxfordshire Blue Tits move more than 20 km as shown by the table of ringing recoveries (Table 5.83). At this time they are particularly attracted to peanuts or fat hung up for them and ringing has shown that more than 100 individuals might pass through an Oxford garden during a winter.

In woodland the Blue Tit is a frequent member of mixed-species winter flocks. These flocks can sometimes be very large, such as 70 birds feeding in Larches in Bagley Wood in January 1937. Morse (1978) found that 87% of Blue Tits encountered in Wytham Woods in winter were in flocks and 94% of such mixed flocks seen contained Blue Tits, twice as many as contained Great Tits. Although they feed throughout the woodland profile, they are especially active in the canopy although they are easily attracted lower down by nuts put out for them. They are amongst the most acrobatic of the flock-members and will feed on insects in flower buds out on the tips of the smallest twigs.

Like the Great Tit, the Blue Tit population of Wytham Woods has been studied since 1947 by members of the Edward Grey Institute (see Great Tit). While the population density of Marley Wood (the area of Wytham which has been studied for the longest period) tends to fluctuate more or less in parallel with that of the Great Tit population there, this does not seem to be true for the population of the Wytham estate as a whole. In Marley, the density varied between nine and 85 pairs between 1947 and 1983, or 0.36 to 3.4 pairs/ha. Because of competition with the Great Tit for nest sites, rather fewer of the Blue Tits nest in boxes than do members of that species. Indeed in some years only about 60% are able to find a box, and the remainder must use natural holes. In a recent study, it was found that removing boxes from part of the wood had no effect on the density of Blue Tits while it had a considerable effect on the Great Tit population there (East and Perrins 1988). The lower dependence of Blue Tits on nestboxes in which to breed means that it is more difficult to assess their density accurately from nestbox studies alone. Harper (Wiggins 1984) found 108 pairs in Bagley in 1984 (0.47 pairs/ha). Ford (1987) reported densities between 0.5 and 7.14 pairs/ha across 20 Oxfordshire woodlands ranging in size from 0.14 to 18 ha. As in the Great Tit, he found that isolated woods held higher densities of Blue Tits (2.93 birds/ha) than did

woodland census plots of similar size within larger blocks of woodland (2.12 birds/ha).

Rather less is known about the factors regulating the Wytham Blue Tit population than is known for the Great Tit although they are generally assumed to be similar. This is because of similarities in their ecology, and the parallel fluctuation in their populations – at least in Marley Wood. However, their survival may be more affected in Oxfordshire by winter weather than the Great Tit. For example, Alexander (1940) found 1.34 pairs/ha in a mixed woodland area of Bagley in 1939, which was reduced to 0.44 pairs/ha in 1940 after a severe winter. For further information about the Wytham tit population study see Perrins (1979).

GREAT TIT
Parus major

The Great Tit is one of the commonest resident species in Oxfordshire, with records from 97.3% of tetrads. This makes it the eighth most widely distributed species in the county. Furthermore, its status has changed little since 1889 when Aplin described it as a common resident. Its ubiquity reflects its tolerance to a wide range of both urban and rural habitats. Although essentially a bird of broadleaved (and especially Oak) woodland where it breeds at its highest densities and with greatest success, the Great Tit will nest in almost any mature woodland, hedgerow, park or garden habitat in the county.

Being largely sedentary in Britain, Great Tit occur in winter in the same rural habitats as when breeding. However they are considerably more abundant in gardens at this time and are frequent visitors to the winter bird table. The availability of food in winter (see below) may account for the fact that very few Oxfordshire Great Tits travel more than 20 km from where

they were ringed as shown by Table 5.84. The longest movements tend to be during hard weather. In more rural habitats it is an important constituent of mixed-species flocks. Morse (1978) found that 79% of all Great Tits encountered in winter in Wytham Woods were in mixed-species flocks and 49% of such flocks contained Great Tits.

The Great Tit has been described as one of the most studied of bird species, and this is in no small degree due to work carried out in Oxfordshire. In 1947, David Lack and John Gibb of the Edward Grey Institute began a population study of this species on the Wytham estate near Oxford. A great attraction of the Great Tit for population studies is that it readily takes to artificial nestboxes, and in 1947, 214 wooden boxes were put up in the 25 ha Marley Wood. From 1958 C.M. Perrins expanded the study to include the rest of the woodlands of the estate (some 390 ha) so that by 1964 there were nearly 1,000 boxes. In the early 1970s they were all replaced with concrete boxes which greatly reduced both the predation on the tits in the boxes, and the amount of maintenance required.

In Marley Wood (the area with the longest run of data), the breeding population has varied from seven to 86 pairs, or about 0.3–3.5 pairs/ha. Several studies have shown that more than 90% of the Great Tit population nest in the boxes so that accurate estimates of population size are possible. Between 1960 and 1986, the population ranged from 121–354 pairs on the whole estate (or 0.31–0.91 pairs/ha).

Breeding densities are also available for

Oxfordshire woods other than Wytham. Alexander (1940) found 0.44 pairs/ha in mixed woodland in Bagley Wood. Harper (Wiggins 1984) found 79 pairs in Bagley in 1984 (0.35 pairs/ha). Ford (1987) found 0.27–2.38 pairs/ha in 20 Oxfordshire woodlands ranging in size from 0.42–18.0 ha. He also noted that Great Tits bred at higher densities in smaller woods than in larger ones since on average he found 2.0 birds/ha in woodland islands, but only 1.38 in census plots of the same size within larger woodland blocks such as Wytham.

Studies of the Wytham Great Tit population have shown that the size of the breeding population is determined largely by juvenile survival. Particularly important to this is the survival of the young birds during the first few months after fledging. Survival is also related to the quality of the beechmast crop in winter since the breeding population increases after a good mast crop and drops after a poor one. Also there are proportionally more yearling breeders in the population after a good mast crop (see Perrins 1979 for a review). Beechmast is an important food for the tits when available. In a good mast year hundreds of Great Tits can be seen on the ground under the Beeches, busily turning leaves in search of mast. In a poor mast year, emigration from the woods may be considerable, and greater numbers of tits of all species are noted in Oxfordshire gardens. Under these conditions, Gosler (1987) found that subdominant individuals were the first to leave the woods. Despite the relationships between juvenile survival, Beech crop and population change, there is a problem since it is known that most juvenile mortality occurs before the tits are able to feed on mast which only become available in October or November (McCleery and Perrins 1989). Winter weather seems to have little effect on the Oxfordshire Great Tit population and this may be because the birds are buffered against its worst effects by the food provided by householders. In a recent survey of winter feeding around Wytham, Riddington found that 71.5% of 253 households provided food and of these, 61.7% provided peanuts and 51.7% provided fat for tits (Riddington pers. comm.).

Despite more than 40 years of study of the Wytham tit population, there are still a great many questions unanswered, especially concerning the importance of immigration and emigration from the wood since about half of the breeding birds in the wood in any one year were not hatched there. For a review of the Wytham Great Tit study up to 1979 see Perrins (1979).

Table 5.84. Great Tit.
Recovery distances of Great Tits ringed in Oxfordshire.

| Month | Distance in km | | | |
	0-9	10-99	100+	TOTAL
January	28	14	1	43
February	32	9	1	42
March	51	13	0	64
April	44	6	1	51
May	54	7	0	61
June	48	8	0	56
July	30	4	0	34
August	25	2	0	27
September	9	2	0	11
October	22	7	0	29
November	26	6	1	33
December	22	15	1	38
Other	4	0	0	4
TOTAL	395	93	5	493

Family: Sittidae
Nuthatches

The Nuthatch is the sole British representative of this family which has another two species in Europe and 25 species world-wide. Structually, behaviourally and ecologically, the Nuthatch shares many features in common with the true tits with which it is closely related and with which it often flocks in winter.

NUTHATCH
Sitta europaea

The status of the Nuthatch has changed little since 1889 when Aplin described it as "... resident in some numbers, but somewhat local...". He also described its habitat requirements as any "... situations which afford large timber". This remains a useful description since in addition to mature broadleaved woodland (especially if it contains Oak), Nuthatches occur in a variety of parkland and mature garden habitats. Nests are usually found in Oak or Beech although there is one report of a nest in an apple tree. They will also use nestboxes.

Nuthatches occupy large territories of 4–5 ha which the pair defends vigorously throughout the year so that they are rarely found in small or isolated woods. Ford (1987), in a study of the birds in such woodlands in Oxfordshire found them breeding in only two out of 20 isolated woods surveyed and at densities of 0.42 and 0.06 pairs/ha. However, he found them in three out of eight control census plots of similar size within larger blocks of woodland. Morse (1978) estimated the population density at 0.36 pairs/ha in Wytham Woods. Gosler (1990) estimated their density there to be about 0.22 pairs/ha or 80–90 pairs. Harper (Wiggins 1984) found 14 pairs in Bagley Wood or about 0.14 pairs/ha. Provided an adequate number of old trees are present, it inhabits parkland and large gardens as well as woodland. There were estimates of 25–30 pairs in Blenheim Park in 1981, and of three or four pairs in the University Parks in 1984. The parkland nature of central Oxford with its many mature trees, enables some to nest in the larger college gardens, in north Oxford, and on the slopes of Headington Hill.

The Oxfordshire Atlas map shows the importance of large woodlands to the Nuthatch as the distribution indicates a strong association with tetrads containing all or part of a wood greater than 12.5 ha (Appendix 5). From autumn

1977 to summer 1978 the OOS and BOS surveyed the distribution of the Nuthatch in the county (Parr 1978). They found them in 20% of tetrads in October and 50% in March when they were more vocal. The Oxfordshire Atlas recorded them from 31.5% of tetrads which probably represents little or no change from the earlier study since (as stated in the earlier report) the limited coverage of that study was biased in favour of tetrads containing suitable habitat for Nuthatch. Because of their strong attachment to a territory, nuthatches are extremely sedentary. Of the 15 Oxfordshire ringing recoveries, none moved more than 9 km.

Radford (1966) stated that Nuthatches often suffered in hard winters, such as 1917 and 1963. This is supported by Overall's figures from his CBC site in Wytham Woods which showed drops of 50–70% after the severe winters of 1971/72, 75/76, 78/79 and 81/82 (Overall 1988). This also might reflect a reluctance to leave the territory when conditions deteriorate

although they will come readily to garden feeders if these are in close proximity to the territory (e.g. Oxford, Woodstock near Blenheim, Kennington near Bagley Wood, Headington Hill and Risinghurst near Shotover).

Despite their extreme territoriality, Morse (1978) found that Nuthatches were regular constituents of mixed-species flocks in Wytham in winter. Of 49 encounters that he had with Nuthatches, 93% were in mixed-species flocks and 19% of flocks contained Nuthatch. On average, a flock contained 1.1 Nuthatch.

A precise account of the population changes which have occurred in the county is impossible partly because of a lack of detailed information in earlier accounts. Aplin (1889) described it as "numerous about many villages where old Elms are found". The loss of the Elm from the county in the 1970s presumably had an effect. The deaths of ancient Oaks at Blenheim, Wychwood and elsewhere, and the loss of mature timber in the gales of 1987 and 1990 has restricted its habitat a little further but there is no evidence for any significant effect of this as yet.

Family: Certhiidae
Treecreepers

The Treecreeper is the sole breeding representative in Britain of this small family. Although few of the places in which it feeds could truly be considered as exclusively available to this species, in practice, few other birds feed on the small invertebrates which it finds in and on the bark of trees and no other species specialises on this ecological niche in the manner of the Treecreeper.

TREECREEPER
Certhia familiaris

The Treecreeper is a fairly common resident in most habitats with trees in Oxfordshire. Aplin (1889) described it as "... a common but not numerous resident", and pointed out that it could be found especially in pollard willows and orchard trees "... to which it is very partial". Radford described it as "moderately common in wooded places" and that its status had not changed since Aplin's day.

The Oxfordshire Atlas map shows that the Treecreeper is widespread in the county. It also shows that its distribution is strongly influenced by the availability of large woodland blocks (see Appendix 5). However, it would be wrong to give the impression that they were found only in woods. It is, for example, also common in parkland and along tributaries of the Thames, and Aplin's comment about pollarded willows is no less true today.

Treecreepers are extremely sedentary in

Oxfordshire. Of the eight ringing recoveries available for analysis, the three longest movements were 19 km in March 1964, 7 km between May and November 1962 and 7 km between January and March 1977. The rest were recovered within 1 km of the place of ringing.

Radford (1966) noted that because of its inconspicuous nature, the Treecreeper was regularly overlooked in the County Bird Report. Inconspicuous it surely is as it scuttles mouse-like along the trunk or under a branch of a tree, but uninteresting it is not since it is one of few small resident species which remains insectivorous throughout the winter. There is much still to learn about how its behaviour allows it to do this. Certainly communal roosting is likely to be important in severe weather, but it is still not clear exactly how they benefit from joining mixed-species flocks of tits in winter. Morse (1978) found that 33% of such flocks in Wytham Woods contained Treecreepers, that on average when present these flocks contained 1.2 birds per flock and that 96% (of 89) of Treecreepers seen were with mixed-species flocks.

In mid-winter Morse (1978) estimated that the population density of Treecreepers in Wytham Woods was 0.18 birds/ha. Ford (1987) found breeding Treecreepers in ten isolated woodlands (out of 20 surveyed) in Oxfordshire where they occurred on average at 0.46 birds/ha compared with 0.11 birds/ha in census plots of the same area in larger woods (mostly in Wytham). Overall (1988) reported a density of 0.15–0.30 pairs/ha on his Wytham CBC plot and Gosler (1990) estimated the Wytham population to be between 78 and 117 pairs. Harper (Wiggins 1984) found 35 pairs in Bagley Wood, a density of about 0.35 pairs/ha. The population is affected by hard winter weather. It was estimated that their numbers might have been reduced by as much as 50–70% after the hard winter of 1917, and W.B. Alexander found none after a harsh winter, in his census plot in Bagley in 1940 where there had been 0.18 pairs/ha in 1939.

Family: Oriolidae
Orioles

One oriole species occurs in Britain, and although it breeds intermittently and in low numbers in the country, it generally occurs as a vagrant.

GOLDEN ORIOLE
Oriolus oriolus

A rare vagrant. In total there have been 17 records of Golden Oriole accepted for Oxfordshire: eight in May, eight in June and one in July. The timing of visits has been erratic: five were reported between 1862 and 1886, only two in the long interval from 1897–1962, ten between 1962 and 1982 and one 1983–1990. Presumably most of these birds were overshooting on migration. None showed any inclination to stay, although one account of nesting at Haseley in the nineteenth century sounded convincing. There were two together in July 1891 and June 1916. All other records were of solitary birds.

Appearances are mostly in woodland and show a haphazard scatter. Recent sites have included Wroxton, Wytham, Freeland, Witney, south Oxford wood, Appleton, Tackley and Childrey.

Family: Laniidae
Shrikes

Four species of shrike have occurred in Oxfordshire. Of these, one formerly bred but is now extremely rare in Britain, another is an occasional winter visitor and the other two are rare vagrants.

Table 5.85. Great Grey Shrike.
Number of occupied sites. 1960-1989.

Period	No. of sites
1960-64	3
1965-69	13
1970-74	25
1975-79	26
1980-85	1
1986-90	1

Table 5.86. Great Grey Shrike.
Times of occurrence, by quarter-month periods. (excluding one undated record in 1960/61) (After Riddington 1991).

Month	Week	No. of birds
October	3	2
	4	6
November	1	6
	2	6
	3	8
	4	8
December	1	12
	2	10
	3	12
	4	10
January	1	13
	2	12
	3	16
	4	13
February	1	13
	2	15
	3	14
	4	14
March	1	11
	2	8
	3	10
	4	9
April	1	2
	2	2

RED-BACKED SHRIKE
Lanius collurio

An extremely rare summer visitor. The Red-backed Shrike has never been common in Oxfordshire. Not only has breeding ceased, but it is rarely seen as a passage visitor any longer. Between 1967 and 1990 there were only two records. Single birds were seen at Aston Upthorpe on 26 August 1978 and at Dorchester Gravel Pits on 31 August 1983.

It was unpredictable and local in its breeding range in the nineteenth century and the first half of the twentieth century. Aplin (1889) met with it on only two occasions in north Oxfordshire where it remained uncommon, but in some years it was easy to find around Oxford, on the Berkshire Downs, in the Thames valley and the Vale of the White Horse. It seems to have flourished in the 1930s when, for example, there were three pairs breeding in one field near Wolvercote.

In 1937 it featured as one of the species scheduled for special attention by the OOS. This showed the beginning of a decrease as several previous nesting sites were found to be deserted (OOS Report 1937). The only place near Oxford where a breeding pair was located was at Southfield Golf Course.

The decline continued uninterrupted, and by the 1960s very few pairs remained anywhere. Three pairs were discovered in 1960, at Henley, Radley and Harwell, and two pairs in 1963. Since then the only breeding record was of a pair which nested unsuccessfully in central Oxfordshire in 1967.

The few remaining Red-backed Shrikes in England prefer a habitat of dry, bushy heathland (Bibby 1973) which is conspicuously lacking in Oxfordshire. Its continued withdrawal from the country, which has been linked with the reduction in insect supplies caused by climatic deterioration (Sharrock 1976), gives little hope for its re-establishment here in the near future.

LESSER GREY SHRIKE
Lanius minor

There is one record of this rare vagrant; an adult bird in full breeding plumage was seen at Standlake on 17 June 1978.

GREAT GREY SHRIKE
Lanius excubitor

The Great Grey Shrike (illustrated below) is an occasional visitor in winter. Alexander (1949) called it "a rare winter visitor", noting that it had been recorded over 20 times "in the last 60 years". Radford was able to amend this status description to an "occasional winter visitor" for it had been seen "nearly 20 times" between 1948 and 1962 in the two counties of Oxfordshire and Berkshire (former boundaries). Since then there has been a striking rise followed by an equally pronounced fall in the number of

winter visits. This is illustrated clearly in the summary of the totals of sites at which it has been found in five-yearly periods between 1960 and 1989 (Table 5.85).

All records have been of single birds apart from an account of two together at a site between Wantage and Didcot. While the overall period of observations extends from 23 October to 14 April, most were seen in the mid-winter months (Table 5.86).

The exceptional period in the late 1960s and the 1970s described above was also noted in neighbouring counties, and was part of a general, sustained influx into Britain. During these years of plenty, some birds over-wintered in areas near Otmoor, Dorchester, Stanton Harcourt, Sandford Sewage Farm, Sonning Eye and Farmoor. One or two stayed for a considerable time: for example, one remained near the river at Farmoor from 25 October 1973 to 20 March 1974. Riddington (1991) found that of the *ca.* 58 records of Great Grey

Shrikes during the period 1940–1990 at least 18 (31.0%) refer to genuine over-wintering birds. The reasons for the influx are not well understood. Lack (1986) mentions breeding success, summer survival, abundant prey and weather as possible factors. As our county is outside the Great Grey Shrikes' normal wintering range, we may have to wait some time for a repetition of the events which allowed us to enjoy its presence regularly.

WOODCHAT SHRIKE
Lanius senator

A rare summer visitor. There are five records for the county. Single birds have been noted at Fifield in May 1905, at Churn on five dates between 14 August and 6 September 1958, at Wheatley on 1 June 1981, at Little Milton from 14 July to 2 August in the same year and at Letcombe Regis on 14 and 15 June 1985.

Family: Corvidae
Crows

Seven corvid species have been recorded in Oxfordshire during the twentieth century. Of these, two are vagrants while the other five are abundant residents. Two species in particular (Magpie and Carrion Crow) have increased dramatically as a result of the relaxation in game keeping during this century. Their populations are now at levels where concern has been expressed over their possible effects on small passerine populations but the evidence that they have had an effect is weak. In this regard, perhaps of greater concern should be and growing population of cats, the result of whose depredations is unknown.

Table 5.87. Jay.
Breeding population densities in three Oxfordshire woodlands.

Site and reference	Area	No. pairs/km²
Wytham Woods Gosler (1990)	390	9.0-11.0
Bagley Wood Wiggins (1984)	227	6.6
Little Wittenham NR Wiggins (1984)	52	11.5

JAY
Garrulus glandarius

Each of the crow species resident in Oxfordshire is associated to some degree with the woodland habitat, but none more so than the Jay. Nesting almost exclusively in mixed and deciduous woodland and in more open but wooded parks and gardens, its noisy, raucous calls will penetrate a woodland and allow its presence to be ascertained with ease. Its colourful pink plumage with prominent white rump and black tail ensure accurate identification, although location of the nest, which is usually in dense cover, is rather more difficult. It is therefore not surprising to note that whilst in the course of the Oxfordshire Atlas it was recorded in 51% of tetrads, 40% of these were in the 'possible' breeding category. However, bearing in mind the sedentary nature of the resident Jays (the furthest recorded movement of an Oxfordshire ringed bird is 33 km), it would be surprising if the majority of these records were not valid. The

distribution map corresponds closely with the distribution of woodlands in the county although there are a few gaps, which are mostly smaller woods. Ford (1987) showed that the presence of Jays in woodland in the breeding season was governed by area and pairs nested only in woods greater than 2.9 ha in size. Accurate estimates of breeding densities in the county are limited. This is due in part to territories of nesting pairs overlapping considerably thus making it a difficult species to census, but estimates at three sites (Table 5.87) give densities of between six and 12 pairs/km².

During the 1980s there appears to have been an increase in the local breeding population with birds noted with increasing frequency away from woodland. They have even nested in central Oxford.

As with other members of the crow family, the diet is catholic. In the breeding season, considerable numbers of large invertebrate prey items are taken as too are small vertebrates including birds, their eggs and nestlings. This habit does not endear the Jay to gamekeepers. After the summer, and through the winter, acorns and beechmast are gleaned from the woodland floor and food caches made. Every year, particularly in October, they become conspicuous as they leave the woods to scour the countryside. Acorns are the main attraction, but grain is taken in years when the favoured foods are in short supply. Gardens are also used where scattered grain, kitchen scraps and peanuts are taken. Some individuals have been known to feed tit-fashion on suspended nut bags although this is a rare occurrence. In 1975, a garden in Stanton St. John was raided by a Jay who, in quick succession lifted, and flew off with, a dozen crocus corms, presumably to store for a later date.

Since acorns and beechmast are so important in the diet of the Jay, if supplies on mainland Europe are restricted due to a poor crop, large numbers of continental birds will irrupt into Britain, including Oxfordshire, in the autumn. Such an irruption took place in 1983 and a strong passage of birds through the county was noted. More than 100 birds were seen heading westwards over Shotover in October and at the end of that month 50 birds were counted in Shotover Country Park. At the time of these influxes, parties in excess of 20 birds are not uncommon.

MAGPIE
Pica pica

There is no mistaking the Magpie. With it's bold, pied plumage and raucous chattering call, it is a familiar resident of the county in both rural and urban settings. The data from the Oxfordshire Atlas show this clearly since, with records coming from 709 (94.2%) tetrads, it is the second most widely distributed member of the crow family in the county. Blank squares are probably a result of limitations imposed by the availability of nest sites and also, in some instances, by persecution on heavily keepered estates. Whilst a large proportion of the records submitted fall into the 'possible' category of recording, this is almost certainly a reflection of low observer coverage. The largely sedentary nature of the species, coupled with other observations and experiences, means that such records can be assumed to be good evidence of breeding pairs.

The success of the species is a reflection of its opportunistic nature, able to exploit a wide variety of habitats in the absence of predators and, persecution. Thus it may be seen in woodlands, on farmland where hedgerows and copses provide nesting opportunities and extending into the parks and gardens of built-up areas. Indeed it is common in the centre of Oxford where it was unknown in the 1940s.

Nests are quite large affairs and are built either into thorn bushes and hedges, or else high up in mature standard trees where the

typically domed nest and the activities around it can easily be observed. Activity around nests can be seen year-round, with nest building noted throughout the winter months although eggs are not usually laid until March.

The Magpie has not always enjoyed such a widespread distribution in Oxfordshire. In the first half of the century it was regarded as common in the north and east of the county and rare or absent from much of the south and west. There was an increase during and after the Second World War and since that time there has been an apparently relentless spread through the county which was still being noted into the mid-1980s. This is part of an expansion witnessed throughout the UK (Marchant et al. 1990). Since then, there seems to have been a more stable population in some areas as the population reached saturation, and even some local declines e.g. Bagley Woods (Wiggins 1984) although elsewhere numbers continue to increase. For example, a CBC plot in Wytham Woods recorded fewer than one pair present between 1971 and 1976, one to two pairs between 1977 and 1983 and up to three pairs from 1984-1989.

Food taken is varied — carrion, invertebrates including ectoparasites of Fallow Deer (e.g. in Magdalen College) and sheep, and items of plant material such as berries and grain, as well as food provided at garden feeding stations. The Magpie will also take the eggs and young of many bird species. The taking of gamebirds brings it into conflict with game-keeping interests and shooting is widely practised. In 1980, one estate claimed that 140 birds were shot in the first five months of the year. Interestingly, the gamekeeper later reported that in 1981, all of the former territories in that area had been filled by incoming birds. Eggs and young of songbirds may also be taken and, although this makes a distressing sight when witnessed in a garden setting, there is currently no evidence to suggest any decline in numbers of these small bird species (Birkhead 1991).

Whilst the Magpie may not be a colonial nester, it is far from being a solitary bird and even during the breeding season may be seen in small parties and in larger, loose-knit flocks. The largest congregations may be seen at communal winter roosts or early in the year before the breeding season. Even so, a flock of 32 in February 1990 is the highest figure recorded although 23 in one tree at Hartslock in 1984 must have made quite an impressive sight.

NUTCRACKER
Nucifraga caryocatactes

The unprecedented invasion of this species into Britain during the autumn of 1968 enabled Oxfordshire to add this species to its list. At Cholsey there were two or three in late December 1968 and in January 1969. Then at Blenheim there was one on 14 April 1969.

JACKDAW
Corvus monedula

The Jackdaw is a very numerous resident with an extensive distribution in Oxfordshire. Whilst each of the resident members of the crow family regularly frequent the towns and villages of Oxfordshire, the Jackdaw has the closest association with Man. As a hole-nesting species, it has been able successfully to exploit the nesting opportunities that exist in buildings and the majority of nests in the county occur in chimney-pots, church towers, barns and a range of older style buildings. In such situations, sizeable colonies thrive, although such habits are not always welcomed. Despite many attempts to prevent entry to potential nest sites, enough holes and crevices exist to ensure continued success in such places. Naturally occurring holes, usually in trees, occasionally in quarries are also used by nesting Jackdaws and sizeable colonies can occur in woodlands and in open wooded parkland where a good number of mature trees exist. Nestboxes, often those intended for Kestrel or Tawny Owl will be taken up by Jackdaws and there are a few instances of nests in Rabbit burrows. Birds nesting around habitation may scavenge for food close to the nest site or move into the open countryside to forage for a wide range of animal and plant material.

The Oxfordshire Atlas data show how widely distributed the species is during the breeding season. The main gaps are in areas where woodlands and man-made structures are absent, although the apparent thinness in distribution in parts of the Chilterns is curious. This may be due to a lack of nesting holes or it may be due to inadequate observer coverage. Also, 24% of the records are in the 'possible' breeding category and a large proportion of these may be of birds away from the nest area. The conspicuous nature of the species in the breeding season

ensures that, in the main, few pairs will have been overlooked.

Like other corvids, Jackdaws are highly sedentary in the county (44 out of 50 recoveries of birds ringed in Oxfordshire were within 9 km of the ringing-site) but one bird ringed in Oxford on 24 February 1933 was at Oosterbeek, Netherlands on 25 April 1934 (488 km E).

Whilst large numbers of birds can be found around towns throughout the year, once the breeding season is finished and through the winter months, large flocks of Jackdaws can be found feeding on pasture, ploughed fields or on stubble. Flocks of several hundred birds, often feeding alongside Rooks, are not uncommon and on several occasions counts of more than 1,000 birds have been made. As with other members of the crow family, refuse tips are also frequented. Winter roosts of several thousand birds are also documented, again congregating with Rooks.

Whilst there would appear to be no evidence of any long-term decline in the population (all previous accounts of the birds of Oxfordshire regard it as a common or very common species), there may be a case for the local monitoring of colonies as older buildings are demolished or modernised with the possible loss of nest sites.

ROOK
Corvus frugilegus

A highly abundant and gregarious species, this familiar member of the crow family enjoys a widespread distribution throughout Oxfordshire. Familiar as a breeding species, the Rook's colonial nesting habit, ensures that they are readily visible, especially as many rookeries are traditional sites occupied year after year. A large proportion of these rookeries are close to and within villages and towns. For some years there has been a small number of birds nesting in the heart of Oxford at the southern end of St. Giles, a remnant of a former, larger rookery, possibly dating from times when this was outside the city walls.

The very conspicuous nature of the Rook, coupled with an early start to the breeding season means that the species is relatively easy to census. The earliest counts in the county were made in 1928 and an area of 580 km^2 in the Oxford district gave a nesting density of 11.6 nests/km^2. Three years later a count in the Thames valley, which included the area surveyed in 1928, yielded a density of 12.4 nests/km^2 and, as part of a BTO survey in 1944, a figure of 17.5 nests/km^2 was obtained.

In 1972 work at the Edward Grey Institute indicated a dramatic decline in the county to less than one half of the 1944 figure. In 1975 the BTO carried out another national Rook survey which, in Oxfordshire, located 21,634 nests equating to a density of nine nests/km^2. Table 5.88 gives a summary of these population changes. The exact reasons for the decline are

unclear although changes in agricultural practices, the onset of Dutch Elm Disease, tree felling and increasing urbanisation have probably all contributed. The 1975 survey also demonstrated how the breeding density varied across the county. The upper Thames valley, with its fertile alluvial soils, provide birds with good feeding conditions and provide a good medium for tree growth. Hence the highest densities occur in this region. East of Oxford and for example around Otmoor where soils are heavier (hardening when dry) feeding conditions are less favourable. Here too there is a tendency for fields to be smaller and the landscape less open — further factors to deter feeding Rooks.

Rookery size varies considerably. Of the 924 rookeries located in 1975, colonies varied from just two or three nests up to rookeries in excess of 300 nests. However most are small with about 300 colonies having fewer than ten pairs (Table 5.89). The choice of tree species in which the rookery was situated is also interesting. The main factor in the choice appears to be the height of the tree and Table 5.90 shows the relative importance of the different species. As can be seen, Elm was of particular importance. This is of great significance since shortly after this survey, the Elm ceased to be a significant part of the landscape and consequently many traditional rookeries were lost.

It is difficult to assess precisely how well the Rook has fared since the mid-1970s. Although the data from the Oxfordshire Atlas show a comparable number of occupied areas, recent numerical information is lacking. A breeding season survey by the BOS in 1991 showed that in their survey area the number of occupied nests located was of the same order as that found in 1975, that is 7,787. This latter survey also revealed that there had been a significant reduction in the proportion of smaller rookeries (i.e. those of fewer than 25 nests).

It would appear though that Rooks have managed to establish themselves in a range of smaller trees including in some areas willows and Hawthorns eight metres in height. Man-made structures have also been used as nest sites and in 1976 nests were built on electricity pylons near Clifton Hampden and Kidlington, a habit that has spread to a number of other locations in the county.

Flocks of birds are easily observed as they feed in the open fields probing for invertebrate prey as well as taking a range of plant material such as grain and even fallen fruit and acorns. From late summer, after the young birds have joined them, these flocks swell dramatically. Numbers in excess of 500 are regularly seen and feeding flocks of over a 1,000 birds have been recorded. Birds may also be seen gleaning fallen seed along road edges and verges in rural areas, particularly early in the morning, or scavenging on refuse tips throughout the day.

Rooks form large winter roosts. In this period, birds are drawn from a wide area to create roosting groups in woodland numbering several thousand birds. A site at Chislehampton, was extensively used until the early 1980s when the wood was felled. In more recent times, sites at Otmoor Spinney and at Cumnor have been used.

The Rook's ability to use a wide range of nest sites coupled with a predominantly agricultural landscape has conferred some degree of success upon the species in Oxfordshire. Indeed, its ability to adapt to changing circumstances appears to have been the key to that success. Whilst the Rook has been subjected to a measure of often unnecessary persecution (including poisoning in recent times), the population appears to be stable. An extensive county-wide survey is now needed, particularly since we are entering a further period of change to the agricultural environment (e.g. a ban on stubble burning) and a new benchmark is required to assess the effects of these developments.

CARRION CROW
Corvus corone corone

With a presence in 94% of Oxfordshire tetrads, the Carrion Crow is a well represented resident in the county. It is also highly sedentary here. While this status has been enjoyed for over a century, the species has increased in number during this period, a trend also borne out by national CBC indices.

During the breeding season, they are predominantly solitary birds, nesting high in mature trees along hedgerows or in parkland and in copses or larger woods, especially towards their edges. They are at all times wary birds, and slip silently off the nest at the approach of a possible intruder. Such behaviour may have led to the relatively high percentage of 'possible' breeding records as birds move into open fields without betraying the exact location of the nest.

Table 5.88. Rook.
Nesting density in Oxfordshire 1928-1975.

Year	Density (nests/km²)
1928	11.6
1931	12.4
1944	17.5
1972	8.2
1975	9.0

Table 5.89. Rook.
Rookery size, 1975.

Rookery size nests	No. of rookeries
1-25	666
26-50	165
51-100	69
101-200	17
201-300	6
301-400	1

Table 5.90. Rook.
Tree species utilised by nesting Rooks, 1975.

Tree species	% of rookeries
Elm	45
Ash	18
Beech	17
Oak	6
Sycamore	3
Scot's Pine	2
Poplar	2
Chestnut	1.5
Other	10.5

the normally solitary Carrion Crow can be found in considerable numbers and quite large congregations can occur. For example, loose flocks of 300 birds were noted at Alkerton Tip in January 1986. Since the 1940s there has been a regular flock of 100–150 Carrion Crows on Port Meadow. These are mainly young or non-breeding birds, which, in the evening, fly over towards Wytham to roost.

The Hooded Crow *Corvus corone cornix* is a rare vagrant to Oxfordshire. During the nineteenth century, small numbers were noted in the county during most winters. It is now an uncommon winter visitor, occurring only sporadically in the county and indications are that it is becoming more rare, there having been no reports since 1982. It was recorded in nine of the years between 1950 and 1964 and in ten of the years in the period 1965–1988. The sightings are mainly of single birds although a pair was seen at Farmoor in December 1975.

Carrion Crows are omnivorous and opportunistic. This makes them very adaptable, a factor which has been instrumental in their success. They can be watched foraging in open fields for invertebrates and grain, patrolling roads for mammals and birds killed by vehicles, or congregating around rubbish tips. In the urban setting, litter bins and general roadside garbage also excite interest from Carrion Crows. They frequently take small mammals and birds, especially if those prey items are sick or injured, and will take the nestlings of a wide range of bird species. To this end, harassment of ground nesters such as Lapwing is common. A rather more unusual feeding record is one of a party of 50 birds aerially feeding at dusk for flying beetles. Water-borne food is gratefully accepted and the edges of lakes, rivers and flood meadows, particularly when flood waters recede, can provide rich pickings. Dead trout at Farmoor are regularly consumed, and when part of the Oxford Canal was drained in 1977, mussels and stranded fish were eagerly taken. It is when feeding opportunities such as these occur that

RAVEN
Corvus corax

The Raven occurs as a rare and irregular vagrant to the county. Until the nineteenth century they were known to be quite common in Oxfordshire and remains of birds of this species have been discovered in archaeological remains from Iron Age to medieval times (Wilson 1987). The last known breeding pair was shot at their nest on top of the Column of Victory in Blenheim Park in 1847.

Records in the present century total 21 sightings of 23 birds, all but five since 1970, with a maximum of six records of seven birds in 1978. Birds have been recorded from sites throughout the county and in all months of the year except July and November.

Some caution must be exercised in the interpretation of records, since birds are kept in captivity and free-flying escapes do occur. A bird over Kidlington in July 1986 was believed to fall into this category and has not been included in the above analysis.

Family: Sturnidae
Starlings

One species of starling is common throughout Europe although it occurs only as a winter visitor in the south. In Britain it is a widespread resident whose numbers are swollen in winter by arrivals fleeing the severe weather of northern and eastern Europe.

STARLING
Sturnus vulgaris

An abundant and extensively distributed resident whose numbers are greatly enhanced by continental immigrants in winter. The Starling is a hole-nesting species, once limited to nesting in trees in woodland, but now in hedgerow habitat as well as in a range of buildings including factories, warehouses, barns and houses. Nests may also be found amongst burrows in Sand Martin colonies, and in 1982 birds nested in the tail-planes of VC10s at RAF Abingdon. The debris from the nest, the loud screeching calls of the young and the conspicuous flights of the adults during nest building and when feeding the young, make the species very obvious during the breeding season. Hence pairs are unlikely to be overlooked, and the results of the Oxfordshire Atlas are considered accurate. Moreover, 86% of registrations were of proven breeding (the highest of all species) indicating the ease of locating nesting birds.

In Aplin's time, the Starling population was increasing in Oxfordshire, as elsewhere in Britain, an observation which Aplin (1889) attributed in part to the loss of predators, notably the Sparrowhawk. Prior to this the species was a very scarce breeder. Increases continued so that by the mid-twentieth century it was extremely common, although in recent years the impression of some local ornithologists is that there has been a slight decline, which agrees with the evidence for a national decline during the 1980s shown in the CBC data (Marchant *et al.* 1990).

In the autumn and winter Starlings become even more prominent. Huge numbers of birds from northern Europe and from more northerly parts of Britain, move into the county. During the day they forage widely, typically feeding in open fields alongside gulls, Lapwings or Golden Plover. They also visit refuse tips, scavenge in towns and villages, and glean food from around farmyards. Flocks enter gardens, taking not only food scattered on tables and on the ground but also woodpecker-fashion, on hanging feeders.

The origin of these wintering birds has been clearly demonstrated with a considerable number of ringing recoveries from almost as far east as Moscow. The maximum distance travelled by a bird ringed in the county is 2,772 km. Figure 5.76 shows the origin of those wintering birds. In addition, some are resident in the county and only migrate when weather conditions become harsh.

Moderate-sized, post-breeding roosts form in the summer, but in winter these roosts may exceed 10,000 birds and flocks estimated to contain at least 100,000 birds have been reported. Roost sites may be used for many years and generally occur in areas of thick scrub or in woodland. Some typical recent roosts are indicated in Table 5.91.

Roosts of the size shown in Table 5.91 provide a most stunning spectacle as they gather from all directions with the approach of sunset. Roosts often build up within a season and then,

Table 5.91. Starling.
Some Oxfordshire winter roosts.

Site	Period	No. of birds
Marston (Oxford)	1950s	10,000
Chalgrove	1970s & 1980s	15,000
Mollington	1981	20,000
Woodcote	1981	20,000
Kidlington	1980-89	<10,000
Harcourt Hill	1987	40,000-100,000
Steventon	1987	70,000

Figure 5.76. Starling.
Ringing recoveries.

just as rapidly, are abandoned mid-way through the winter. The reason for this abrupt desertion is unclear, although where roosts are in deciduous or mixed woodland, it may be that birds move off to seek denser evergreen vegetation once all leaf cover has been lost.

There is no doubt as to the success of the Starling in Oxfordshire. 'Garrulous', 'gregarious' and 'greedy' are terms one might use to describe the Starling; more appropriate adjectives might be 'social' and 'opportunist'.

Its aggressive behaviour at the bird table and on farmland are reasons for its poor image, but on closer inspection it is found to be an attractive bird worthy of study. Despite its rather messy habits it is probably more beneficial than harmful, devouring many soil-dwelling invertebrate pests and it will be interesting to watch how the Starling adapts to the various changes that the twenty-first century will undoubtedly bring.

Family: Ploceidae
Sparrows

The two species of sparrows share many ecological features with the finches and buntings. Both these species are resident in Oxfordshire although the Tree Sparrow has declined considerably in the last 30 years.

HOUSE SPARROW
Passer domesticus

The House Sparrow is an abundant and widespread resident in Oxfordshire occurring in close association with human habitation. This is demonstrated by the results of the Oxfordshire Atlas in which birds were recorded in 94.6% of tetrads. Vacant squares are those with few buildings. Nests are most commonly built on ledges in buildings of all types and, in favourable situations, large colonies may prosper. Older properties, with easy access to roof spaces are most often used and thatched roofs are especially favoured. Many modern buildings do not provide such easy nesting opportunities, and along with barn conversions and the general improvements to older houses, have possibly lead to a slight decline in numbers in recent years. House Sparrows will also take over the nests of other birds such as Tree Sparrows, House Martins and Swallows and will often oust box-nesting Blue Tits.

House Sparrows are essentially sedentary. Ringing records show that of 385 recoveries of birds ringed in Oxfordshire, only five were found outside the county and only one of these travelled more than 100 km, i.e. a bird ringed in Kidlington in October 1966 which was found dead three weeks later in Southampton. Another interesting ringing recovery is of a bird that was shown to have lived at least seven years. However, the distribution of recoveries through the year, which for such a bird as the House Sparrow generally reflect the distribution of mortality, is interesting. Figure 5.77 shows this pattern for the 364 recoveries that were within 9 km of the ringing site. Some 75% of recoveries occurred between March and July with a peak in May, while the coldest period of December to February claimed only 18%. While it seems likely that the species is buffered against winter weather by exploiting feeding stations provided by householders, the summer recoveries might reflect heavy losses to cats during the breeding season.

During the autumn and winter, large flocks may be seen foraging on open fields, away from buildings, or around farmyards. Parties of several hundred birds are not uncommon and during the 1960s, flocks of several thousand were recorded. Whether this decrease in winter flock size is another indication of a decline is unclear; it may be that with more food provided in domestic gardens, birds are dispersed more widely.

House Sparrows may attain pest status in agricultural and horticultural situations, despoiling grain and other harvested crops and damaging growing plants. Aplin (1889) described this problem in some depth. At that time the population was undergoing a rapid expansion, and the species was treated as vermin. In some villages, church wardens would offer a reward for all dead sparrows.

It is hardly surprising that such a common species is hardly ever mentioned in the local bird reports and the problems inherent in the censusing of House Sparrows do not allow easy

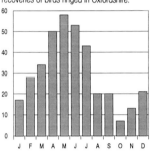

Figure 5.77. House Sparrow.
Monthly distribution of 364 local (<9 km) recoveries of birds ringed in Oxfordshire.

Table 5.92. Tree Sparrow.
Maximum size of winter flocks recorded in Oxfordshire in each five-year period 1955-1989.

Period	Number
1955-59	100
1960-64	100
1965-69	2000
1970-74	1000
1975-79	500
1980-84	200
1985-89	100

Table 5.93. Tree Sparrow.
Occupancy of nestboxes at Coneygree Wood, 1958-1971. (After Scroggs 1974).

Year	No. of boxes occupied	No. available
1958	0	12
1959	1	36
1960	11	36
1961	22	36
1962	20	24
1963	20	24
1964	24	24
1965	23	24
1966	24	24
1967	23	24
1968	23	24
1969	22	24
1970	18	24
1971	17	24

Table 5.94. Tree Sparrow.
Total number of clutches laid at Coneygree Wood 1958-1971. (After Scroggs 1974).

Year	No. of boxes occupied	No. of clutches laid
1958	0	0
1959	1	2
1960	11	–
1961	22	54
1962	20	42
1963	20	41
1964	24	53
1965	23	56
1966	24	60
1967	23	58
1968	23	64
1969	22	41
1970	18	39
1971	17	27

population monitoring. Between 1966 and 1969 A.S. Cheke ringed 5,500 House Sparrows in Wytham Village alone. Apart from their phenomenal success they do possess other interesting facets. Observations at one colony included a female bird that removed an egg from the nest of another bird and then replaced it with one of her own. Thus any ornithologist wishing to look at social interactions in a species needs to look no further than the House Sparrow.

TREE SPARROW
Passer montanus

The Tree Sparrow is generally a colonial, hole-nesting species, using natural cavities in trees, especially pollarded willows along rivers, and holes in buildings, particularly more isolated barns and farm outhouses. They will also take over nestboxes intended for tits, and pairs have been noted in old Kingfisher, Willow Tit and Sand Martin nests. They may themselves be ousted from nest sites by the slightly larger House Sparrow.

Although widely distributed, the Tree Sparrow has a very scattered distribution with large areas in the southern half of the county devoid of breeding birds. Most occupied tetrads are in the lower-lying parts of the county, but a full explanation of this distribution pattern cannot be made. However, since each tetrad may hold only one or two nesting pairs, often in an isolated corner of the countryside, it is possible that some may have been overlooked.

Outside the breeding season, Tree Sparrows form mixed flocks of variable size with finches and buntings, foraging over stubble or around farmyards. Parties of up to 50 birds are not uncommon in most winters, but flocks of 2,000 have been recorded in the county (Table 5.92).

All of the previous accounts of the birds of

Oxfordshire describe the Tree Sparrow as 'common', although, in the absence of any locally derived numerical data, it is difficult to assess precisely how the species has fared in the long term. It is known that it undergoes fluctuations in population and a considerable increase in numbers occurred in the 1960s and 1970s. The national CBC data for farmland plots demonstrate this rise and subsequent fall and was mirrored on the few such plots that exist in the county. The change is presumably reflected in the maximum size of winter flocks reported (Table 5.92), as the population seems to be mainly sedentary (15 out of 19 recoveries of Oxfordshire-ringed Tree Sparrows were within 9 km of the ringing site).

In the BOS area, the status of the Tree Sparrow has altered similarly. The decennial report for the period 1962–1971 (Brownett 1974) describes the species as 'abundant', yet by the end of the next decade it was assigned the lower grade of 'fairly numerous' (Easterbrook 1983).

Scroggs (1974), studied a colony of Tree Sparrows in Conygree Wood, Great Tew, where the species entered the site in 1959 and had taken over nestboxes. Occupancy of this site is shown in Tables 5.93 and 5.94, and at its peak, over 60 clutches with a mean of five eggs per clutch were laid. From these, a hatching rate of 70–80% was obtained and a fledging rate of between 60% and 70%.

A similar colonisation occurred at Wytham Woods (Seel 1968) and although it did not commence until 1961, by 1964 16% of the 910 available nestboxes were occupied by Tree Sparrows. A further indication of the population expansion was documented by Brucker (pers. comm.) in a study of birds nesting in bankside willows along the River Thame. In 1961 the population was estimated to be at least 200 pairs; additional observations in 1964 indicated that a further increase had taken place. However from this time there was a steady decline and in the mid-1970s, long stretches of the river where they were previously found, were devoid of them. Similarly, there were no Tree Sparrows nesting in the boxes at Wytham by this time (Gosler 1990).

Tree Sparrows are affected by a number of constraints. The availability of nest sites is one such factor, and the loss of hedgerows and the onset of Dutch Elm Disease are likely to have significantly reduced the number of suitable nest-holes. Indeed, the reason for the dearth of Tree Sparrows over much of the southern part of the county could be associated with the way this has been changed into a vast open prairie. Further limits to the population may be related to the availability of food during the winter months, as fallen grain is less available now because of more efficient farming practices, while the seeds of various weeds are also much less abundant because of autumn sowing and herbicide use. Interspecific competition with House Sparrows may also be implicated. These cannot explain entirely the population dynamics of the species and another unknown factor must be involved.

Although the Tree Sparrow is easily overlooked and rarely reported through the OOS, the Atlas results indicate that there are hitherto unknown factors governing their distribution in Oxfordshire and further fieldwork would be desirable to improve our understanding of this species in the county.

Family: Fringillidae
Finches

Of the 13 species of finch recorded in Oxfordshire, six are resident, another three are winter visitors (although one has bred), and the rest are vagrants or irruptive. The availability of weed or cereal seed in autumn and winter is important to many of these birds. Hence many have declined during the last 30 years because of more efficient farming methods, the increase in autumn sowing, stubble-burning and the use of herbicides. Recently introduced checks on some of these practices can only be beneficial to many of these species.

Table 5.95. Chaffinch.
Breeding densities observed in some Oxfordshire woods.

Site and reference	Area ha	No. of pairs	Density pairs/km²
Bagley Wood Wiggins 1984	227	193	85
Little Wittenham NR Wiggins 1984	52	38	73
Wytham Wood CBC Overall 1988	6.7	6.3*	94
West Oxfordshire Ford 1984			
(a) 13 sites	0.9*	23	197
(b) 5 sites	3.7*	20	109
(c) 1 site	18	11	61
*mean figures			

Figure 5.78. Chaffinch.
Ringing recoveries. All recoveries over 100 km from the ringing site are shown.

● Recoveries of birds ringed in Oxfordshire
○ Origin of birds recovered in Oxfordshire

CHAFFINCH
Fringilla coelebs

A highly successful and adaptable bird, the Chaffinch is the second most widely distributed species in Oxfordshire, with breeding season records obtained from all but five tetrads during the course of the Oxfordshire Atlas. It nests in a wide range of habitats including woodlands of all kinds, scrub and hedgerow, parks and gardens. Chaffinches not easily overlooked and for the majority of tetrads the higher categories of breeding evidence have been obtained.

During the winter, the number of birds in the county is increased by an influx of Chaffinches from elsewhere in Britain and northern Europe. These continental birds tend to be larger than our own. Considerable movements of birds over the county may be witnessed from vantage points on the Downs, Chilterns or on Shotover, especially in October and early November. The majority of these movements are made early in the morning at low level.

Numbers and locations of birds seen in the county will depend upon food availability, both here and on the continent. An important food source for Chaffinches is beechmast and the relative abundance of beechmast in the mainland of Europe and in Britain, influences the numbers seen from year to year (see also Brambling). However, beechmast is not the only food; stubble fields and farmyards, as well as domestic gardens, are highly attractive to foraging finch flocks. The numbers likely to be encountered range from flocks of 200 birds which are recorded in most years, to flocks numbering several thousand (as at Blenheim in January 1977).

Many of the Chaffinches seen in Oxfordshire in winter are birds that have bred here. However, as previously noted, ringing data have shown very large numbers of them to be of continental origin as shown by Figure 5.78. Since a number of the records relate to recoveries during the spring or autumn migration, it is assumed that many have breeding grounds further to the east or north.

Breeding densities vary according to habitat. Surveys of a number of woodland sites give densities of between 61 and 197 pairs/km², although for smaller sites densities may be three times this figure due to the increased habitat diversity at the edge (Table 5.95). Little information is available for Oxfordshire farmland but a national average derived from CBC data gives a figure of 25.6 pairs/km². This would give a county population in the order of 65,000 pairs.

Newton (1967) demonstrated behavioural and ecological differences between the resident population and the continental visitors. Residents tend to remain close to their territories throughout the year and, if the weather is fine, males will burst forth into song. Continental birds are found in the large flocks, collecting where ever food is plentiful and roosting communally. Diet also differs, with resident birds taking a much wider range of food.

BRAMBLING
Fringilla montifringilla

The description of the Brambling's status given by Aplin (1889) remains true today. He called it a "winter visitor of irregular occurrence" and commented that "in some years hardly any will be noticed, while in others very large flocks appear".

Bramblings rarely arrive before October, and in some winters numbers build up in the later months. Very few linger later than mid-April by which time the males are resplendent in their breeding plumage.

As the main source of winter food is beechmast, Bramblings are most frequently found in the Chiltern Beechwoods or in parks such as Blenheim. Although mast is more plentiful at the beginning of winter, Ross (1980) describes birds still finding it at Blenheim as late as the first week in April. They also join mixed flocks of seed-eaters ranging through the county, and occasionally visit gardens.

Their appearances are so irregular that in some winters no flocks of more than ten birds are seen, while in others three-figured flocks are frequent.

There was one quite exceptional period. This was between 1967 and 1972 when vast assemblies were discovered in south Oxfordshire. In January and February 1967 more than 2,000 gathered with a mixed finch flock at Sutton Courtenay to feed on weed seeds covering a long mound of top soil which had been piled up before the extraction of gravel to be used in building Didcot Power Station. No fewer than 114 were ringed. Then from mid-November 1971 Oxfordshire's largest ever flock, estimated at 4,000–8,000, were following the plough at a site a few miles from the above-mentioned Sutton Courtenay flock. One hundred and fifty of these were ringed. Finally, 1,500 were present at Harwell (also in south

Oxfordshire) in January 1972. Concentrations on this scale are sometimes reported in central Europe, but they have not occurred in this county since. There is one continental recovery of a bird ringed in Oxfordshire. An adult male at Charlbury on 13 February 1979 was at Aalborg, Denmark on 5 May the same year.

With beechmast showing such dominance as a winter food source, a relationship between the success or failure of the mast crop and numbers of Bramblings visiting from year to year would seem likely, but this is not found. For example, in some seasons when there is an abundance of beechmast few Bramblings appear. This is not surprising if the mast crop were also good in the source area from which the birds come since they are essentially irruptive in Britain. Jenni (1987) found that Brambling invasions in central and southern Europe could be predicted from the amount of beechmast and snow cover (which restricts access to that food) in northern Europe. A statistical analysis (see Appendix 5) of the data in Table 5.96 shows that these two factors are both highly significant predictors of the numbers of Bramblings reaching Oxfordshire in winter.

Once here, if the beechmast crop in Oxfordshire is poor or depleted, Bramblings disperse widely and often associate with finches and buntings to explore other feeding possibilities. Unfortunately the stubbles and stackyards to which they once resorted for seeds are not so readily available in times of efficient modern farming. In recent years some Bramblings have discovered gardens as one alternative. Since 1970 visits to bird tables have increased. Nearly all garden reports are in March when they feed greedily, presumably fattening up in preparation for migration. They take any grain seeds provided, and demonstrate a willingness to consume peanuts and sunflower seeds. At such times they are more likely to be found partnering Greenfinches than their usual companions, Chaffinches, who seem unable to deal with these larger food items.

SERIN
Serinus serinus

There are four records of this rare visitor, three of which occurred during the Oxfordshire Atlas study. In September 1985, two juvenile Serins were seen in Holywell Meadow, Oxford and in June 1986, at a location south of Oxford, a male was found in song in mature gardens, but was not seen or heard on subsequent visits. In 1988 a male held territory for at least two weeks in May and June, at a site by the River Thames in the south-east of the county. Although the latter bird was found in the Atlas survey area, it was actually recorded in Berkshire and Buckinghamshire. The only other Oxfordshire record is of a bird at Crowmarsh Battle in May 1904.

The Serin has been slowly expanding its

Table 5.96. Brambling.
Winter flock sizes of Brambling in Oxfordshire in relation to the quality of the beechmast crop in northern Europe and the amount of snow in Germany taken as representative of snow fall in northern Europe generally. Beechmast and snowfall data are from Jenni (1987). The largest Brambling flock size is taken as representative of the number of Bramblings in the county in that winter.

Winter	Largest Oxon flock	Beech crop	Snow cover
1955/56	100	poor	light
1956/57	9	good	light
1957/58	5	poor	average
1958/59	15	good	light
1959/60	26	poor	light
1960/61	29	good	light
1961/62	59	poor	light
1963/64	200	poor	heavy
1964/65	100	good	heavy
1965/66	500	poor	heavy
1966/67	2000	poor	average
1967/68	1	good	average
1969/70	500	poor	heavy
1970/71	200	good	heavy
1971/72	7000	poor	heavy
1972/73	200	poor	average
1973/74	150	poor	heavy
1975/76	50	poor	average
1976/77	19	good	light
1977/78	19	poor	light
1978/79	200	poor	heavy
1979/80	0	good	light
1980/81	250	good	heavy
1981/82	30	poor	heavy

range across continental Europe for over a century and the first breeding in Britain occurred in 1967. Many ornithologists expected it to maintain its advance across this country as it has done elsewhere but to date this has been a rather slow process. It will be interesting to see if this attractive little finch ever colonises Oxfordshire to any significant degree.

GREENFINCH
Carduelis chloris

The Greenfinch is a common resident in Oxfordshire. Although found as a breeding bird of the wider countryside, mostly at the woodland edge and in extensive, dense hedgerows and scrub, it is equally likely to be seen around towns and villages. In such locations, dense shrubs and hedges, especially evergreens, in parks, gardens and churchyards provide excellent nesting opportunities. Indeed, of all the finches, the Greenfinch has the closest association with human habitation.

The Oxfordshire Atlas demonstrated the wide distribution of the species with the main gaps occurring in the more intensively cultivated areas with little habitation. The conspicuous nature of the species, being both very vocal and very visible, coupled with a long breeding season, means that it is unlikely to have been overlooked. However, there is a chance that a degree of over-recording may have taken place since birds are known to travel several kilometres from their nest sites in search of food. Hence a number of registrations may have been of birds feeding, but not breeding in a tetrad and this may account for some of the 55 'possible' records.

Although Greenfinches are more sedentary than the other finches that occur in Oxfordshire, ringing data suggest that birds disperse widely from their natal site in their first year. There are also some winter movements but only a small proportion travel further than 100 km. The movements that occur follow a north-east to south-west pattern and are of three categories (Holmes 1981). There are some birds, breeding in Oxfordshire, that winter further south and west. Others, breeding to the north and east of the county, over-winter here, whilst another group are essentially transient since they breed north and east of here and pass through on their way to wintering grounds to either the south or west. There are two foreign recoveries of birds ringed in Oxfordshire, one from Guernsey and another from Dieppe, France. In addition, a bird ringed in County Wicklow, Eire in March 1983 was recovered the following month at Thame.

A noticeable feature of Greenfinches in winter is the formation of large flocks, typically in the company of buntings and other finches. These flocks forage over open fields in search of grain. Groups of 50 birds are seen in most winters and parties of up to 200 birds appear with some regularity. However, larger flocks have

occasionally been noted; 300 were at Hartslock in November 1981, and flocks of 400–600 birds were seen at Adderbury in February and December 1967, Great Tew in January 1972, and at Somerton in September 1972. The largest flocks were noted in 1967 when over 2,000 birds were present at Cholsey during February and March and a similar number at Sutton Courtenay in February. In some years large flocks are not evident since birds may be more generally distributed. For example, in 1982, a party of 200 was the only sizeable flock noted, yet 120 individuals were ringed in a Charlbury garden in January and February indicating a rapid passage of birds through garden feeding stations.

The Greenfinch is, of course, familiar across the county as a regular visitor to gardens where it will eagerly take peanuts and sunflower seeds. Newton (1967), examined several hundred birds and found that nearly all had been feeding on peanuts which comprised up to 97% by volume of the winter diet of Greenfinches. It has been suggested that the utilisation of this artificially provided food has enabled the species to overcome some of the natural fluctuations in population that might result from variations in the availability of naturally occurring seeds. As with many other granivores in the county, the ban on stubble burning after 1991 and the expansion in set-aside land in the county should benefit Greenfinches.

GOLDFINCH
Carduelis carduelis

A very numerous resident. Although found in 74.6% of tetrads during the Oxfordshire Atlas fieldwork, breeding was confirmed in only 26%. They appear to be more plentiful in the low-lying areas to the east and south of Oxford. Breeding was mostly noted in gardens, orchards, parks, and farms with fewer in more open areas of countryside.

Parties of up to 200 can still be found in autumn, usually feeding on thistles and teasel. Some observers believe that fewer are present now than 30 or more years ago, but there are no data to substantiate this.

The break-up of these flocks occurs abruptly in September and October when most of the local Goldfinches leave. Apparently they move southward, some going as far as western France or Spain. Seven recoveries of birds ringed in Oxfordshire either during or shortly after the breeding season have been made between Deauville in northern France and Cordoba in southern Spain (Figure 5.79). Four of these were found in late October or November, indicating that the movement is made with alacrity well before the onset of cold weather in Britain.

A small wintering population remains, but in cold weather they are almost entirely absent. I. Newton's counts (OOS Report 1963) at Port Meadow made at fortnightly intervals from January 1962 until March 1963 (Figure 5.80) show how few stayed in the first three months of both years when temperatures were exceptionally low. In contrast, during mild winters small numbers remain throughout, as demonstrated in the summary of the results of a survey made by 34 members of the OOS during the mild winter of 1988/89 (Brucker 1989) given in Table 5.97.

Table 5.97 shows a steady decline in November and December giving the impression of a gradual movement out of the area. Remaining birds split from large flocks to forage individually in small parties. A noticeable increase in January included the appearance of larger flocks. There seems little doubt that these were incoming birds. By February many had left and flock size reduced as birds again spread out in search of food. March brought no overall change in total numbers present, but flock size increased considerably.

An essentially similar pattern was revealed in a follow-up survey made by 14 OOS members from November 1989 to March 1990, which was an exceptionally mild period. Once again there was a pronounced peak in mid-winter, although this time it came a month earlier, in December. Flock sizes were also consistently higher, increasing from an overall average of 4.3 in winter 1988/99 to 9.2. At least some individuals were presumed to have remained in the area all winter. One was retrapped at Charlbury in December 1988 which had been caught there the previous October. A pair, thought to be the same birds, were ever present in a Raspberry growing area at Kingston Bagpuize, and parties at Port Meadow remained of constant size in both winters.

The amount of available food is the single most important factor determining the numbers that over-winter. It is noticeable how efficient they are in exploiting limited resources, finding food in such places as roadside verges, and the few untidy corners of farms.

During the winter surveys observers were asked to note the types of food taken. Teasel, which was found throughout the winter, provided the main source (48%), and thistles were still important in November (14%). These were supplemented by seeds from a wide variety of plants including Alder, Burdock, Knapweed, Mugwort, Fat Hen, Lavender, Groundsel, Dandelion, Daisy, Cosmos, and African Marigold.

A signal that winter is over is when returning migrant Goldfinches come flooding in. When they arrive in April many are already paired and begin their search for breeding sites. This may be interrupted by cold weather when they may gather again briefly in flocks on a Dandelion patch or in some weedy corner. One party was noted feeding on split pine cones.

'Charms' of these elegant little finches have always been an attractive part of the Oxfordshire scene, and to nineteenth century bird catchers they were an irresistible temptation. Yarrell (1876) comments that, "Gay plumage, lively habits, an agreeable form and song, with an endearing disposition, are such strong recommendations, that the Goldfinch has been, and will probably long be, one of the most favourite cage birds".

Five years later an Act was passed banning the taking of them, but this had little impact, for Aplin (1889) described how "26 dozen" were netted by three bird catchers in 1882, and in 1884 a Banbury man took 160 in September and October. Eventually the practice died out, and depleted populations began to recover.

In the second half of the twentieth century there was concern about the widespread use of herbicides for weed control which reduced available supplies of seed in the countryside. That this was not a totally new anxiety can be appreciated on reading Yarrell (1876), who

Figure 5.79. Goldfinch.
Foreign ringing recoveries of Goldfinch and Linnet involving Oxfordshire.

● Goldfinches
○ Linnets

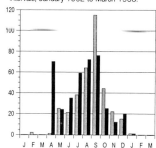

Figure 5.80. Goldfinch.
Port Meadow counts made at fortnightly intervals, January 1962 to March 1963.

Table 5.97. Goldfinch.
Monthly winter counts in Oxfordshire 1988-1989.

Month	Records	Total no.	Max flock	Mean flock
November	26	129	20	4.9
December	42	93	17	2.2
January	59	342	30-40	5.7
February	41	142	18	3.4
March	26	142	45	5.4

Table 5.98. Siskin.
Maximum winter flock size.

Winter	No.
1973/74	30
1974/75	30
1975/76	70
1976/77	50
1977/78	60
1978/79	50
1979/80	80
1980/81	40
1981/82	400
1982/83	50
1983/84	450
1984/85	150
1985/86	150
1986/87	50
1987/88	100
1988/89	150

gives as a reason for its growing scarcity, "The continually increasing cultivation of waste lands, and the extirpation of weeds from those already under tillage or used as pasture, essential to the system of high farming which has of late years conferred so many benefits on the nation at large".

Despite all these difficulties Goldfinches seem to survive, and will be helped by the more sympathetic attitudes being displayed today. For example, they are being assisted by E. Maddock who showed in her contribution to the BTO Garden Bird Feeding Survey how she attracted them regularly to her garden in urban Headington by supplying them with seeds. In 1984 she set up a Teasel plant. After Goldfinches came to it following an early snowfall and consumed all the seeds, she re-charged it with bought seeds and the visits continued. Eventually they also showed a readiness to take food from the ground. Chicory seeds proved a less expensive alternative, and since then a wide range of other seeds have been provided, either grown naturally or purchased. By these means feeding flocks have been drawn in throughout every winter month in the period 1984-1990. A typical example is that of the winter of 1987-1988 when maximum numbers were: five in October, six in November, nine in December, 12 in January, 23 in February, 27 in March, seven in April. The highest count was in February 1989 when 45 were present.

SISKIN
Carduelis spinus

Known primarily as a very frequent or regular winter visitor, the Siskin also occasionally breeds.

Aplin (1889) regarded the species as a winter visitor although birds remaining through into the late spring did raise the possibility that small numbers stayed to breed. Similarly, Alexander (1947) called it a winter visitor but cited two records of nesting near to Oxford which he considered to be escaped captive birds. This general pattern is also described by Radford (1966) with winter flocks in excess of 50 birds mentioned.

Since the mid-1960s the situation has changed. Larger numbers are recorded in most winter periods and birds frequently remain in the county during the summer, with a handful of instances of probable and confirmed breeding. The period of the Oxfordshire Atlas for example recorded birds in five tetrads with probable breeding in two, although some of these records could refer to late, over-wintering birds which may often be heard in song before departing. However, since these birds were all noted in large woodland areas after the usual departure dates, one assumes them to be at least potential breeders. Summering was first noted during the 1970s when in two seasons (1972 and 1978) birds were seen in Wytham. It was not until 1984 that breeding was confirmed when two

pairs bred at a site near Oxford. It is interesting to note that in the winter prior to this, Siskin numbers reached an all-time high in Oxfordshire with flocks of over 30 birds noted on 13 occasions plus one flock in excess of 450 birds feeding on riverside Alders in the vicinity of Nuneham Courtenay and Radley.

As already implied, numbers of Siskin appearing during the winter vary quite considerably. Table 5.98 shows the maximum flock size recorded in Oxfordshire in each winter period. This gives some impression of peak years although it is more usual to find a wide distribution of birds in small to moderate sized flocks. In 1981/82, 11 flocks of between 30 and 80 birds were noted plus a flock of 100 birds at Adderbury, 65 of which were caught and ringed. In some seasons birds are apparently scarce and in 1986/87 most records were of single birds, widely dispersed and there are records of only two flocks of more than 20 birds.

Whilst numbers vary, the pattern of the appearance of Siskin is fairly consistent. The first birds arrive in September with a larger influx in October. Numbers are generally low in November and peak in December and January with a further influx into the county. In good years numbers may remain high through into February but there is a gradual decline and most birds depart by April. However, birds are now summering in the county it is difficult to assign accurate first and last dates. During the winter, it is clear that these flocks are highly mobile and wander widely in search of food.

Siskin flocks are most often discovered in Alders alongside rivers and other wet areas. Birch seeds are also taken as too are seeds of certain conifers such as Larch and Cypress. Birds are also attracted to garden feeding stations, especially in the second half of winter, presumably as natural food becomes more difficult to obtain. These birds readily take

peanuts in hanging feeders and especially from net bags. This seems to have been a recently acquired habit and, from 1970, the incidence of this behaviour first appeared in the OOS reports at a time when it was first being recognised elsewhere in the country.

What is the origin of Siskin that overwinter in the county? Most birds wintering in southern Britain are thought to be of Scottish origin and five records of Oxfordshire-ringed birds fit this picture. However the remaining recoveries probably relate to birds on passage through the county. In addition, a Russian-ringed bird was found at Botley in February 1987, and a bird ringed in Charlbury in January 1989, was recovered in May of that year in Norway, showing that some of these birds are of continental origin.

The increase of Siskin wintering locally, their emergence as a garden visitor and their inclusion on the list of breeding birds in the county is surely to be welcomed. Whilst this attractive little finch will continue to occur as a winter visitor, one hopes that sufficient suitable woodland habitat will remain to allow its breeding status to continue and increase.

LINNET
Carduelis cannabina

Although the Linnet can still be described as a very numerous resident, they occur in substantially reduced numbers than formerly. Much of their favoured breeding habitat has gone. Abundant stretches of Gorse on the Chiltern slopes or the Corallian limestone hills in mid-Oxfordshire where Aplin found so many no longer exist. Important sites today include wasteland near gravel pits and rubbish tips, or areas of soil disturbance where weeds grow. There are fewer dense hedgerows, and nests are more frequently sited in small conifers or closely clipped hedges in gardens. The Oxfordshire Atlas showed Linnets to be more common in the low-lying clay vales to the south and east of Oxford, and scarcer in the wooded areas.

Most local birds appear to leave the county abruptly in the autumn. For example, a juvenile ringed in Abingdon on 10 August 1967 had reached Segovia in Spain by 22 October. The map of winter recoveries (Figure 5.79) shows a similar distribution to that of the Goldfinch, although there is no evidence that they travel together. Some Linnets are to be found in the county during the winter, and these have been the subject of two surveys.

Newton studied Linnet flocks on Port Meadow in 1962 and 1963. He found the largest concentrations in April, when they returned from migration, and post-breeding gatherings in September (Figure 5.81). In the two exceptionally cold periods from January to March, in both years, Linnets were almost totally absent. This was not a typical pattern, for analysis of the total number of flocks exceeding

100 reported in the period 1979 to 1988 demonstrates marked influxes in January, (Figure 5.82).

The four highest counts in this period ranged from 400–650, and were in January, September and two in October. Surveys by members of the OOS in the winters of 1988–1989, (Brucker 1989) showed a pattern of flocks leaving by mid-November, a build up in January, and the return of migrants from late March (Table 5.99).

A follow-up survey in the winter of 1989-1990 showed a similar sequence, although flock sizes were generally larger. One exceptional group of 200–300 feeding in a mustard field near Fulbrook on 3 November was a reminder of earlier times.

The origin of the mid-winter flocks is uncertain, but the possibility that they come from northern Britain is suggested by the only recoveries of birds ringed in Oxfordshire at that time of year. One ringed in Charlbury on 15 January 1973 was in Scunthorpe on 15 February 1975. The other was also ringed in Charlbury but on 4 December 1975. It was recovered in Doncaster on 10 June 1978. Another clue was the sighting of three parties of 15–20 flying purposefully in a south westerly direction at intervals during the hour after dawn over Otmoor on 11 January 1990. Linnets returning in spring mostly seem already to be paired, although they still gather in flocks at times.

Linnet populations remained at a high level in the times of agricultural depression between the two wars when there were many weedy corners in Oxfordshire's small mixed farms. In the second half of the twentieth century, reduction in marginal lands, the burning of stubbles, the sowing of winter cereals, and the persistent use of herbicides had the cumulative effect of depleting supplies of the weed seeds that these ground-feeding finches rely upon. There were still flocks of more than 1,000 in the

Table 5.99. Linnet.
Counts of Linnets in Oxfordshire, 1988-1989.

Month	No. of records	No. of birds	Max flock	Mean flock
November	12	248	ca 100	20.6
December	5	62	30	12.4
January	19	319	115	16.7
February	6	124	60	20.6
March	21	560	ca 100	26.6

Figure 5.81. Linnet.
Port Meadow counts made at fortnightly intervals, January 1962 to March 1963.

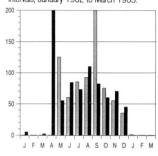

Figure 5.82. Linnet.
Monthly distribution of flocks exceeding 100 birds, 1979-1988 inclusive.

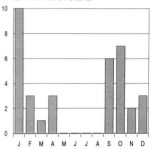

Figure 5.83. Twite.
Monthly distribution of records.

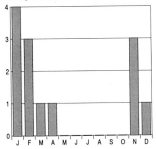

Figure 5.84. Redpoll.
Ringing recoveries involving Oxfordshire.

Single recovery of bird
in Oizy, Belgium

● Recoveries of birds ringed in Oxfordshire
○ Origin of birds recovered in Oxfordshire

early 1960s, but by the 1980s only occasional flocks in the low hundreds. There are some hopeful signs for the future. They have shown a great liking for the seeds of Oilseed Rape which is being grown in ever increasing abundance. It is hoped that the 'set-aside' programme will make available a greater quantity of weed seeds, at least in the initial stages. Any move towards greater diversity in farming locally might also be in their favour.

TWITE
Carduelis flavirostris

A rare winter visitor. The early history of the Twite in Oxfordshire was clouded with uncertainty, as there were some possible records, but none were considered totally acceptable. The problems of separating this species from the Linnet continue to cause difficulties.

Between 1958 and 1989 a total of 13 records were published in annual reports. Most were of one to four birds usually associating with parties of Linnets or Redpolls. The only larger party was one of ten birds at Blewbury in February 1960. No obvious pattern in their occurrences here is discernible except there were three records in the extremely cold early months of 1979. As shown in Figure 5.83. the period of sightings extends from November to April: the earliest was on 5 November, and the latest on 10 April.

REDPOLL
Carduelis flammea

A very frequent winter visitor and a scarce breeding species, the earlier avifaunas of Oxfordshire give a similar description noting the Redpoll (illustrated below) to be an occasional breeder mostly along the Rivers Thames and Cherwell. Since 1968 there have been details of at least possible breeding in every year except two, but it may well have been overlooked. Records of confirmed breeding are confined to four years in this period; Christmas Common in 1969, Ditchley Park in 1972 and University Parks, Oxford in 1977 which was the best year for breeding with confirmed breeding at a west Oxfordshire site, at South Stoke and at one other location. Five other sites provided possible or probable records. These records all come from a period when the British breeding population

was at a very high level as shown by the national CBC index data (Marchant *et al.* 1990). Redpoll bred again in the University Parks in 1979. The Oxfordshire Atlas located birds in 14 tetrads although no proof of breeding was obtained in this period. There was a wide spread of occupied sites, many along river valleys and a number in well wooded areas, including two on the Chilterns, and at a cluster of four tetrads in SP44.

In the winter, Redpoll are much more conspicuous. An immigration of birds occurs in October although many individuals move through the county to over-winter further south. However, from autumn to March, flocks of up to 30 birds are seen in most winters. Larger parties occur at the peak of population abundance (e.g. 130 at Stanton Harcourt in December 1973, 100 at Headington in October 1975, and at least 200 at Waterperry Wood in the winter of 1976). In 1978/79 large numbers of Redpoll were present at Charlbury and over 60 birds were trapped. The few retraps suggest a very mobile population of birds homing in on particularly good feeding areas. Two of these birds were controls and these, along with other ringing recoveries are shown in Figure 5.84.

In the 1980s, the largest flock was one of 60 birds seen at Sunningwell in February 1985 and the general situation in that decade was one of a wide distribution of small flocks. These winter flocks are most frequently seen feeding in the company of Siskin, Goldfinches or Blue Tits on Birch, Alder or Larch seeds. A wide range of other seeds (e.g. willowherbs, Mugwort, thistles and a variety of grasses including reeds) may be taken. The preference for these seed species determines the bird's distribution.

The majority of records relate to the British race of the Redpoll, *C.f. cabaret* also called the Lesser Redpoll. There have also been two recent records of the 'Mealy' Redpoll, *C.f. flammea*, on 18 February 1975 and 23–27 February 1986, to add to the five records given by Radford (1966).

COMMON CROSSBILL
Loxia curvirostra

The Crossbill is a frequent but irruptive winter visitor to Oxfordshire and a rare breeding species.

Both Aplin (1889) and Radford (1966) detailed invasions of Crossbills and Radford

documented concentrations of up to 200 birds in 1935 and 1962. These sources give details of only five confirmed or probable breeding records for Oxfordshire.

Between 1965 and 1988 there have been between one and 15 reports of Crossbills in Oxfordshire in any one year although there were five years without sightings. Birds have been seen in all months and up to 80 birds noted in any one year. The years of maximum sightings are those when continental birds irrupt from their usual breeding areas as a result of food shortage, and a large influx into Britain occurs. 1972 and 1985 were such years. In the latter, parties of birds were present from June until November with up to 35 present at the Warburg Nature Reserve, Bix, a flock which included several juveniles. In 1986, large numbers of birds were also seen; up to 40 at Bernwood in July may have been migrants but it is felt that they were probably birds from the previous year's irruption that had remained to breed. A further irruption occurred in 1990/91 with probable breeding again noted.

In contrast to most other finches, Crossbills may breed very early in the year nesting almost exclusively in coniferous woodlands. Thus it is possible to see young birds on the wing in April and it is also possible to see non-breeding birds about at this time. This has certain implications for the interpretation of breeding season records and especially for the Oxfordshire Atlas records. Although in this survey birds were noted in ten tetrads, the late dates of some of the 'possible' breeding records suggest that they were probably passage birds. However, the survey recorded confirmed breeding in two tetrads, one on the eastern edge of the county and one in the BOS area in the north. In the case of the latter, breeding was reported in 1986 and 1987 and was the first instance of confirmed breeding in the BOS area, and indeed in Oxfordshire since 1964. It is important to note that irruptions had taken place one or two years previously in both cases.

For some of the reasons outlined, it is quite difficult to accurately assess the breeding status of the Crossbill in Oxfordshire. Conifer plantations are seldom visited by birdwatchers especially during the first three months of the year and this may lead to a paucity of reliable breeding season records. For a more reliable appreciation, organised fieldwork recognising this early nesting season is required.

SCARLET ROSEFINCH
Carpodacus erythrinus

A very rare vagrant. There has been one record of this species; a single bird at Adderbury on 31 January 1912. It was reported in the *Zoologist* (1912, p. 460) and was considered by the ornithologists of the time to be an acceptable record.

BULLFINCH
Pyrrhula pyrrhula

The Bullfinch is a very widely distributed and numerous resident in Oxfordshire woodlands, scrub and dense hedgerows. Sometimes only a small thicket of Hawthorn or Blackthorn may hold a nesting pair and gardens with an abundance of shrubs and dense vegetation may similarly provide adequate cover for nesting. It is the least conspicuous of the commoner finch species and usually remains within, or close to, thick vegetation, so that often all one sees is the flash of a white rump as the bird flits from bush to bush or hears its soft, piping notes. These factors must be considered in relation to the Oxfordshire Atlas results. Although 70% of the records submitted fall in the lower categories of recording, it is felt that the overall distribution pattern is accurate. This is based primarily upon the often protracted breeding season of the species, i.e. late April to mid-September, making them less difficult to overlook. One would expect few records from the intensively agricultural parts of the county where suitable hedgerows are absent or few in number. Gaps also exist in the Chilterns, and whilst this may be due to low levels of recording, some of the mature Beechwoods have little by way of a shrub layer and hence nesting opportunities for Bullfinches may be restricted.

The Oxfordshire Bullfinch population is largely sedentary with the most distant recovery for a bird ringed in the county being 21 km. Aplin (1889) and Alexander (1947) both mention that there is an influx of birds into the county during the winter although there is little evidence for this from ringing studies. However, Newton (1972) notes that a bird trapped in Oxford during the winter did show features of the northern subspecies. A feature of Bullfinches during the winter is their congregating into small flocks. Since the mid-1960s, the largest

party reported was of 30 birds which, when compared to the flocks of over 100 birds mentioned by Radford is possible further evidence of a decline.

Seasonal fluctuations in Bullfinch numbers may occur due primarily to the availability of food. Seeds, soft fruit and buds form the diet of Bullfinches although young are fed on a mixture of seeds and invertebrates (Newton 1972). From May onwards, adults feed on the seeds of a wide variety of plants including docks, nettle and Bramble whose seed crops are consistent in quantity from year to year. Birds also feed upon seeds of Privet, Birch and particularly Ash, plants whose seed production varies considerably from year to year and whose availability is important in the success of the species especially through the winter. As seeds diminish in number, Bullfinches feed on buds of trees, Hawthorn and Crab Apple especially, but only when the seed supply is exhausted. It is then that birds may move into commercial and domestic orchards and damage the buds of fruit trees so that control measures may be required.

All of the earlier accounts describe the Bullfinch as a common resident and fluctuations in population were noted by Aplin (1889) and Radford (1966). A marked increase occurred from about 1955 to about 1970. During this period, Bullfinches colonised more open habitats and attained pest status in fruit growing areas. Further evidence for the build up of numbers is provided by Radford who cited the increase at a Sonning Common garden from 12 in 1955 to 66 in 1961, and the increase in ringing figures at a Cholsey site from 0–67 in the 13 years after 1949.

Newton (1972) reports densities as high as 50 pairs/km² in deciduous woodland around Oxford, although this is unlikely to be true for the whole of the county, and the national average from CBC plots of 20 pairs/km² is more likely. More recently, there is some evidence of a decline in the local population caused by the loss and unsympathetic management of hedgerows. A decline from six pairs to just one on the CBC plot at Grimsbury Reservoir was attributed to such activities. A further contributory factor may be the destruction of low thickets by the increasing number of deer in woodland. National CBC indices also provide evidence of a general reduction in the population. Gosler (1990) notes a considerable decline since the time of Newton's (1964) study in Wytham Woods. At one Kidlington garden, small parties made regular visits between 1965 and 1976, stripping the buds from plum and apple trees and attempting to nest in 1975. In the period 1977–1989, Bullfinches made only eight (brief) visits to the site. In 1990, a representative of one of the county's largest fruit growing areas reported that the Bullfinch was no longer of significance in terms of crop damage, and had virtually disappeared from the orchard scene.

HAWFINCH
Coccothraustes coccothraustes

The Hawfinch, largest of our finches, is a scarce bird of Oxfordshire woodlands and parklands, occasionally venturing into mature gardens or orchards. It is a shy and secretive species, spending a good deal of its life in the woodland canopy and thus is easily overlooked and is probably under-recorded.

Since the mid-1960s, Hawfinches have been recorded in every year, with at least one confirmed breeding record in most years, although in the latter half of the 1980s the number of records has declined. Figure 5.85 gives the distribution of all records in the county. Of the more recent records, a number have been single sightings, but certain sites

have been regular breeding grounds. Wychwood, Blenheim, Eynsham Hall Park, Boar's Hill, Rousham, Great Tew, Sandford-St. Martin and Middleton Stoney have provided the most breeding season records, and Radley, Ducklington, Charlbury, Woodcote and Bradwell Grove to a lesser degree. The Oxfordshire Atlas obtained records from just 30 tetrads which is thought to be an underestimate of the true population, especially in the south-east corner of Oxfordshire and in particular along the Chilterns.

Aplin (1889) gives details of eight likely breeding areas, but noted that there were far more records in the winter months, and attributed this to migrant birds into the county. Indeed, the Hawfinch had formerly been regarded as a winter visitor. Whether this was the case, is still unclear. Radford (1966) notes that Tucker believed that large flocks (over 50 birds) at sites such as Watlington Hill, probably represented a large part of the breeding population of the Chilterns rather than any long distance migration. In addition to the sites mentioned by Aplin and the winter records from Watlington, Radford notes only Wytham and Great Tew from where Hawfinches were recorded, and those were both in the winter.

The paucity of winter records in recent times suggests a decline, since the majority of reports are of small parties (two to four birds) or single birds. There are exceptions; 24 birds were seen at Middleton Stoney in 1971 and 18 birds there in 1974. There were at least 16 at Heythrop in 1983 and, in 1983 and 1985, ten at Woodcote. In the first three months of 1984 up to 12 birds were seen at Blenheim and a party of 11 birds on Christchurch Meadows, Oxford in February 1986 is the last sizeable winter flock recorded.

During a prolonged and regular period of observation in the gardens of Blenheim Palace between 1984 and 1990, a steady decline from 122 to 12 'bird-days' (Table 5.100) has been traced (D. Doherty, pers. comm.), although there has been no obvious habitat change. Birds were most frequently seen in the spring and breeding was proved in 1985 and 1986.

With its heavy bill the Hawfinch can crack open relatively large seeds (stones) such as Cherries or Damsons. Indeed, excellent views of them can be obtained in the Cherry trees in the vicinity of Jarn Mound on Boar's Hill as family parties forage in the tree canopy in June/July. Flocks of up to 20 birds have been seen here. However, there is evidence of a decline as in successive years of the 1980s they became more difficult to find. Hornbeam is also highly favoured and the presence of good numbers of this tree species on the Chilterns prompts further suspicion of under-recording. Birds have also been seen on Hawthorn, which appears to be important in the second half of the winter period, on seeds or berries of Ash, Lime, Holly and Yew. These are all native tree species normally well distributed in a mixed deciduous woodland.

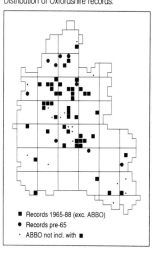

Figure 5.85. Hawfinch.
Distribution of Oxfordshire records.

■ Records 1965-88 (exc. ABBO)
● Records pre-65
· ABBO not incl. with ■

Table 5.100. Hawfinch.
Counts at Blenheim Palace gardens.

Year	No of 'bird-days'
1984	122
1985	93
1986	58
1987	37
1988	18
1989	29
1990	12

Family: Emberizidae
Buntings

The buntings are generally large-billed seed-eaters, showing many similarities to the finches. Most of the seven species occurring in Oxfordshire show associations with farmland and downland. Three are vagrants or occasional visitors; one, the Cirl Bunting, was a localised breeder which is now possibly extinct; the remaining three, Yellowhammer, Reed Bunting and Corn Bunting are widespread breeders which are largely resident.

Table 5.101. Snow Bunting.
Incidence of records per decade.

Decade	No. of records	No. of years
1950s	1	1
1960s	6	3
1970s	6	4
1980s	14	6

LAPLAND BUNTING
Calcarius lapponicus

A very rare vagrant although this species is probably under-recorded. Not only can it be difficult to identify, but it is likely to appear in areas of open countryside not well watched during the winter. There was a female on Aldfield Common near East Hendred on 23 March 1983. There is a record of a bird heard calling at Churn on 3 October 1984, but the bird was not seen. There have been one or two other records from the Berkshire Downs which were regarded by the observers as 'possible'.

SNOW BUNTING
Plectrophenax nivalis

An occasional winter visitor, the Snow Bunting has been recorded approximately 33 times in Oxfordshire. Some individuals stay for a few days, and one female remained for nearly two months at Farmoor Reservoir in the winter of 1990/91. There have been three observations of two birds, and one of three. All the rest are singles.

Aplin (1889) and Alexander (1947) were unable to document more than six sightings. These were in 1878, 1879, 1893, 1928, and 1944. However, they were encountered with increasing frequency in the period 1950–1990 (Table 5.101). Today, Farmoor Reservoir proves the main attraction with 15 out of 20 records

between 1974 and 1990. Apart from one seen on the Berkshire Downs in this period all the others were at gravel pit sites.

YELLOWHAMMER
Emberiza citrinella

The Yellowhammer (illustrated below) is a familiar and typical resident bird of the Oxfordshire countryside. Abundant and with an extensive distribution, it is a conspicuous bird throughout the year and the distinctive 'little-bit-of bread-and no-cheese' song, can be heard throughout the summer from roadside and farmland hedgerows in the open countryside. These features, coupled with the agricultural nature of the county, place it as the ninth most widely distributed breeding species, being recorded in 733 (97.3%) tetrads during the course of the Oxfordshire Atlas. The high percentage of probable and confirmed breeding records amongst this total further underline the ease with which the species may be located. Heavily wooded or built-up areas account for most gaps on the distribution map although in districts where breeding density is low, one or two pairs may have been overlooked.

Yellowhammers in Oxfordshire are very sedentary and there are few recoveries outside the county of birds which were ringed here. Indeed, in mild winters birds may remain close to their breeding areas, although in harsher conditions their behaviour changes and birds

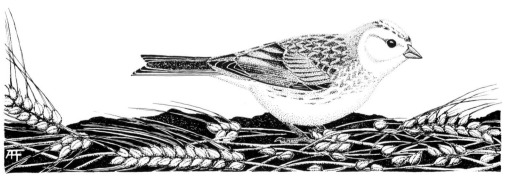

flock together more readily. Parties seen are never huge and congregations of 100 birds, usually with finches or sparrows and most often on stubble fields or around farmyards especially stockyards, may be considered large. During the hard winter of 1982, 120 were counted near Kidlington, the largest of several flocks seen, whilst in 1980, 200 birds feeding on old stubble at Hinksey is the largest flock recorded locally. In autumn and winter, birds may also form communal roosts, and such a gathering involving 60 birds was noted at Waterperry in 1968 and over 75 roosted near Swinford in 1984.

The earlier accounts of the birds of Oxfordshire all regard the Yellowhammer as a common or abundant resident and there is little indication of any medium or long-term change to this situation since the last of these (Radford 1966). There is some evidence of small fluctuations from year to year but these are based on limited, local observations. In 1965 for example, three pairs nested along a 70 m stretch of country road where normally one might expect no more than one pair. Also in the 1960s, occupied territories on a 110 ha farmland CBC plot at Kidlington varied between 13 and 25 pairs.

CIRL BUNTING
Emberiza cirlus

Once a scarce breeding species with a very local distribution, the Cirl Bunting has been recorded in the county only once since 1985. The species has never been well represented here; Aplin (1889) gives no definite breeding records but noted birds in a number of sites in north Oxfordshire during the summer, and also reckoned breeding to occur along parts of the Chilterns. Similarly, Alexander (1947) gives the Chilterns as the only regular breeding area in the county. The Chilterns area for a long time appears to have been the stronghold for the species and Radford (1966) describes the Cirl Bunting as resident at Chinnor, Crowell, Watlington and around Berrick Salome. Birds were seen in the area, although less widely distributed, until the 1980s but in the later years records were never annual.

R.S.R. Fitter kept notes of all registrations of Cirl Buntings in the vicinity of Chinnor Hill between 1953 and the present (Table 5.102). These findings indicate a peak population in the late 1950s/early 1960s which declined after the prolonged hard winter of 1963/64 although the hard but shorter cold spell in the previous winter appears to have had little effect. The generally low numbers in the early part of the study may also have been due to a succession of severe winters. The loss of Elms in the area in the 1970s may also have contributed to the decline. The last encounter in this study area (the parishes of Chinnor and Crowell) was in 1978, although other observers have recorded birds in the area on two other occasions; a single in July 1979 and a pair in May 1983. The actual location of the latter record may have been from outside Fitter's area. This study also demonstrated the long song period of the species (Figure 5.86) and, at least to those observers attuned to it, the song helps in the location of this thinly distributed species.

In addition to the Chilterns population, breeding is known to have occurred at a number of sites elsewhere in the county. The Goring, Cholsey and Streatley areas provided regular summer records in the 1960s and early 1970s with confirmed breeding on a number of occasions. Figure 5.87 (Sharrock 1976) shows the distribution in the county at the time of the National Atlas. Breeding took place near Kennington and in an area near West Challow in the early 1960s but both sites were apparently deserted soon after. In the period 1974-1976, birds were discovered during the summer near Milton. Until 1979 there was usually a scattering of records from around the county during both the winter and the summer periods.

There were no records in the first two years of the 1980s but a pair of birds were seen in a flock of Yellowhammers in Wytham Wood in January 1982. In this year a national BTO survey failed to find any evidence of breeding in Oxfordshire. In December 1983, a single bird was seen at Cuxham and in 1983 and 1984, two birds were seen in the winter to the east of Farmoor village and a male was observed at the site in June 1984. In 1985, a bird was noted at a site just to the west of Oxford and which provided the only record for the Oxfordshire Atlas. On 24 February 1991, a single bird was noted at Kidlington, keeping company with a mixed flock of finches and buntings on a 'set-aside' field.

Nationally, the Cirl Bunting is in decline, possibly due to climatic factors (Sitters 1983), but more likely because of agricultural changes

Table 5.102. Cirl Bunting.
Number of contacts, visual or auditory, in the vicinity of Chinnor Hill 1954-1978.

Year	Number of contacts
1954	12
1955	14
1956	23
1957	44
1958	20
1959	32
1960	44
1961	57
1962	68
1963	13
1964	22
1965	25
1966	10
1967	5
1968	8
1969	11
1970	2
1971	1
1972	2
1973	3
1974	0
1975	0
1976	1
1977	0
1978	3

Figure 5.86. Cirl Bunting.
Song period on Chinnor Hill based upon the number of auditory contacts in each month.

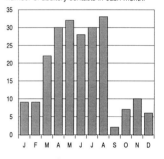

Figure 5.87. Cirl Bunting.
Breeding distribution 1968-1972 (after Sharrock 1976).

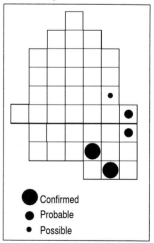

● Confirmed
● Probable
• Possible

Table 5.103. Reed Bunting.
Number of territories held by buntings on a Kidlington farmland CBC plot (110 ha) 1964-1970.

	Number of occupied territories		
Year	Reed Bunting	Corn Bunting	Yellowhammer
1964	5	3	18
1965	7	3	17
1966	8	2	18
1967	9	5	13
1968	18	2	21
1969	15	5	25
1970	16	4	20

which have reduced the seed availability in autumn and winter (Evans 1991). Devon is the only remaining British stronghold. We can only be optimistic that recent changes in English agriculture might be beneficial to this once common bird and we see a revival in its fortunes. It may be significant that the 1991 record was of a bird with other seed-eaters on 'set-aside' land.

LITTLE BUNTING
Emberiza pusilla

A very rare vagrant. An adult male was found on 19 March 1988 at the Lashford Lane Fen Nature Reserve, feeding with Reed Buntings near the bird table. It remained until at least 20 April, watched from the hide by many observers. It was frequently heard in full song. Although nearly all British records have been in autumn, there have been two similar spring records in neighbouring counties. One visited Iver in Buckinghamshire, 18 March to 26 April 1987 and in 1991 one appeared at Chippenham in Wiltshire from 28 March to 10 April.

REED BUNTING
Emberiza schoeniclus

The Reed Bunting is the most common and familiar passerine associated with waterside habitats in Oxfordshire. It is principally a resident of river valleys where it nests in undergrowth along the banks or in the hedgerows and overgrown ditches close to the river. It has also made considerable use of the nesting opportunities provided by the many new gravel pits in the county. Other still waters, provided that there is plenty of low vegetation present, will also be used. The easily recognised, if none-too-melodious song and its conspicuous nature, have ensured that 88% of registrations for the Oxfordshire Atlas are in the higher categories of recording. The results are believed to be an accurate representation of the breeding distribution during the study.

Reed Buntings are present in their breeding grounds from mid-April to the end of August and during the winter birds may be seen feeding alongside finches, sparrows and other buntings on arable land throughout the county. These feeding groups may be large and flocks containing over 100 birds (e.g. Kidlington in January 1981) have been noted. The roosting behaviour of Reed Buntings is also well documented in Oxfordshire. During the early 1970s, up to 400 birds used a reedbed at Grimsbury Reservoir whilst a similar habitat at Duke's Lock held as many as 200 birds. A number of smaller sites are also regularly used in this fashion.

Many of the birds at these roosts, which reach their peak in the autumn, have been trapped and ringed and when added to other ringing data show that there is considerable movement of Reed Buntings into and through the county. The data show such movements during the winter

from north and east (eg, the Midland counties, Cambridgeshire, Bedfordshire) and the continued migration of these, and of birds breeding locally, to points south and west (e.g. Devon, Dorset and Hampshire). Continental birds also occur during the winter and there are two records of birds from Belgium while the occurrence of birds ringed at Dungeness, Kent in October gives further evidence of an easterly passage of birds from mainland Europe.

Another feature of Reed Buntings in winter, particularly if the conditions are harsh, is their appearance at garden feeding stations. This occurs mostly in the second half of the winter period and although numbers are generally few, flocks of up to 20 birds have been seen. Interestingly, the majority of birds coming into gardens are males.

The status of the Reed Bunting has always been described as common, and previous accounts of the county's birds also note the association with the river valleys (Aplin 1889, Radford 1966). However, during the 1960s and 1970s a rapid increase in the Reed Bunting population occurred. One consequence of this was that birds began moving out of the typical wetland habitats into drier areas, far away from ponds or streams. This pattern occurred throughout the country and was graphically illustrated by Gordon (1972) who reported the findings from two farmland CBC plots. One, at Kidlington (110 ha) bordered the River Cherwell and whilst it had some marshy areas, two-thirds comprised well-drained land used for arable crops. The increase in the number of territories held by Reed Buntings at the site is shown in Table 5.103.

The colonisation of the dry areas took place mainly in Hawthorn hedges or hedges with trees and the suggestion of this representing an overspill from preferred wetland sites was supported by the fact that singing by territory-holding birds usually took place much later than in the wetter habitats. The increase in population on this site was aided by a good system of hedgerows and a management

regime which allowed the proliferation of a diverse plant community. In addition to providing an abundance of seeds, this would also attract a host of insects which are vital to the nestlings and which form an important part of the diet of the adults during the breeding season. In the course of the spread, territories overlapped with other bunting species, (as is also shown on Table 5.103), though with no reduction in their numbers. At a second CBC plot at Little Milton, a parallel if less dramatic increase also occurred, as the site which usually held no birds, had four pairs by 1968. At the start of the 1990s, populations at both sites had returned to the pre-1960s level.

Radford (1966) notes one or two instances of nesting in sites up to 4 km from water. These reports are added to in an account in the same book, of birds of the Lambourn Downs (then in Berkshire, now partly in Oxfordshire), by E.L. Jones who noted their presence far from water in patches of 'thorn savanna'. This nesting behaviour has continued to be noted into the 1980s with pairs noted at East Hendred Down, at an elevation of 200 m, and apparently associated with a patch of Gorse. An association with Gorse was also noted on an area of waste scrub land in the Sutton Courtenay area where three nests were located (R. Wiggins, pers. comm.).

In the north of the county, the BOS reported a doubling in the population density during the 1960s and 1970s, to 80 pairs per 10 km square. The population has now reverted to the pre-1960s level as seen in figures from the Grimsbury CBC plot which fell from 21 pairs in 1975 to six in 1986.

Although the Reed Bunting population may no longer be at a peak, it has demonstrated that this is an adaptable species. Fisher (1941) recorded nine territory-holding males on a 1.2 km stretch of the River Thames above Godstow. In 1981, a count along the same stretch of river held five pairs but in the intervening period a new road had been cut through the area. However, the lake that had been created in the next field to build the fly-over provided a new habitat where there were at least six pairs (J. Brucker, pers. comm.). Furthermore, it is one of the few species which has readily taken to breeding and feeding in fields of rape which are now a conspicuous part of the Oxfordshire landscape. Further aspects of the Reed Bunting's ecology were studied at Oxford by R. Prys-Jones (1977).

CORN BUNTING
Miliaria calandra

A very numerous and widespread resident, the Corn Bunting is strongly, but not exclusively, associated with Oxfordshire's open, upland areas. From the low dry-stone walls and hedges separating the rolling fields of growing cereals, the jangling song can be heard throughout the summer, often with only the ubiquitous Skylark or Yellowhammer for company. The distribution of the species, as shown by the Oxfordshire

Atlas map is rather patchy, being largely absent from much of the upper Thames valley, the Chilterns and urban areas. It is also apparently less well represented along much of the western edge of the county and, since much of this comprises open, arable land, this absence is curious. The species' far-carrying song, and obvious territoriality, has ensured that the majority of registrations are of either probable or confirmed breeding and although the late breeding season of the Corn Bunting may have led to a few pairs being overlooked, the overall picture is believed to be accurate.

The habitat preferences of the Corn Bunting were shown during an Annual Breeding Season Survey carried out by the BOS in 1985. Covering 100 km², 54 pairs were located, and of those where the principal habitat category was specified, 97% were in arable land, and of these, 70% were associated with barley. Furthermore, a survey in the region in 1957 had shown that breeding occurred on the fairly flat plateaux between river valleys and that there were no records from the steeper slopes. Since the Corn Bunting is much more common in the southern half of the BOS area many of these observations could tentatively be extrapolated to include the rest of the county and go some way towards explaining the distribution.

The association between Corn Buntings and barley was also noted in the south of the county (R. Wiggins, pers. comm.). In an investigation of 109 tetrads, a minimum of 1,000 singing males were counted, the majority of which were close to barley fields. A single 80 ha field of barley near Appleford held between 40 and 45 singing birds. Careful searching in fields of other crops proved fruitless.

During the winter, birds congregate into flocks and wander throughout the wider countryside but avoid built-up areas unless agricultural buildings are present. Parties of up to 100 birds are not uncommon, especially in

hard weather, and flocks of 200 have been noted, usually on stubble. Roosting is another feature of birds in autumn and winter with as many as 1,000 birds seen at some sites such as Cholsey. Here, Shaw (1981) trapped and ringed 172 birds between 1976 and 1980 and showed that, on average, only 25% of the birds in the roost were males. This fits with other similar studies elsewhere in the country and may be explained by the known polygamy of the species.

The status of breeding Corn Buntings in Oxfordshire is not thought to have changed greatly, as each of the earlier accounts (Aplin 1889, Radford 1966) refer to it as being common but with a local distribution. Several attempts have been made to assess the numbers present in the county. Between 1928 and 1930, 575 km² of Berkshire and Oxfordshire were surveyed although the survey area did not include a large area between Marcham and the Downs which is a well known traditional locality for the species. Fifty-five singing males were located. An interesting feature of this work was that there was a clear association between their distribution and the geology, with Corn Buntings most numerous on chalk and limestone. Another survey in 1957, organised by B. Campbell, covered approximately 1,200 km² and 401 singing males were located. The important features in this work were that most birds were found on open, arable land and on light, well-drained soils over chalk and limestone. The study also showed how the ideal conditions for Corn Buntings are a combination of open fields of well-grown corn with isolated song perches. These conditions exist in areas such as along the Chiltern scarp and foothills, the Downs and the clay vale east of Oxford and give rise to the greatest concentrations of Corn Buntings in Oxfordshire.

A BOS survey in 1964 reported 131 singing males in 600 square kilometres, an addition of ten birds to the total found in 1957. Owing to the incomplete nature of these surveys it is difficult to say if a significant population change has occurred but assuming from subjective evidence that it has not, this would suggest a density of between ten and 60 pairs per 10 km square with the upper range more likely. Assuming the association between Corn Buntings and barley growing to hold across the county, it will be interesting to see how the species fares in the future if the decline in barley acreage which peaked in the 1970s and early 1980s, continues.

CHAPTER SIX

A Future for Birds in Oxfordshire

The publication in 1966 of Dr Mary Radford's account of the birds of Oxfordshire was prompted by a need to summarise all the data gathered in annual reports since 1922. A secondary motive was a sense of unease about threats to the environment. In her introduction, Radford states that her book is "written partly with a view to the future and the preservation of the present avifauna". However, this is not a dominant theme in the main text.

Neither she, nor her contemporaries, could have predicted the speed with which Oxfordshire was to be so radically altered on such an extensive scale. Nevertheless, there were, in those days, signs of an awareness of the dangers ahead, encouraging not only the publication of the avifauna, but also the formation of the Berkshire, Buckinghamshire and Oxfordshire Naturalists' Trust (BBONT) in 1959, of local groups of the Royal Society for the Protection of Birds, and of several local Natural History Societies within the county.

Today conservation is high on the public agenda. In the present book there is a clear concern to assess the environmental pressures which have confronted Oxfordshire's birds, and make precise statements about their present status so that future changes can be readily identified. We need now to look ahead, but any attempt to make forecasts must have as a prerequisite, an examination of past events and recent trends.

The most conspicuous changes have been in agriculture, which remains the dominant factor with some 70% of Oxfordshire land use now devoted to it. Throughout the first half of the twentieth century most farms in the county were still engaged in essentially traditional mixed farming practices involving a combination of tillage and stock. These provided a diversity of habitats favourable to birds and other wildlife. In the first three decades after the Second World War there was an emphasis nationally on food production. Farmers were encouraged by government grant-aid programmes to bring an ever-increasing amount of land into use, which involved embarking on extensive drainage schemes, and removing hedgerows. Advances in mechanisation and chemical technology further facilitated the rapid switch to a local concentration on cereal growing which transformed much of Oxfordshire into extensive tracts of arable 'prairie' land. There was a degree of uniformity in this highly organised environment (undesirable in its effect on the landscape), not only in the type of crops grown, but also in the timing of farming operations which severely restricted opportunities for birds to feed and breed. Habitat changes have always occurred, but it was the rapidity and scale of the process which was so damaging since few refuges were left for wildlife, and suitable habitat was greatly fragmented. For bird life there were many reductions and losses, and very few gains in the farmland of our county.

Such advances were made by the use of intensive farming methods that by the mid-1980s more food was being grown than was required. Thus regulations and 'quotas' were introduced to control over-production. Agricultural policies were re-directed creating 'set-aside' schemes to encourage farmers to take fields considered surplus to requirements out of use, and introducing measures to prompt the planting of hedges and woodland areas. Early responses to these initiatives are already showing benefits to bird life. At this time also a greater variety of crops were planted, the most conspicuous of which was Oilseed Rape, which quickly proved attractive to nesting Reed Buntings and Sedge Warblers, and feeding Linnets, Woodpigeons and Swifts.

Many farmers are sympathetic and relish the ways in which the new political climate is enabling them to restore wildlife habitats on their land. However, future economic and political pressures will undoubtedly become increasingly severe. Their choice of actions is likely to be considerably restricted by the Common Agriculture Policy of the European Community quota system, and by not merely national, but international requirements. New regimes supported by modern technology are likely to change the appearance of our countryside again, and pose a fresh set of problems for bird populations. Further scientific progress will make improved chemicals available to farmers. Insecticides will more selectively target harmful species, but this could reduce overall numbers available to insectivorous birds. Herbicides will be more effective in eradicating 'stubborn' weeds such as the thistles which have been so beneficial for wintering birds. We can expect that more sophisticated machinery will be invented to improve efficiency. Farmers will find it difficult to survive in a competitive world if they ignore these developments.

There are some corners of the county in which the changes have not been so extensive. These include the private estates, of which there are a considerable number in Oxfordshire. One example is at Blenheim park where the present Duke of Marlborough instituted a landscape reclamation scheme in conjunction with the Countryside Commission. Between 1981 and 1990, some 900 individual trees were planted, with another 1,000 in groups, and a further 20,000 in woodland areas. The underlying concept has been to introduce a mixture of species which will provide a continuous canopy, with opportunities at 40, 100, 150 and 200 years of re-planting in groups. Another private area which is being carefully maintained is the Ministry of Defence land at Otmoor. The protection offered here has enabled this to become the most important area locally for breeding waders and many warblers, and wintering owls and harriers. A new management scheme initiated by the Ministry of Defence conservation section, and supported by English Nature and the National Rivers Authority gives promise that this locality may become even more attractive for wildlife.

Recent industrial developments in our county have in many ways been of benefit to birds. The excavation of more than 50 gravel and sand pits in the second half of this century has provided new lakeland habitats for a range of waterfowl. Great Crested Grebes, Canada Geese, Coots and many duck species have prospered. There is no sign of an end to this activity, although new methods of immediate in-filling, if adopted generally, could result in fewer waters becoming available. Work has commenced recently in the Yarnton/Cassington area north of the Thames, and these places will surely be mentioned frequently in the next avifauna. The large reservoirs at Farmoor and Grimsbury should continue to provide welcome resting and feeding places for migrants and wintering wildfowl, and such opportunities will be increased if the proposed new reservoir is built in the Vale of the White Horse. Thames Water Utilities have added to the value of Farmoor Reservoir in recent years by installing floating platforms to encourage Common Terns to breed, and by creating shallow lakes at a

'scrape' suitable for waders between the reservoir and the river. Although still in their early stages, both these projects are already proving successful.

Limestone extraction has practically ceased in Oxfordshire, and the future of quarry habitats must be considered, especially at Shipton-on-Cherwell which is the largest 'hole' dug in the county. At the moment these areas provide much needed nesting sites for such species as Stock Dove, Little Owl, Kestrel, Little Ringed Plover, Ringed Plover and Redshank.

Some of the quarry and gravel pit sites have been used for the disposal of the ever-growing quantities of human refuse. This has sometimes occurred at the expense of wildlife habitat although the rubbish tips have provided feeding opportunities for vast numbers of gulls, corvids, Starlings and other. More efficient methods of waste disposal could cause a reduction in this food source but is generally to be welcomed.

The 'Beeching' closure of many railway lines produced new wild areas, but these gains were in no way balanced by the losses caused by the building of many miles of roads across the countryside. Ornithologists joined in the battle to achieve the least damaging route for the M40, and must be prepared to review future road plans. 'Waste' areas, important to wildlife were often built upon as villages and towns expanded considerably in the post war years. An example of one of the first attempts made by local societies interested in conservation to resist such pressures was the opposition to the establishment of an industrial site at Trap Grounds near Port Meadow in the mid-1980s. Bird conservationists have discovered the need to examine all planning applications with care.

Possibly the greatest future cause for anxiety will be 'people pressure'. Oxfordshire's population rose by at least 7.6% in the decade 1981 to 1991 according to the national census. Population in the United Kingdom as a whole is forecast to rise from 57 million now to 61 million by about 2030. It is inevitable that this county will share in this continued increase especially with the M40 now providing easy access to London and the Midlands. Inevitably also, demands for additional house building and industrial development will be considerable. Not only will Oxfordshire become more densely populated, but people will have more leisure time and be more mobile. Predictions of traffic growth are horrendous. As more and more people seek recreational enjoyment in the countryside many present problems will intensify. In Mary Radford's day, Lapwings bred on Port Meadow, and Tree Pipits and Woodlarks on Shotover. Bird populations have been much reduced in these attractive open places within easy reach of the city as Oxford citizens have found more time to relax in them. The gravel pit lakes are in great demand for fishing and boating activities. The larger ones, which are best for birds, are particularly sought after, and the futures of the two key lakes at Dorchester (Queenford Pit) and Stanton Harcourt (Dix Pit) are under threat. In areas of open countryside, places which were previously quiet and comparatively undisturbed, less productive agriculturally, but attractive to birds, are being considered for golf courses. Few parts of our county are free from some kind of human enterprise destructive to wildlife. It seems that only those corners owned by wildlife trusts, the Ministry of Defence, or on private estates are relatively secure.

Fortunately, local political developments give cause for quiet optimism. In 1990 the West Oxfordshire District Council was prompted by continued demands for mineral extraction in its area to ask its planners to produce a draft report on the *After use of the Gravel Pits in the Stanton Harcourt area*. The Oxfordshire County Council has also recently appointed an ecologist to work in their planning department. Although his brief is wide and he will have an overview of all planning developments, his first concern will be to create a long-term strategy for the Windrush valley, which will take account of all the demands for land, but which will ensure a place for wildlife. In this, the active co-operation of ornithologists has already been sought, and plans made for all biological records relating to the area to be kept on a central computer.

Another hopeful sign in 1991 was the production by the Oxfordshire County Council of a strategy document entitled *Oxfordshire's Natural Heritage* which is intended to promote plans to conserve the counties' wildlife both in town and country. It aims to ensure that the necessary breadth of conservation information appears on planner's desks when decisions have to be made about developments. Such moves are encouraging. We are losing battles at present as a result of the lack of considered planning in the past. Difficulties will remain in the next few years, but the prospects for conserving the environment in the twenty-first century seem brighter.

A possible threat to the continued application of these more enlightened attitudes is local authority re-organisation which is promised for the mid-1990s by the major political parties. It is to be hoped that recent progress is in no way interrupted by the turmoil that this is bound to cause.

In such a situation it is clear that involvement in conservation matters is now a necessity for birdwatchers. Both the Banbury and Oxford Ornithological Societies are becoming increasingly active in commenting on planning proposals, and in supporting or initiating schemes to enhance environments for birds. From 1989 they have combined with other organisations with an interest in local conservation such as English Nature, BBONT and the RSPB to form the Oxfordshire Bird Conservation Co-ordinating Group which meets regularly to liaise and form joint policies.

There has never been a greater need for accurate information about local bird populations. In the past, much of our pleasure has come from making casual observations in spare moments. Notes of these, collected over 70 years in the annual county bird reports have produced a considerable knowledge as shown in the species' accounts in this book. But in many important instances our understanding has proved incomplete. The BTO has shown that 39 of Britain's most common species have declined since the 1960s, mainly because of intensive farming practices (Marchant *et al.* 1990). We have been unable to quantify or trace the majority of these changes locally as there is a lack of systematically collected data. The need for accurate monitoring of the more common species is particularly acute. We also need to concentrate more on site-related studies which are proving of great value, especially those involving regular watching by individuals or groups. The speed and efficiency with which birdwatchers produced evidence for the Oxfordshire Atlas demonstrates that there are many competent observers ready for future challenges.

The ready accessibility of the data is vital if prompt and informed responses to damaging planning applications are to be made. Developments in the use of computers, now at an advanced stage in Banbury, have considerable implications. We look forward to the time when their general use will enable us to use records not only on a local basis, but nationally, to organise our fieldwork results and facilitate immediate, precise responses when needed.

Support of national organisations will remain a priority for local birdwatchers. Care has always been taken to respond fully to requests from the British Trust for Ornithology and the Wildfowl and Wetlands Trust because their research produces unparalleled data on the national progress of bird species. The Royal Society for the Protection of Birds has increased its local involvement, not only in protecting rare species (such as the Montagu's Harrier), but in initiating schemes for the re-introduction of Red Kites and by working with local farmers to encourage Stone Curlews to recolonise former breeding areas in the county. All such efforts deserve our continued co-operation.

As we move towards the twenty-first century there is concern about world-wide environmental issues. It is beyond our brief to comment on global warming, acid rain, the destruction of the ozone layer and tropical forests, and other such gloomy prospects. Even on a local basis it is difficult to forecast future winners and losers in our avifauna. Presumably gardens will become even more important as havens for a growing number of species as they take advantage of the feeding opportunities they provide on an ever expanding scale. There is hope for the retention of some of Oxfordshire's recently created lakelands, which should ensure the continued success of the species they have attracted. Wetland birds such as the Snipe and Redshank seem unlikely to return in strength as so many suitable habitats have been lost forever. Similarly there seems little likelihood that heathland birds like the Nightjar will reappear without strenuous efforts to restore lost habitat. What is on the horizon for agriculture is not clear. Even farmers have little idea which new crops will be introduced. Linseed and Sainfoin are being grown more extensively at present, and Soya Bean is being considered, but this is an area of considerable speculation. Thus it is clearly impossible to predict the consequences for birds of these inevitable, but unknown changes. And it is anyone's guess which species might storm across Britain in the manner of the Collared Dove, although the call of the Cetti's Warbler could become a regular feature of Oxfordshire's reedy places.

What is without doubt, is that the actions of ornithologists will be critical. We will need a clear awareness of any changes in our bird populations. All organisations must work actively together to protect habitats, and ensure there are places for birds in our small corner of the world. In the 1960s, when Mary Radford wrote her book, the words "conservation" and "environment" were yet to come into everyday usage. Now we are supported by a general appreciation of 'green' issues. Our active involvement is vital, and could be productive. The next avifauna will demonstrate what degree of success we have achieved.

References

NOTE: OOS REPORT CITATIONS — A number of literature citations in the text refer to notes or articles which have appeared in the county bird reports. Please note that the year given for the reference is the year to which the report refers and not the year of publication which is usually one or two years after this.

ALEXANDER, W.B. (1940) Note on the effect of the cold weather 1939-40 on the bird population as shown in the census figures at Bagley Wood. OOS Report for 1940: 7-8.

ALEXANDER, W.B. (1947) A *Revised List of the Birds of Oxfordshire*. OOS. Oxford.

ALEXANDER, W.B. (1952) *An annotated list of the Birds of Berkshire*. OOS. Oxford.

APLIN, O.V. (1889) *The Birds of Oxfordshire*. Clarendon Press. Oxford.

BAATSEN, R.G. (1990) Red-crested Pochard in the Cotswold Water Park. Hobby. Wiltshire Ornithological Society.

BACON, P.J. (1980) Status and dynamics of a Mute Swan population near Oxford between 1976 and 1978. *Wildfowl* 31: 37-50.

BAKER, S.E.C. (1942) *Cuckoo Problems*. Witherby. London.

BATTEN, L.A. (1973) Population dynamics of suburban Blackbirds. *Bird Study* 20: 251-258.

BATTEN, L.A., BIBBY, C.J., CLEMENT, P., ELLIOTT, G.D. and PORTER, R.F. (1989) *Red Data Birds in Britain*. T. and A.D. Poyser, London.

BAYLISS, M.J. (1981) Birdwatching in Oxford City — Corpus Christi Sports Ground gains a new warbler. OOS Newsletter 10: 7-9.

BAYLISS, M.J. (1982) Birds of Oxford City. OOS Report for 1982: 56-66.

BBONT (1990) BBONT Conservation Factsheet.

BELL, B.D., CATCHPOLE, C.K. and CORBETT, K.J. (1968) Problems of censussing Reed Buntings, Sedge Warbler and Reed Warbler. *Bird Study* 15: 16-21.

BERTHOLD, P. and TERRILL, S.B. (1988) Migratory behaviour and population growth of Blackcaps wintering in Britain and Ireland: some hypotheses. *Ring. and Migr.* 9: 153-159.

BEVEN, G. (1964) The feeding sites of birds in grassland with thick scrub. *London Naturalist* 43: 86-109.

BIBBY, C. (1973) The Red-backed Shrike: a vanishing British species. *Bird Study* 20: 103-110.

BIBBY, C. (1989) A survey of breeding Wood Warblers *Phylloscopus sibilatrix* in Britain, 1984-1985. *Bird Study* 36: 56-72.

BIRKHEAD, T.R. (1991) *The Magpies*. T. and A.D. Poyser. London.

BLAKER, G. B. (1934) *The Barn Owl in England and Wales*. RSPB. London.

BLOXHAM, C. (1982) *Portrait of Oxfordshire*. Robert Hale. London.

BOND, J. and OVER, L. (1988) Oxfordshire and Berkshire - Ordnance survey historical guides. George Philip and Ordnance Survey. London and Southampton.

BROOKE, M de L. (1990) *The Manx Shearwater*. T. and A.D. Poyser. London.

BROOKE, M de L. and DAVIES, N.B. (1987) Recent changes in host usage by Cuckoos *Cuculus canorus* in Britain. *J. Animal Ecology* 56: 873-883.

BROWNE, P.E. and DAVIES, M.G. 1949. *Reed Warblers*. Foy Publications, East Molesey, Surrey.

BROWNETT, A. (1974) A Study of birds in the South Midlands. BOS. Banbury.

BRUCKER, J.W. (1974) The day of the terns. OOS Report for 1974. 26-27.

BRUCKER, J.W. (1975) House Martin nests in an area of North Oxford. OOS Report for 1975. 43-48.

BRUCKER, J.W. (1989) OOS Newsletter, Oct. 1989: 2-4.

BUCKLEY, J. (1973) The prey of Short-eared Owls wintering on the Berkshire Downs. British Birds 66: 143-146.

CAMPBELL, B. (1960) The Mute Swan census in England and Wales, 1955-56. Bird Study 7: 208-223.

CAMPBELL, B. and FERGUSON-LEES, J. (1972) A Field Guide to Bird's Nests. Constable. London.

CAMPBELL, J.M. (1975) The status of the Great Crested Grebe in Oxfordshire. OOS Report for 1975: 50-53.

CADBURY, C.J. (1980) The status and habits of the Corncrake in Britain 1978-79. Bird Study 27: 203-218.

CATCHPOLE, C.K. (1974) Habitat selection and Breeding success in Reed Warbler. J. Animal Ecology 43: 363-380.

CHANCE, E. (1922) The Cuckoo's Secret. Sidgwick and Jackson. London.

CHANCE, E. (1940) The truth about the Cuckoo. Country Life. London.

CHANDLER, R.J. (1981) Influxes into Britain and Ireland of Red-necked Grebes and other waterbirds during the winter of 1978/79. British Birds 74: 55-81.

CHRISTIE, D. (1975) October Reports. British Birds 68: 85-88.

CLARK-KENNEDY, A.W.M. (1869) The Birds of Berks and Bucks. Simpkin, Marshall and Company. London.

COLLINS, A. (1983) Breeding birds of the South Oxford Canal. OOS Report for 1983: 33-39.

COULSON, J.C. (1961) Movements and seasonal variation in mortality of Shags ringed on the Farne Islands, Northumberland. British Birds 54: 225-235.

COWLEY, E. (1979) Sand Martin population trends in Britain, 1965-1978. Bird Study 26: 113-116.

CRAMP, S. and SIMMONS, K.E.L. (Eds) (1977-1988) The Birds of the Western Palearctic. Vols I-V. Oxford University Press. Oxford.

CROWLEY, T.E. (1976) Birds and Molluscs. OOS Report for 1976: 30-33.

DANIEL, M. (1988) Black-tailed Godwits in Oxfordshire. OOS Newsletter, Autumn 1988: 7-8.

DAVENPORT, D.L. (1982) Influxes into Britain of Hen Harriers, Long-eared Owls and Short-eared Owls in winter 1978/79. British Birds 75: 309-316.

DAVIES, N.B. (1982) Territorial behaviour of Pied Wagtails in winter. British Birds 75:261-267.

DAVIES, N.B. and BROOKE, M. de L. (1989) An experimental study of co-evolution between the Cuckoo, Cuculus canorus, and its hosts. I. Host egg discrimination. J. Animal Ecology 58: 207-224.

DAVIES, N.B. and BROOKE, M. de L. (1989) An experimental study of co-evolution between the Cuckoo, Cuculus canorus, and its hosts. II. Host egg markings, chick discrimination and general discussion. J. Animal Ecology 58: 225-236.

DAVIES, N.B. and HOUSTON, A.I. (1983) Time allocation between territories and flocks and owner-satellite conflict in foraging Pied Wagtails, Motacilla alba. J. Animal Ecology 52: 621-634.

DAVIS, P.G. (1982) Nightingales in Britain in 1980. Bird Study 29: 73-79.

DAY, J. (1988) Marsh Harriers in Britain. RSPB Conservation Review 2: 17-19.

DEAN, A.R. (1981) Seasonality of Herring Gulls in the West Midlands. British Birds 80: 632-633.

EAST, M. and PERRINS, C.M. (1988) The effect of nest boxes on breeding populations of birds in broadleaved temperate woodlands. Ibis 130: 393-401.

EASTERBROOK, T.G. (1983) Birds of the Banbury Area 1971-1981. BOS. Banbury.

ELKINS, N. (1983) Weather and Birds. T. and A.D. Poyser. Calton, Staffs.

ELLIOTT, G. (1988) Montagu's Harrier Conservation. RSPB Conservation Review 2: 20-21.

ELTRINGHAM, S.K. (1963) The British population of the Mute Swan in 1961. Bird Study 10: 10-28.

EVANS, A. (1991) Save the Village Bunting. Birds 13(5): 29-31.

FISHER, J. (1941) Watching Birds. Pelican. London.

FITTER, R.S.R. (1983) The Cirl Bunting in the Chinnor Area. OOS Newsletter 13: 5-6.

FITTER, R.S.R. (Ed.) (1985) The Wildlife of the Thames Counties. Robert Dugdale/BBONT. Oxford.

FLEMMING, T.H. (1981) Winter roosting and feeding behaviour of Pied Wagtails *Motacilla alba* near Oxford, England. *Ibis* 153: 463-476.

FORD, H.A. (1987) Bird communities on habitat islands in England. *Bird Study* 34: 205-218.

FOX, A.D. and SALMON, D.G. (1989) The winter status and distribution of the Gadwall in Britain and Ireland. *Bird Study* 36: 37-44.

FULLER, R. J. (1982) *Bird Habitats in Britain*. T. and A.D. Poyser. Calton, Staffs.

FULLER, R.J., BAKER, J.K., MORGAN, R.A., SCROGGS, R. and WRIGHT, M. (1985) Breeding populations of the Hobby *Falco subbuteo* on farmland in the southern Midlands of England. *Ibis* 127: 510-516.

FULLER, R. J. and STEEL, D. T. (1990) Coppicing in Brasenose Wood, Oxfordshire: the response of breeding birds. *Fritillary* 1: 5-15

GARCIA, E. (1981) An experimental and observational study of interspecific territoriality between the Blackcap *Sylvia atricapilla* L. and the Garden Warbler *S. borin* Boddaert. Unpublished D.Phil thesis, University of Oxford,

GARSON, P.J. (1978) A study of territorial and breeding behaviour in the Wren. *Troglodytes troglodytes*. Unpublished D.Phil thesis, University of Oxford.

GASTON, A.J. (1975) Factors affecting the evolution of group territories in babblers and Long-tailed Tits. Unpublished D.Phil thesis, University of Oxford.

GEER, T.A. (1979) Sparrowhawk (*Accipiter nisus*) predation on tits (*Parus* spp.) Unpublished D.Phil thesis, University of Oxford.

GIBBINGS, R. (1957) *Till I end my song*. London.

GLEN, N. (1985) The co-operative breeding behaviour of the Long-tailed Tit (*Aegithalos caudatus*). Unpublished DPhil thesis, University of Oxford.

GLUE, D. (1982) *The Garden Bird Book*. Macmillan, London.

GLUE, D. (1990) Breeding biology of the Grasshopper Warbler in Britain. *British Birds* 83: 131-145.

GOODACRE, M.J. (1959) The origin of winter visitors to the British Isles. *Bird Study* 6: 37-50.

GOODACRE, M.J. (1960) The origin of winter visitors to the British Isles. *Bird Study* 7: 108-110.

GORDON, M. (1972) Reed Buntings on an Oxfordshire farm. *Bird Study* 19: 81-90.

GOSLER, A.G. (1986) Oxford — harbinger of British ornithology. *BTO News* 147: 12.

GOSLER, A.G. (1987) Pattern and Process in the bill morphology of the Great Tit *Parus major*. *Ibis* 129: 451-476.

GOSLER, A.G. (1987b) A Study of the daily attendance and departure patterns of wintering gulls (*Larus* spp.) at the Sutton Courtenay landfill site, Oxfordshire. Unpublished report to the Amey Roadstone Corporation Ltd.

GOSLER, A.G. (1987c) Gull catching at Sutton Courtenay. *OOS Report for 1987*: 37-39.

GOSLER, A.G. (1988) A Study of the daily attendance and departure patterns of wintering gulls (*Larus* spp.) at the Sutton Courtenay landfill site, Oxfordshire. II The effectiveness of scaring. Unpublished report to the Amey Roadstone Corporation Ltd.

GOSLER, A.G. (1990) The Birds of Wytham — an historical survey. *Fritillary* 1: 29-74.

GRAY, D.B. (1974) Breeding behaviour of Whinchats. *Bird Study* 21: 280-282.

GRAY, I.L. (1987) The feeding ecology of the Sparrowhawk *Accipiter nisus* outside the breeding season. Unpublished D.Phil thesis, University of Oxford.

GRIGG, D. (1989) *English Agriculture — an Historical Perspective*. Blackwell. Oxford.

HALE, W.G. (1980) *Waders*. Collins. London.

HANSON, W.J. (1960) Cheltenham Grammar School Biology Reports 4: 27-30.

HARRISON, C. (1982) *An Atlas of Birds of the Western Palaearctic*. Collins. London.

HARRISON, G.R., DEAN, A.R., RICHARDS, A.J. and SMALLSHIRE, D. (1982) *The Birds of the West Midlands*. West Midlands Bird Club. Studley.

HICKLING, R. (1983) *Enjoying Ornithology*. T. and A.D. Poyser. Calton, Staffs.

HIRONS, G. (1981) Breeding behaviour of *Scolopax rusticola*. Unpublished final report to Natural Environmental Research Council.

HIRONS, G. (1985) The effects of territorial behaviour on the stability and dispersion of Tawny Owl (*Strix aluco*) populations. *J. Zool., Lond.* (B) 1:21-48.

HOLMES, P. (1981) An analysis of the movements of Greenfinches and Reed Buntings through Oxfordshire. *OOS Report for 1981*: 36-38.

HOLMES, P.R., CHRISTMAS, S.E. and PARR, A.J. (1987) A study of the return rate and dispersal of Sand Martins *Riparia riparia* at a single colony. *Bird Study* 34: 12-19.

HORSFALL, J. A. (1981) The time budget of the Coot, *Fulica atra*. Unpublished DPhil thesis, University of Oxford..

HUDSON, R. and MARCHANT, J.H. (1984) Population estimates for British breeding birds. Report to Nature Conservancy Council CSD, Report 602. BTO. Tring.

JENNI, L. (1987) Mass concentrations of Bramblings *Fringilla montifringilla* in Europe 1900-1983: their dependence upon beechmast and the effect of snow cover. *Ornis Scandinavica* 18: 84-94.

JONES, S. (1983) *The Buckinghamshire Bird Report.* 1983.

JOURDAIN, F.C.R. (1926) The Birds of Oxfordshire. in Walker, J.J. (ed): The Natural History of the Oxford District. Oxford University Press, London.

JOYCE, B., WILLIAMS, G. and WOODS. A. (1988) Hedgerows: still a cause for concern. *RSPB Conservation Review* 2: 34-37.

KELLY, G. (1986) *The Norfolk Bird Atlas.* Norfolk and Norwich Naturalists Association. Norwich.

KENWARD, R.E. (1979) Winter predation by Goshawks in lowland Britain. *British Birds* 72: 64-73.

KNIGHT, R. (1977) BTO Golden Plover Survey. OOS Report 1977: 23-26

KNIGHT, R. (1982) Breeding waders of wet meadows in Oxfordshire. OOS Report for 1982: 37-45.

KNIGHT, R. (1985) BTO Waterways Bird Survey. BOS Annual Report 1985: 35-38.

KNIGHT, R., WILLIAMS, H. and SCROGGS, R. (1980) Annual breeding season survey — Lapwing. BOS Report 1980: 30-50.

LACK, D. (1943) *The Life of the Robin.* Witherby.

LACK, D. (1956) *Swifts in a Tower.* London.

LACK, D. and LACK, E. (1952) The breeding behaviour of the Swift. *British Birds* 45: 186-215.

LACK, D. (1965) *Enjoying Ornithology.* Methuen. London.

LACK, P. (1986) *The Atlas of Wintering Birds in Britain and Ireland.* T. and A.D. Poyser. Calton, Staffs.

LANGSLOW, D.R. (1977) Movements of Black Redstarts in Britain. *Bird Study* 24: 169-178.

LEACH, I.H. (1981) Wintering Blackcaps in Britain and Ireland. *Bird Study* 28: 5-15.

LEAN, G. (1989) Observer Magazine for 4th June 1989, p.22.

LEWINGTON, I. (1988) Black-headed Wagtail in Oxfordshire. *Birding World* 1: 212.

LLOYD, G., TASKER, M. and PARTRIDGE, K. (1991) *The Status of Seabirds in Britain and Ireland.* T. and A.D. Poyser, London.

MAGEE, J.D. (1965) The breeding distribution of the Stonechat in Britain and the causes for its decline. *Bird Study* 12: 8326289.

MARCHANT, J.H. (1984) 1982-83 CBC Index Report. *BTO News* 134: 7-10.

MARCHANT, J.H., HUDSON, R., CARTER, S.P. and WHITTINGTON, P. (1990) *Population Trends in British breeding birds.* BTO. Tring.

MASSINGHAM, H.J. (1940) *Chiltern Country.* London.

McCLEERY, R.H. and PERRINS, C.M. (1989) Great Tit. In Newton, I. (Ed.) *Lifetime reproduction in Birds:* 35-54. Academic Press. London.

MEAD, C. (1983) *Bird Migration.* Country Life Books.

MEAD, C. (1984) Sand Martins slump. *BTO News* 133:1.

MEAD, C. and SMITH, K. (1982) *The Hertfordshire Breeding Bird Atlas.* HBBA. Tring.

MEEK, E.R. and LITTLE, B. (1977) The spread of the Goosander in Britain and Ireland. *British Birds* 70: 229-237.

METEOROLOGICAL OFFICE (1981) *The Thames Valley.* The Climate Of Great Britain Series. Meteorological Office. Bracknell.

MILBLAD, T. (1978) Unusual song of Grasshopper Warbler. *British Birds* 71: 139.

MONK, J.F. (1963) The past and present status of the Wryneck in the British Isles. *Bird Study* 10: 112-132.

MONTIER, D. (Ed.) (1977) *Atlas of breeding birds of the London area.* Batsford. London.

MOORE, N.W. (1962) The heaths of Dorset and Their conservation. *J. Ecology* 50: 369-91.

MOREL, G. and ROUX, F. (1962) Donnes nouvelles sur l'avifaune du Sengal. *L'Oiseau* 32: 498.

MOREAU, R. (1951) The British status of the Quail and some problems of its biology. *British Birds* 44: 257-276.

MORSE, D.H. (1978) Structure and foraging patterns of flocks of tits and associated species in an English woodland during winter. *Ibis* 120: 298-312.

MURTON, R.K. and RIDPATH, M.G. (1962) The autumn movements of the Woodpigeon. *Bird Study* 9: 7-41.

NATURE CONSERVANCY COUNCIL (1984) *Nature Conservation in Great Britain.* NCC. Shrewsbury.

NEWTON, I. (1964) The ecology and moult of the Bullfinch. Unpublished D.Phil thesis, University of Oxford.

NEWTON, I. (1967) The adaptive radiation and feeding ecology of some British finches. *Ibis* 109: 33-98.

NEWTON, I. (1972) *Finches.* Collins, London.

NEWTON, I. (1979) *Population Ecology of Raptors.* T. and A.D. Poyser. Calton, Staffs.

NICHOLSON, E.M. (1951) *Birds and Men.* Collins. London.

NICHOLSON, E.M. (1983) Jubilee Speech. *BTO News* 127:2.

NORRIS, A.S. (1977) Unusual song of Grasshopper Warbler. *British Birds* 70: 502-503.

NORRIS, C.A. (1947) Report on the distribution and status of the Corncrake. *British Birds* 40: 226-244.

O'CONNOR, R.J. (1980) Population regulation in the Yellowhammer *Emberiza citrinella* in Britain. In Oelke, H. (Ed.). *Proc. VI Int. Con. Bird Census Work,* 190-200,

O'CONNOR, R.J. and MEAD, C.J. (1984) The Stock Dove in Britain, 1930-80. *British Birds* 77: 181-201.

O'CONNOR, R.J. and MORGAN, R.A. (1982) Some effects of weather conditions on the breeding of the Spotted Flycatcher *Muscicapa striata* in Britain. *Bird Study* 29: 41-48.

O'CONNOR, R.J. and SHRUBB. M. (1986) *Farming and Birds.* Cambridge University Press. Cambridge.

O'MEARY, M. (1979) Distribution and numbers of Corncrakes in Ireland in 1978. *Irish Birds* 1: 381-405.

OGILVIE, M.A. (1981) The Mute Swan in Britain, 1978. *Bird Study* 28: 87-106.

OGILVIE, M.A. (1986) The Mute Swan, *Cygnus olor,* in Britain 1983. *Bird Study* 33: 121-137.

OKE, T.R. (1975) Urban heat island dynamics in Montreal and Vancouver. *Atmospheric Environment* 9: 191-200.

OKE, T.R. (1976) The distinction between canopy and boundary layer heat islands. *Atmosphere* 14: 268-77.

OVERALL, R. (1988) Wytham Woods, Oxford: 1971-1987. OOS Report 1988. 28-30.

PARR, A.J. (1978) Nuthatch survey. OOS Report for 1978. 29-32.

PARRINDER, E. (1987) As LRPs spread north. *BTO News* 153: 6-7.

PARRINDER, E.D. (1989) Little Ringed Plovers *Charadrius dubius* in Britain in 1984. *Bird Study* 36: 147-153.

PARSLOW, J.L.F. (1967) Changes in status among breeding birds in Britain and Ireland. *British Birds* 60: 401-402.

PEPLER, G.R.M. (1966) Recent work at Sand Martin colonies in Oxfordshire and Berkshire, 1962-1966. OOS Report for 1966: 34-37.

PERRINS, C.M. (1971) Age of first breeding and adult survival rates in the Swift. *Bird Study* 18: 61-70.

PERRINS, C.M. (1979) *British Tits.* Collins. London.

PERRINS, C.M. and REYNOLDS, C.M. (1967) A preliminary study of the Mute Swan (*Cygnus olor*). *Wildfowl Trust Ann. Rep.* 18: 74-84.

PERRY, S.G. (1986) Birds of south-west Oxfordshire. OOS Report for 1986: 5-9.

PFORR, M. and LIMBRUNNER. A. (1981) *The Breeding Birds of Europe.* Croom Helm. London.

PHILLIPS, J.S. (1973) Stonechats in young Forestry plantations. *Bird Study* 20: 82-84.

PHILLIPS, J.S. and GRIEG-SMITH, P. (1980) Breeding and wintering sites of Stonechats. *Bird Study* 27: 255-256.

PICKLES, M. (1960) The Birds of Blenheim Park. OOS. Oxford.

POLLARD, J. (1982) The Shearwater Osprey. *Hobby* 1982: 37-40. Wilts. Orn. Soc.

PRYS-JONES, R.P. (1977) Aspects of Reed Bunting ecology, with comparison with the Yellowhammer. Unpublished D.Phil thesis, University of Oxford.

PURSEGLOVE, J. (1988) *Taming the Flood.* Oxford University Press. Oxford.

RACKHAM, O. (1986) *The History of the Countryside.* J.M. Dent and Sons Ltd. London.

RADFORD, M.C. (1966) *The Birds of Berkshire and Oxfordshire.* Longmans. London.

RATCLIFFE, D.A. (1984) *New Phytol.* 98: 73-100.

RIDDINGTON, R. (1988) Synoptic influence on the form of Oxford's urban heat island. Unpublished B.A. Hons. dissertation, University of Oxford.

RIDDINGTON, R. (1990) The Great Grey Shrike in Oxfordshire. OOS Report for 1990: 26-29.

ROSS, C. (1980) Wintering Bramblings. OOS Newsletter 7: 8.

SCOTT, D.K. (1984) Winter territoriality of Mute Swans *Cygnus olor. Ibis* 126: 168-176.

SCOTT, D.K. and BIRKHEAD, M.E. (1983) Resources and reproductive performance in Mute Swans, *Cygnus olor. J. Zool. Lond.* 200: 539-547.

SCROGGS, R. (1974) Tree Sparrows in Conygree Wood. in: Brownett, A. (ed.).A Study of birds in the South Midlands. BOS.

SEARS, J. (1986) A study of Mute Swans in relation to lead poisoning. Unpublished DPhil thesis, University of Oxford.

SEARS, J. (1989) A review of lead poisoning among the River Thames Mute Swan *Cygnus olor* population. *Wildfowl* 40: 151-152.

SEEL, D.C. (1968) Breeding seasons of the House Sparrow and Tree Sparrow *Passer* spp. at Oxford. *Ibis* 110: 129-144.

SHARROCK, J.T.R. (1976) *The Atlas of Breeding Birds in Britain and Ireland.* T. and A.D. Poyser. Calton, Staffs.

SHAW, B. (1981) A ringing study of Corn Buntings. OOS Report 1981: 33-35.

SHAWYER, C.R. (1987) *The Barn Owl in the British Isles. Its past, present and future.* Hawk Trust. London.

SHRUBB, M. (1988) Nesting Lapwings in England and Wales in 1987. BTO News 156: 6-7.

SIMMS, E. (1971) *Woodland Birds.* Collins. London.

SIMMS, E. (1985) *British Warblers.* Collins. London.

SITTERS, H.P. (1982) The decline of the Cirl Bunting in Britain, 1968-80. *British Birds* 75: 105-111.

SITTERS, H.P. (1983) Cirl Bunting Survey 1982 – Provisional results. *BTO News* 127: 4.

SITTERS, H.P. (1986) Woodlarks in Britain, 1968-83. *British Birds* 79: 105-116.

SITTERS, H.P. (Ed.) (1988) *Tetrad Atlas of the Breeding Birds of Devon.* Devon Birdwatching and Preservation Society. Yelverton.

SMITH, C.G. (1954) *Climate.* In Martin, A.F. and Steel, R.W. (Eds.) The Oxford Region.

SMITH, C.G. (1980) Two hundred years of Oxford weather. In Rowley, T. (ed.) The Oxford Region.

SMITH, K.W. (1983) The status and distribution of waders breeding on wet lowland grasslands in England and Wales. *Bird Study* 30: 177-192.

SNOW, B.K. and SNOW, D.W. (1984) Long term defence of fruit by Mistle Thrushes. *Ibis* 126: 39-49.

SNOW, D.W. (1958) *A Study of Blackbirds.* British Museum (Natural History) London.

SNOW, D.W. (1966) The migration and dispersal of British Blackbirds. *Bird Study* 13: 237-255.

SNOW, D.W. (1969) Some vital statistics of British Mistle Thrushes. *Bird Study* 16: 34-44.

SNOW, D.W. and MAYER-GROSS, H. (1967) Farmland as a nesting habitat. *Bird Study* 14: 43-52.

SOUTHERN, H.N. (1954) Tawny Owls and their prey. *Ibis* 96: 384-410.

SOUTHERN, H.N. (1970) The natural control of a population of Tawny Owls *Strix aluco. J. Zool. Lond.* 162: 197-285.

SPENCER, R. (1975) Changes in the distribution of recoveries of ringed Blackbirds. *Bird Study* 22: 177-190.

SPENCER, R. (1989) Rare breeding birds in the United Kingdom in 1987. *British Birds* 82: 498.

STANDLEY, P.I., BROUGH, T., FLETCHER, M.R., HORTON, N. and ROCHARD, J.B.A. (1981) The origins of Herring Gulls wintering inland in south-east England. *Bird Study* 28: 123-132.

STEEL, D (1984) *The Natural History of a Royal Forest (Shotover). Pisces Publications.* Oxford.

STEEL, D. and VARLEY, P. (1991) The BBONT Habitat Survey of Oxfordshire. BBONT. Oxford

STROUD, D.A., PIENKOWSKI, M.W. and MUDGE, G.P. (1989) Review of the protection afforded to bird species by the network of proposed and designated special protection areas in Great Britain. Nature Conservancy Council. Peterborough.

STUART-WHORTLEY, A.J. (1896) *The Partridge*. Longmans and Co. London.

STUBBS, C.E. (1903) Notes on Oxford Ornithology. in Aplin, O.V. (Ed.) *Zoologist* 1903: 445-453.

TANSLEY, A.G. (1939) The British Islands and their Vegetation. Cambridge University Press. Cambridge.

TAYLOR, D.W., DAVENPORT, D.L. and FLEGG, J.J.M. (1982) *The Birds of Kent*. The Kent Ornithological Society. Meopham.

TAYLOR, K., HUDSON, R. and HORNE, G. (1988) Buzzard breeding distribution and abundance in Britain and Northern Ireland in 1983. *Bird Study* 35: 109-118.

THOMPSON, D.B.A. and GRIBB, N.S. (1986) Ecology of Corn Buntings (*Milaria calandra*) in NW England. *British Ecological Society Bulletin* 17: 2.

TICEHURST, N.F. (1957) *The Mute Swan in England*. Cleaver-Hume. London.

TOYNTON, P. (1975) The Aston Rowant National Nature Reserve. OOS Report for 1975: 38-40.

TUBBS, C.R. (1986) *The New Forest*. Collins. London.

TURNER, A. and ROSE, C. (1989) *A Handbook to the Swallows and Martins of the World*. Christopher Helm. London.

TYRVAINEN, H. (1975) The winter irruption of the Fieldfare and the supply of rowan berries. *Ornis Fennica*. 52: 23-31.

VINNICOMBE, K. (1982) Population fluctuations of the Little Grebe. *British Birds* 75: 204-217.

WALKER, J. J. (Ed.) (1926) The Natural History of the Oxford District. Oxford University Press. London.

WARDE FOWLER, W. (1885) *Summer studies of birds and books*. Macmillan. London.

WARDE FOWLER, W. (1886) *A Year with the Birds*. Macmillan. London.

WARDE FOWLER, W. (1913) *Kingham, old and new*. Oxford University Press. Oxford.

WHITE, G. (1788) *A Natural History of Selbourne*.

WIGGINS, R. (1984) A comparison of bird breeding species and their population densities in two Oxfordshire woodlands. OOS Report for 1984. 31-38.

WIGGINS, R.H. (1985) The Birds of Little Wittenham. Northmoor Trust.

WILLIAMS, G. (1987) *Birds* 11(6): 47.

WILLIAMS, G. and BOWERS, J.K. (1987) Land Drainage and Birds in England and Wales. *RSPB Conservation Review* 1: 25-30.

WILLIAMSON, K. (1969) Habitat preferences of the Wren on English farmland. *Bird Study* 16: 53-59

WILSON, R. (1987) Archaeological Animals of the Upper Thames Valley. Abingdon, Oxford.

WINSTANLEY, D., SPENCER, R. and WILLIAMSON, K. (1974) Where have all the Whitethroats gone? *Bird Study* 21: 1-14.

WOOD, P.C. (1939) Redshank census 1939. OOS Report for 1939: 38-40.

WOODELL, S.R.J. (1985) Vegetation. In Fitter (Ed.) *The Wildlife of the Thames Counties*: 24-37.

WYLLIE, I. (1981) *The Cuckoo*. Batsford. London.

WYLLIE, I. (1987) *The Cuckoo*. Shire Publications. Aylesbury, Bucks.

YARRELL, W. (1837-1884) *A History of British Birds*. Van Voorst. London.

YURDAN, M. (1988) *Oxfordshire and Oxford – Shire County Guide*. Shire Publications. Aylesbury, Bucks.

Appendix 1

A complete systematic list of bird species recorded in Oxfordshire (see also Appendix 2). Species bracketed have not occurred during the twentieth century and a list of species which have occurred but which are believed to have escaped from captivity appears at the end of this list. All records of birds in the county are required and will be welcomed by the county recorder c/o OOS, especially if they include details of numbers or behaviour. For a more fully annotated list, please contact the county bird recorder at the OOS address (Appendix 7).

Red-throated Diver	*Gavia stellata*	Teal	*A. crecca*
Black-throated Diver	*G. arctica*	Mallard	*A. platyrhynchos*
Great Northern Diver	*G. immer*	Pintail	*A. acuta*
Little Grebe	*Tachybaptus ruficollis*	Garganey	*A. querquedula*
Great Crested Grebe	*Podiceps cristatus*	Shoveler	*A. clypeata*
Red-necked Grebe	*P. grisegena*	Red-crested Pochard	*Netta rufina*
Slavonian Grebe	*P. auritus*	Pochard	*Aythya ferina*
Black-necked Grebe	*P. nigricollis*	Ring-necked Duck	*A. collaris*
Fulmar	*Fulmarus glacialis*	Ferruginous Duck	*A. nyroca*
Manx Shearwater	*Puffinus puffinus*	Tufted Duck	*A. fuligula*
Storm Petrel	*Hydrobates pelagicus*	Scaup	*A. marila*
Leach's Petrel	*Oceanodroma leucorhoa*	Eider	*Somateria mollissima*
Gannet	*Sula bassana*	Long-tailed Duck	*Clangula hyemalis*
Cormorant	*Phalacrocorax carbo*	Common Scoter	*Melanitta nigra*
Shag	*P. aristotelis*	Velvet Scoter	*M. fusca*
Bittern	*Botaurus stellaris*	Goldeneye	*Bucephala clangula*
Little Bittern	*Ixobrychus minutus*	Smew	*Mergus albellus*
Night Heron	*Nycticorax nycticorax*	Red-breasted Merganser	*M. serrator*
Squacco Heron	*Ardeola ralloides*	Goosander	*M. merganser*
Little Egret	*Egretta garzetta*	Ruddy Duck	*Oxyura jamaicensis*
Grey Heron	*Ardea cinerea*	Honey Buzzard	*Pernis apivorus*
Purple Heron	*A. purpurea*	Red Kite	*Milvus milvus*
(Black Stork	*Ciconia nigra*)	White-tailed Eagle	*Haliaeetus albicilla*
White Stork	*C. ciconia*	Marsh Harrier	*Circus aeruginosus*
Glossy Ibis	*Plegadis falcinellus*	Hen Harrier	*C. cyaneus*
Spoonbill	*Platalea leucorodia*	Montagu's Harrier	*C. pygargus*
Mute Swan	*Cygnus olor*	Goshawk	*Accipiter gentilis*
Bewick's Swan	*C. columbianus*	Sparrowhawk	*A. nisus*
Whooper Swan	*C. cygnus*	Buzzard	*Buteo buteo*
Bean Goose	*Anser fabalis*	Rough-legged Buzzard	*B. lagopus*
Pink-footed Goose	*A. brachyrhynchus*	Golden Eagle	*Aquila chrysaetos*
(Lesser White-fronted Goose	*A. erythropus*)	Osprey	*Pandion haliaetus*
White-fronted Goose	*A. albifrons*	Kestrel	*Falco tinnunculus*
Greylag Goose	*A. anser*	Red-footed Falcon	*F. vespertinus*
Snow Goose	*A. caerulescens*	Merlin	*F. columbarius*
Canada Goose	*Branta canadensis*	Hobby	*F. subbuteo*
Barnacle Goose	*B. leucopsis*	(Gyr Falcon	*F. rusticolus*)
Brent Goose	*B. bernicla*	Peregrine	*F. peregrinus*
Egyptian Goose	*Alopochen aegyptiacus*	Black Grouse	*Tetrao tetrix*
Ruddy Shelduck	*Tadorna ferruginea*	Red-legged Partridge	*Alectoris rufa*
Shelduck	*T. tadorna*	Grey Partridge	*Perdix perdix*
Wood Duck	*Aix sponsa*	Quail	*Coturnix coturnix*
Mandarin	*A. galericulata*	Pheasant	*Phasianus colchicus*
Wigeon	*Anas penelope*	Golden Pheasant	*Chrysolophus pictus*
American Wigeon	*A. americana*	Lady Amherst's Pheasant	*C. amherstiae*
Gadwall	*A. strepera*	(Andalusian Hemipode	*Turnix sylvatica*)

Water Rail	*Rallus aquaticus*	Little Tern	*S. albifrons*
Spotted Crake	*Porzana porzana*	Whiskered Tern	*Chlidonias hybridus*
Corncrake	*Crex crex*	Black Tern	*C. niger*
Moorhen	*Gallinula chloropus*	White-winged Black Tern	*C. leucopterus*
Coot	*Fulica atra*	Guillemot	*Uria aalge*
Crane	*Grus grus*	Razorbill	*Alca torda*
(Little Bustard	*Tetrax tetrax*)	Little Auk	*Alle alle*
Oystercatcher	*Haematopus ostralegus*	Puffin	*Fratercula arctica*
(Black-winged Stilt	*Himantopus himantopus*)	(Pallas' Sandgrouse	*Syrrhaptes paradoxus*)
Avocet	*Recurvirostra avosetta*	Rock Dove / Feral Pigeon	*Columba livia*
Stone Curlew	*Burhinus oedicnemus*	Stock Dove	*C. oenas*
Little Ringed Plover	*Charadrius dubius*	Woodpigeon	*C. palumbus*
Ringed Plover	*C. hiaticula*	Collared Dove	*Streptopelia decaocto*
Kentish Plover	*C. alexandrinus*	Turtle Dove	*S. turtur*
Dotterel	*C. morinellus*	Ring-necked Parakeet	*Psittacula krameri*
Golden Plover	*Pluvialis apricaria*	Cuckoo	*Cuculus canorus*
Grey Plover	*P. squatarola*	Barn Owl	*Tyto alba*
Sociable Plover	*Chettusia gregaria*	(Scops Owl	*Otus scops*)
Lapwing	*Vanellus vanellus*	(Eagle Owl	*Bubo bubo*)
Knot	*Calidris canuta*	Little Owl	*Athene noctua*
Sanderling	*C. alba*	Tawny Owl	*Strix aluco*
Little Stint	*C. minuta*	Long-eared Owl	*Asio otus*
Temminck's Stint	*C. temminckii*	Short-eared Owl	*A. flammeus*
Pectoral Sandpiper	*C. melanotos*	Tengmalm's Owl	*Aegolius funereus*
Curlew Sandpiper	*C. ferruginea*	Nightjar	*Caprimulgus europaeus*
Purple Sandpiper	*C. maritima*	Swift	*Apus apus*
Dunlin	*C. alpina*	Alpine Swift	*A. melba*
Ruff	*Philomachus pugnax*	Kingfisher	*Alcedo atthis*
Jack Snipe	*Lymnocryptes minimus*	Bee-eater	*Merops apiaster*
Snipe	*Gallinago gallinago*	Roller	*Coracias garrulus*
Great Snipe	*G. media*	Hoopoe	*Upupa epops*
Woodcock	*Scolopax rusticola*	Wryneck	*Jynx torquilla*
Black-tailed Godwit	*Limosa limosa*	Green Woodpecker	*Picus viridis*
Bar-tailed Godwit	*L. lapponica*	Great Spotted Woodpecker	*Dendrocopos major*
Whimbrel	*Numenius phaeopus*	Lesser Spotted Woodpecker	*D. minor*
Curlew	*N. arquata*	Woodlark	*Lullula arborea*
Spotted Redshank	*Tringa erythropus*	Skylark	*Alauda arvensis*
Redshank	*T. totanus*	Sand Martin	*Riparia riparia*
Greenshank	*T. nebularia*	Swallow	*Hirundo rustica*
Lesser Yellowlegs	*T. flavipes*	House Martin	*Delichon urbica*
Green Sandpiper	*T. ochropus*	Richard's Pipit	*Anthus novaeseelandiae*
Wood Sandpiper	*T. glareola*	Tree Pipit	*A. trivialis*
Common Sandpiper	*Actitis hypoleucos*	Meadow Pipit	*A. pratensis*
Spotted Sandpiper	*A. macularia*	Rock Pipit	*A. spinoletta*
Turnstone	*Arenaria interpres*	Water Pipit	*A. petrosus*
Red-necked Phalarope	*Phalaropus lobatus*	Yellow Wagtail	*Motacilla flava*
Grey Phalarope	*P. fulicarius*	Grey Wagtail	*M. cinerea*
Pomarine Skua	*Stercorarius pomarinus*	Pied Wagtail	*M. alba*
Arctic Skua	*S. parasiticus*	Waxwing	*Bombycilla garrulus*
Long-tailed Skua	*S. longicaudus*	Dipper	*Cinclus cinclus*
Great Skua	*S. skua*	Wren	*Troglodytes troglodytes*
Mediterranean Gull	*Larus melanocephalus*	Dunnock	*Prunella modularis*
Little Gull	*L. minutus*	Robin	*Erithacus rubecula*
Black-headed Gull	*L. ridibundus*	Nightingale	*Luscinia megarhynchos*
Common Gull	*L. canus*	Bluethroat	*L. svecica*
Lesser Black-backed Gull	*L. fuscus*	Black Redstart	*Phoenicurus ochruros*
Herring Gull	*L. argentatus*	Redstart	*P. phoenicurus*
Iceland Gull	*L. glaucoides*	Whinchat	*Saxicola rubetra*
Glaucous Gull	*L. hyperboreus*	Stonechat	*S. torquata*
Great Black-backed Gull	*L. marinus*	Wheatear	*Oenanthe oenanthe*
Kittiwake	*Rissa tridactyla*	Black-eared Wheatear	*O. hispanica*
Sandwich Tern	*Sterna sandvicensis*	Ring Ouzel	*Turdus torquatus*
Roseate Tern	*S. dougallii*	Blackbird	*T. merula*
Common Tern	*S. hirundo*	Fieldfare	*T. pilaris*
Arctic Tern	*S. paradisaea*	Song Thrush	*T. philomelos*
(Sooty Tern	*S. fuscata*)	Redwing	*T. iliacus*

Mistle Thrush	*T. viscivorus*	Serin	*Serinus serinus*
Cetti's Warbler	*Cettia cetti*	Greenfinch	*Carduelis chloris*
Grasshopper Warbler	*Locustella naevia*	Goldfinch	*C. carduelis*
Aquatic Warbler	*Acrocephalus paludicola*	Siskin	*C. spinus*
Sedge Warbler	*A. schoenobaenus*	Linnet	*C. cannabina*
Marsh Warbler	*A. palustris*	Twite	*C. flavirostris*
Reed Warbler	*A. scirpaceus*	Redpoll	*C. flammea*
Icterine Warbler	*Hippolais icterina*	Common Crossbill	*Loxia curvirostra*
Dartford Warbler	*Sylvia undata*	Scarlet Rosefinch	*Carpodacus erythrinus*
(Barred Warbler	*S. nisoria*)	Bullfinch	*Pyrrhula pyrrhula*
Lesser Whitethroat	*S. curruca*	Hawfinch	*Coccothraustes coccothraustes*
Whitethroat	*S. communis*	Lapland Bunting	*Calcarius lapponicus*
Garden Warbler	*S. borin*	Snow Bunting	*Plectrophenax nivalis*
Blackcap	*S. atricapilla*	Yellowhammer	*Emberiza citrinella*
Yellow-browed Warbler	*Phylloscopus inornatus*	Cirl Bunting	*E. cirlus*
Wood Warbler	*P. sibilatrix*	Little Bunting	*E. pusilla*
Chiffchaff	*P. collybita*	Reed Bunting	*E. schoeniclus*
Willow Warbler	*P. trochilus*	Corn Bunting	*Miliaria calandra*
Goldcrest	*Regulus regulus*		
Firecrest	*R. ignicapillus*		
Spotted Flycatcher	*Muscicapa striata*	*Escapes (see Appendix 2)*	
Pied Flycatcher	*Ficedula hypoleuca*		
Bearded Reedling	*Panurus biarmicus*	Sacred Ibis	*Threskiornis aethiopicus*
Long-tailed Tit	*Aegithalos caudatus*	Flamingo sp	*Phoenicopterus* sp.
Marsh Tit	*Parus palustris*	Black Swan	*Cygnus atratus*
Willow Tit	*P. montanus*	Trumpeter Swan	*Cygnus buccinator*
Coal Tit	*P. ater*	Swan/Chinese Goose	*Anser cygnoides*
Blue Tit	*P. caeruleus*	Bar-headed Goose	*Anser indicus*
Great Tit	*P. major*	Emperor Goose	*Anser canagicus*
Nuthatch	*Sitta europaea*	Hawaiian Goose	*Branta sandvicensis*
Treecreeper	*Certhia familiaris*	Taverner's Canada Goose	*Branta canadensis taverneri*
Golden Oriole	*Oriolus oriolus*	Ashy-headed Goose	*Chloephaga poliocephala*
Red-backed Shrike	*Lanius collurio*	Chiloe Wigeon	*Anas sibilatrix*
Lesser Grey Shrike	*L. minor*	Spotbill Duck	*Anas poecilorhyncha*
Great Grey Shrike	*L. excubitor*	Bahaman Pintail	*Anas bahamensis*
Woodchat Shrike	*L. senator*	Cinnamon Teal	*Anas cyanoptera*
Jay	*Garrulus glandarius*	Lanner	*Falco biarmicus*
Magpie	*Pica pica*	Reeve's Pheasant	*Syrmaticus reevesii*
Nutcracker	*Nucifraga caryocatactes*	Manchurian Crane	*Grus japonensis*
(Alpine Chough	*Pyrrhocorax graculus*)	Crowned Crane	*Balearica pavonina*
Jackdaw	*Corvus monedula*	Palm Dove	*Streptopelia senegalensis*
Rook	*C. frugilegus*	Lutine Cockateil	*Nymphicus hollandicus*
Carrion Crow	*C. corone*	Eastern Rosella	*Platycercus eximius*
Raven	*C. corax*	Peach-faced Lovebird	*Agapornis roseicollis*
Starling	*Sturnus vulgaris*	Quaker Parakeet	*Myiopsitta monachus*
(Rose-coloured Starling	*S. roseus*)	Cedar Waxwing	*Bombycilla cedrorum*
House Sparrow	*Passer domesticus*	Black-headed Sibia	*Heterophasia melanoleuca*
Tree Sparrow	*P. montanus*	Crested Cardinal	*Paroaria coronata*
Chaffinch	*Fringilla coelebs*	Zebra Finch	*Poephila guttata*
Brambling	*F. montifringilla*	Village Weaver	*Ploceus cucullatus*

Appendix 2

Additional species on the county list not otherwise mentioned.

I Species recorded before 1900

The main systematic list describes species recorded between 1900 and 1990. There are a number of species seen before 1900 which have not occurred since. Study of bones by Wilson (1987) produced the discovery of two wing tip bones (carpometacarpals) of Pygmy Cormorant, *Phalacrocorax pygmeus*, from a sixteenth century well in Stert Street, Abingdon. This species is not on the British list. Nineteenth century records have mostly been obtained from Aplin (1889). They are listed here together with the years in which they were seen.

Black Stork *Ciconia nigra* 1865
Lesser White-fronted Goose *Anser erythropus* 1888
Gyr Falcon *Falco rusticolus* 1847
Black-winged Stilt *Himantopus himantopus* 1812
Andalusian Hemipode *Turnix sylvatica* 1844
Little Bustard *Tetrax tetrax* 1835, 1849, 1859
Sooty Tern *Sterna fuscata* 1867
Pallas's Sandgrouse *Syrrhaptes paradoxus* 1888
Scops Owl *Otus scops* 1858
Eagle Owl *Bubo bubo* 1843, 1873
Barred Warbler *Sylvia nisoria* 1898
Alpine Chough *Pyrrhocorax graculus* 1881
Rose-coloured Starling *Sturnus roseus* 1837, 1838, 1850's

II Escapes and feral species

In addition to the species presented in the systematic list, an increasing number have been recorded in Oxfordshire which are believed to have escaped from captivity. Some of these have established viable, breeding, feral populations and have become so conspicuous a part of the county's avifauna that we have included full accounts of them in the earlier section. Examples are the Feral Pigeon and the Ring-necked Parakeet.

In other cases, it is less clear whether the birds concerned had escaped or were genuine vagrants. Some records in the main systematic list clearly refer to birds which have escaped from collections but they are included in that list because at least some of the accounts of those species are considered to be of truly wild birds. Species in this category are: Bean Goose, Pink-footed Goose, White-fronted Goose, Greylag Goose, Barnacle Goose, Brent Goose, Egyptian Goose, Ruddy Shelduck, Ferruginous Duck, Red-crested Pochard, Wood Duck, Mandarin, Golden Eagle, Peregrine and Raven.

It is not only escaped waterfowl and raptors which have complicated the situation, since an increasing variety of cagebirds are found. Our records of escaped birds are incomplete because observations have not been submitted systematically over the years. Nor have summaries been made consistently in the bird reports. However an impressive number have been mentioned in those reports.

Here we have listed all those species which are believed to have escaped from captivity since 1900, together with the year in which they were seen if they were recorded only once: Crowned Crane, Manchurian Crane 1927, Cattle Egret 1971, Emperor Goose, Bar-headed Goose, Ashy-headed Goose 1975, Palm Dove, Quaker Parakeet 1979, Crested Cardinal, Cedar Waxwing, Eastern Rosella, Peach-faced Lovebird, Village Weaver 1980, Flamingo sp., Sacred Ibis, Swan Goose, Taverner's Canada Goose 1982, Hawaiian Goose 1983, Black Swan, Trumpeter Swan, Lanner 1985, Chiloe Wigeon 1986, Chinese Goose, Spotbill Duck, Bahaman Pintail, Cinnamon Teal, Reeve's Pheasant, Zebra Finch 1988, Lutine Cockateil and Black-headed Sibia 1989.

A species warranting a more detailed account is the Snow Goose *Anser caerulescens*, since a flourishing feral colony has bred regularly in the county for four years, and it may be possible to admit it fully to the Oxfordshire list in the future.

During 1979, up to four Snow Geese were reported from different localities in Oxfordshire. A skein of 24 passed eastwards over Holywell Meadow, Oxford on 1 March 1980. In the summer of 1980, a pair raised five goslings at a gravel pit in the county. Two broods were raised in 1981 and breeding has occurred in every year since then, although there has been movement from one gravel pit to another within the complex.

During September 1986, 16 unringed Snow Geese took up residence at Blenheim and have returned each winter and by 1989/90 the flock had almost doubled in size. Birds depart in the second half of April to return to the nesting area. Failed and non-breeders return to Blenheim in early June, while those with goslings usually return in mid-July when young are able to fly strongly enough. It will be interesting to see whether this pattern will continue and the Oxfordshire population expand.

Appendix 3

Names of animals (other than birds) and plants mentioned in the text, listed in alphabetical order within kingdoms.

Animals

Ant	*Hymenoptera: Formicidae*
Bullhead	*Cotus gobio*
Drinker Moth	*Philudoria potatoria*
Fallow Deer	*Dama dama*
Five-spot Burnet Moth	*Zygaena trifolii*
Fox	*Vulpes vulpes*
Grey Squirrel	*Sciurus carolinensis*
Leeches	*Annelida: Hirudinea*
Mink	*Mustela vison*
Mouse, Wood	*Apodemus sylvaticus*
Rabbit	*Oryctolagus cuniculus*
Rat, Common or Brown	*Rattus norvegicus*
Stickleback	*Gasterosteus / Pungitius* spp
Vole, Bank	*Clethrionomys glareolus*
Vole, Field	*Microtus terrestris*
Vole, Short-tailed	*Microtus agrestis*

Plants

Alder	*Alnus glutinosa*
Ash	*Fraxinus excelsior*
Beech	*Fagus sylvatica*
Birch, Silver	*Betula pendula*
Blackthorn	*Prunus spinosa*
Bramble	*Rubus fruticosus*
Buckthorn	*Rhamnus catharticus*
Burdock	*Arctium* spp
Charlock	*Sinapsis arvensis*
Cherry	*Prunus* spp
Chicory	*Cichorium intybus*
Cosmos	*Cosmea* spp
Cotoneaster	*Cotoneaster* spp
Crab Apple	*Malus sylvestris*
Cypress	*Cupressus* spp
Daisy	*Bellis perennis*
Damson	*Prunus* sp
Dandelion	*Taraxacum* spp
Docks	*Rumex* spp
Dogwood	*Cornus sanguinea*
Elm	*Ulmus* spp
Fat Hen	*Chenopodium album*
Fritillary	*Fritillaria meleagris*
Fumitory	*Fumaria* spp (mostly *F. officinalis*)
Gorse	*Ulex europaeus*
Groundsel	*Senecio vulgaris*
Hawthorn	*Crataegus monogyna*
Hazel	*Corylus avellana*
Holly	*Ilex aquifolium*
Honeysuckle	*Lonicera* spp
Hornbeam	*Carpinus betulus*
Ivy	*Hedera helix*
Juniper	*Juniperus communis*
Knapweed	*Centaurea* spp
Larch, European	*Larix decidua*
Larch, Japanese	*Larix kaempferi*
Lavender	*Lavandula* spp
Lime	*Tilia* spp
Ling or Heather	*Calluna vulgaris*
Marigold, African	*Tagetes erecta*
Meadowsweet	*Filipendula ulmaria*
Mistletoe	*Viscum album*
Mugwort	*Artemesia vulgaris*
Nettle	*Urtica dioica*
Oak	*Quercus* spp (mostly *Q. robur*)
Orchid, Green-winged	*Orchis morio*
Pine, Corsican	*Pinus nigra*
Pine, Lodgepole	*Pinus contorta*
Pine, Scots	*Pinus sylvestris*
Poplars	*Populus* spp
Privet	*Ligustrum vulgare*
Reed, Common	*Phragmites australis*
Sainfoin	*Onobrychis viciifolia*
Spindle	*Euonymus europeaus*
Spruce, Norway	*Picea abies*
Spruce, Sitka	*Picea sitchensis*
Sycamore	*Acer pseudoplatanus*
Teasel	*Dipsacus fullonum*
Wayfaring-tree	*Viburnum lantana*
Whitebeam	*Sorbus aria*
Willow	*Salix* spp
Willowherb, Great	*Epilobium hirsutum*
Willowherbs	*Epilobium* spp
Yew	*Taxus baccata*

Appendix 4

List of place names mentioned in the text.

This gazetteer is intended to complement the maps presented in the introductory chapters. It lists in alphabetical order, all Oxfordshire localities mentioned in the text. Grid references, where provided, are for the appropriate 10km square. The inclusion of sites in this list does not necessarily imply that they are accessible to the general public and readers are asked to consult the relevant Ordnance Survey maps or suitable guide books when in doubt.

Adderbury	SP 4735	Cuxham	SU 6695
Aldfield Common	SP 4687	Day's Lock	SU 5693
Alkerton	SP 3742	Ditchley	SP 3921
Appleford	SU 5293	Dorchester	SP 5794
Appleton	SP 4401	Ducklington	SP 3507
Ardley	SP 5427	East Hendred	SU 4588
Ascott-under-Wychwood	SP 3018	Ewelme	SU 6491
Asthall	SP 2811	Farmoor	SP 4506
Aston Upthorpe	SU 5586	Fawler	SP 3517
Aynho	SP 5133	Fiddler's Island	SP 4907
Balscote	SP 3941	Fifield	SP 2418
Banbury	SP 4540	Filkins	SP 2404
Beard Mill	SP 3905	Forest Hill	SP 3507
Beckley	SP 5610	Foxcombe Wood	SP 4901
Benson	SU 6191	Freeland	SP 4112
Berinsfield	SU 5796	Fulbrook	SP 2613
Berrick Salome	SU 6294	Glympton	SP 4221
Bix (Warburg NR)	SU 7285	Godstow	SP 4809
Bladon	SP 4414	Great Milton	SP 6202
Blewbury	SU 5385	Great Rollright	SP 3231
Bloxham	SU 4335	Great Tew	SP 3929
Boars Hill	SP 4802	Grove	SU 4090
Boarstall Decoy	SP 6215	Harcourt Hill	SP 4904
Bradwell Grove	SP 2308	Hartslock	SU 6179
Brightwell Baldwin	SU 6595	Harwell	SU 4989
Bruern	SP 2620	Haseley	SP 6401
Buckland	SU 3498	Headington	SP 5407
Cassington	SP 4510	Henry Stephen/CS Lewis NR	SP 5606
Caversham	SU 7175	Heythrop	SP 3527
Chadlington	SP 3221	Hinton Waldrist	SU 3798
Charney Bassett	SU 3894	Holton Wood	SP 5908
Childrey	SU 3687	Holywell Meadow	SP 5206
Chimney	SP 3115	Iffley	SP 5203
Chinnor	SP 7500	Ipsden	SU 6385
Chislehampton	SU 5998	Jarn Mound	SP 4802
Cholsey	SU 5886	Kennington	SP 5202
Christchurch Meadows	SP 5105	Kiddington	SP 4122
Clanfield	SP 2801	Kidlington	SP 4913
Claydon	SP 4550	Kingham	SP 2523
Clifton Hampden	SU 5495	King's Lock	SP 4710
Combe	SP 4115	Lechlade	SU 2199
Cornbury Park	SP 3518	Letcombe Regis	SU 3886
Cowleaze Wood	SU 7295	Little Milton	SP 6100
Crowell	SU 7499	Little Wittenham	SU 5693
Crowmarsh Gifford	SU 6189	Lower Heyford	SP 4824
Cumnor	SP 4705	Magdalen College	SP 5206

Marsh Baldon	SU 5699	Standlake	SP 3903
Marston	SP 5204	Stanford in the Vale	SU 3493
Medley	SP 4907	Stanton Harcourt	SP 4105
Middle Aston	SP 4726	Stanton St John	SP 5709
Middleton Stoney	SP 5323	Steventon	SU 4691
Milton	SP 6302	Stonesfield	SP 3917
Minster Lovell	SP 3110	Stonor	SU 7388
Mollington	SP 4447	Streatley	SU 5980
Nettlebed	SU 6986	Sunningwell	SP 4900
Newbridge	SP 4001	Sutton	SP 4106
North Aston	SP 4729	Sutton Courtenay	SU 5093
Northmoor	SP 4202	Swinbrook	SP 2812
Nuneham Courtenay	SU 5599	Swyncombe	SU 6890
Osney	SP 5006	Tackley	SP 4720
Oxford	SP 5106	Tadmarton	SP 3937
Parson's Pleasure	SP 5207	Tadpole Bridge	SP 3300
Pigeon Lock	SP 4819	Taynton	SP 2313
Pixey Mead	SP 4809	Tetsworth	SP 6802
Port Meadow	SP 4908	Tiddington	SP 6504
Preston Crowmarsh	SU 5298	Trap Grounds	SP 5007
Rousham	SP 4724	Tubney	SU 4398
Rushey	SP 3200	University Parks	SP 5107
Ryecote	SP 6604	Vicarage Pit	SP 4005
Sandford-on-Thames	SP 5301	Warborough	SU 5993
Sandford St Martin	SP 4226	Wardington	SP 4946
Shifford	SP 3701	West Challow	SU 3688
Shilton	SP 2608	West Hendred	SU 4488
Shiplake	SU 7678	Weston-on-the-Green	SP 5318
Shipton on Cherwell	SP 4816	Wheatley	SP 5905
Shrivenham	SU 2489	Wolvercote	SP 4809
Sibford Ferris	SP 3537	Woodcote	SU 6481
Somerton	SP 4928	Woodeaton	SP 5311
Sonning Common	SU 7080	Wootton, Woodstock	SP 4319
South Stoke	SU 5983	Wroxton	SP 4141
St Giles	SP 5107	Wytham	SP 4708

Appendix 5

This appendix presents the results of statistical analyses carried out on Oxfordshire (unless otherwise stated) Atlas or record data and mentioned in the species accounts. In general, we have looked simply for an association between the presence of a species and the presence of a particular habitat feature such as woodland or another species. Only statistically significant results have been presented. The analysis of an association with woodland was carried out by scoring whether or not a tetrad contained a block of woodland of more than 12.5 ha (i.e. one eighth of a 1 km square).

Atlas data (see Chapter 4)

To test whether the number of species recorded in a tetrad reflected the pattern of diversity over a larger area, two analyses were carried out. First we looked for a correlation between the species count of a tetrad and that of a neighbouring tetrad. The tetrad to the east of a particular tetrad was used but since tetrads at the eastern margin of the county cannot be used, these tetrads were omitted from the analysis. This gave a sample of 672 tetrads. This simple analysis gave a correlation coefficient of 0.439 which was highly significant ($P<0.0001$). Secondly, a oneway Analysis of Variance (ANOVA) was carried out on the species counts grouped by 10 km square. The results showed that the variation between tetrads within their 10 km squares was significantly less than that across tetrads between 10 km squares ($F_{38,414}=10.21$, $P<0.0001$). Hence there is significant variation between 10 km squares which is reflected at the tetrad level. Although these regional effects could partly reflect observer differences, it is far more likely that they reflect genuine differences in environmental quality for birds since in most cases, many observers were involved in fieldwork in any one 10 km square so that observer differences are likely to even out over the whole area.

Marsh Tit

[1] The association across tetrads between Marsh Tit and Willow Tit: $X^2_1=110.5$, $P<0.001$.
[2] The association across tetrads between Marsh Tit and woodland: $X^2_1=48.2$, $P<0.001$.
[3] The dissociation between Marsh and Willow Tit in Hertfordshire calculated from data in Mead and Smith 1982: $X^2_1=29.6$, $P<0.001$.

Willow Tit

Association of Willow Tits with woodlands: $X^2_1=9.1$, $P<0.01$.

Coal Tit

Association of Coal Tits with woodlands: $X^2_1=87.2$, $P<0.001$.

Nuthatch

The association across tetrads between Nuthatch and woodland: $X^2_1=96.2$, $P<0.001$.

Treecreeper

The association across tetrads between Treecreeper and woodland: $X^2_1=12.3$, $P<0.001$.

Brambling

The occurrence of Bramblings in Oxfordshire in relation to snowfall and beech crop in northern Europe. The data for these predictors were extracted from Jenni (1987) and are presented with the account for Brambling. The analysis was carried out as a two-way Analysis of Variance (unbalanced design with an interaction term fitted) using a General Linear Model. The number of Brambling (log_e transformed) in the county in a winter was taken as the dependent variable with snow and beech crop as predicting factors. Both factors and the interaction between them were significant determinants of the variation in Brambling numbers from year to year: Beech $F=11.28$ $P=0.004$, Snow $F=10.41$ $P=0.001$, interaction $F=4.19$ $P=0.033$.

Appendix 6

Contributors to the Atlas of Breeding Birds of Oxfordshire 1985-88.

Listed below are the names of those who contributed to the fieldwork for the Oxfordshire Atlas project. Names given in bold print also acted as 10km square leaders, so helping to organise and co-ordinate fieldworkers and increasing the efficency of their work. We have taken great care in preparing this list but we should like to apologise to anyone that might, nevertheless, have been missed.

Mr	R	Absalom	**MR**	**P**	**CHANDLER**
Mr	T	Akriotis	Mrs	S	Chasemore
Mr	D	Alexander	Mr	SJ	Claridge
Mrs	J	Allen	Mr	J	Claydon
MR	**M**	**AMPHLETT**	Mr	B	Clements
Mr	F	Ball	Mr	M	Clist
Mr	P	Barnett	Dr	FAL	Clowes
Miss	S	Barrett	Miss	T	Clowser
Mr	MJ	Bayliss	Mr	S	Coble
Mr	P	Beaumont	Mr	JP	Cockett
Mr		Bell	Mr	M	Cockett
Mr	IC	Bell	Dr	A	Cole
Mrs	F	Berrill	Mr	A	Collins
Mr	J	Best	Mrs	A	Coombes
Mr	A	Birds	Mr	J	Cooper
Mr	CR	Bishop	Mr	D	Cooper
Mrs	B	Blackwell	Mrs		Cooper
Mr	S	Blackwell	Mr	B	Cooper
Dr	JM	Blakey	Mr	J	Coppock
Ms	C	Blundell	Mr	L	Cornwallis
Mr	JC	Booth	Mr	W	Corris
Mr	P	Bowler	Mr	AB	Cox
Mr	R	Bowles	Mrs	AB	Cox
Mr	R	Bradford	Mr	P	Critchley
Mr	A	Brampton	Mr	M	Crockford
Mr	E	Bridge	Mr	RJ	Cross
Mr	B	Brightwell	**MR**	**M**	**DANIEL**
Mr	E	Bristow	Mr	D	Dean
MR	**A**	**BROWNETT**	Mr	C	Dee
MR	**JW**	**BRUCKER**	Mr	D	Doherty
Mr	N	Bucknell	Mr	P	Douthwaite
DR	**SF**	**BURCH**	Mr	N	Dummigan
Mr	R	Burgess	Dr	E	Dunn
Mr	N	Burman	**MR**	**T**	**EASTERBROOK**
Mr	P	Burman	Mr	SB	Edwards
Mr	AW	Busby	Mr	RP	Edwards
Mr	PM	Butcher	Mrs	J	Edwards
Mrs	FH	Butcher	Mr	A	Edwards
Mr	R	Butler	Mr	K	Edwards
Miss	T	Byatt	Dr	P	Edwards
Mrs	V	Caird	Mr	M	Elliott
Mr	JC	Callow	Mr	C	Emary
Dr	B	Campbell	Mr	N	Evans
MR	**JM**	**CAMPBELL**	Dr	PGH	Evans
Mr	WD	Campbell	Mr	M	Eyre
Mrs	F	Castle	Mr	G	Ferguson

Mr	H	Ferrar		**MR**	**J**	**KEARVELL**
Mr	O	Field		Mr	S	Kellagher
Mr	RSR	Fitter		Dr	M	Kelsey
Mr	J	Fletcher		Mrs	J	Kench
Mr	A	Ford		Mrs		Kerslake
Dr	D	Foskett		Mr	P	King
Mr	R	Fox		Mr	R	Knight
Mr	R	Fox		Mrs	D	Knight
Mr	I	Francis		Mrs	DL	Laforte
Mr	JK	Freestone		Mr	H	Lemon
Mrs	B	Fuller		Mr	I	Lewington
Mrs	J	Garlick		Mr	R	Lewington
MR	**J**	**GEARING**		Mr	LR	Lewis
Mrs	M	Gearing		Mr	M	Lewis
Mr	P	Gipson		Mr	NV	Linklater
Mr	R	Godden		Mr	P	Llewellyn
Mr	TJ	Godfrey		Mr	D	Lloyd
Mrs	M	Gordon		Mr	R	Louch
DR	**A**	**GOSLER**		Mr	B	MacDonald
Mr	A	Grantham		Mr	M	MacFadyen
Mr	I	Gray		Miss	EM	Maddock
Mr		Green		Mr	P	Madeley
Mr	E	Green		Mrs	M	Madeley
Mrs	J	Green		Mr	PM	Mansfield
Mr	AP	Gresswell		Mrs	J	Margetts
Mrs	J	Griffiths		Mrs		Martin
Mr	E	Grimes		Mr	D	Mason
Mr	NJ	Hallam		Mr		Mason
Maj.	TT	Hallchurch		Mr	D	Massie
Mr	R	Halsey		Mr	M	Meardon
Mr	J	Harding		Mr	AS	Melville
Mr	T	Harris		Dr	J	Mercer
Mr	M	Hart		Mr	K	Middleton
Mrs	P	Hartridge		Mrs	J	Millen
Miss	FE	Harvey		Mrs	J	Monk
Miss	R	Herbert		Dr	JA	Morton
Mr	L	Herdsfield		Mr	A	Nash
Mr	AR	Heryet		**MR**	**JDA**	**NICHOLLS**
Mr	S	Heskett		Mr	R	Nicholls
Mrs	I	Hill		Mr	KJ	Norledge
Mr	J	Hird		Mr	M	North
Mr	J	Hobson		Mr	WH	North
Mr	GJ	Holloway		**MR**	**E**	**NORVELL**
Miss	S	Hopewell		**MR**	**M**	**OLIVER**
Mr	M	Hopkins		Mr	TG	Osmond
Mr	M	Hopkins		**MR**	**R**	**OVERALL**
MR	**D**	**HORTON**		**MR**	**I**	**PACKER**
Mr	R	Horwood		Mr	S	Parr
Dr	GT	Houlsby		Mr	C	Passingham
Mrs	J	Houlsby		Mr	R	Payne
Mr	DE	Hughes		Mr	LW	Penson
Mr	RW	Hummel		Dr	CM	Perrins
Mr	J	Humphreys		**MR**	**A**	**PETERS**
Mrs	M	Hunt		Mr	N	Phillips
Mr	R	Hurley		Mrs	M	Pickworth
Mr	R	Hurst		Mr	CB	Pierce
Mr	M	Ingram		**MR**	**P**	**POOL**
Mr	MV	Jackson		Mrs	CE	Pool
Ms	CM	Jackson-Houlston		Mr	C	Rasmussen
Mr	M	Jaunet		Mr	D	Rear
Mr	B	Jefferson		Mr	DL	Redhead
Mrs	V	Jefferson		Dr	DJ	Reynolds
MS	**A**	**JONES**		Mr	R	Riddington
Mr	D	John		Mr	D	Ridge
Mr	DWM	Jordan		Mr	A	Riza
MR	**T**	**JUNIPER**		**MR**	**A**	**ROBERTS**

Mr	J	Roberts
Mr	CMA	Roberts
Mr	C	Robinson
Mr	G	Roger
Mr	C	Rogers
Mr	G	Rollason
Mr	M	Rose
Mr	D	Rose
MRS	**C**	**ROSS**
Mr	PJ	Russell
Mr	L	Salmon
Mrs	V	Salt
Mr	J	Sapey
Mr	G	Saunders
MR	**B**	**SCAMPION**
Mr	R	Scase
Mrs	W	Scase
Mrs	J	Scott
MR	**RW**	**SCROGGS**
Mrs	E	Seagar
Mr	RV	Seagrove
Dr	J	Sears
Mr	W	Sell
Mr	V	Shadbolt
Mr	B	Shaw
Mr	RT	Sherwood
Mrs	H	Smith
MR	**G**	**SMITH**
Mr	K	Smith
Mr	DB	Smith
Mr	M	Spiller
Mr	M	Stainton
Mr	B	Stayte
Dr	D	Steel
Mr	M	Stevens
Dr	TA	Stevens
MR	**T**	**STEVENSON**
Mr	R	Stone
Mr	c	Story
Mr	G	Sumner
Mr	M	Sutton
Mr	S	Swinstead
Mr	A	Symonowicz
Mr	KM	Talbot

Mr	M	Taylor
Mr	W	Temple
Mr	NS	Thom
Mr	LS	Tiller
Mr	T	Tims
Mr	P	Tonge
Mrs		Tonkiss-Cameron
Mr	R	Trinder
MRS	**J**	**TROTMAN**
Mr	MW	Tucker
Mrs	B	Turtle
Miss	D	Vincent
Mr	J	Walford
Mr	AM	Walker
Mr	JR	Walsh
Mrs	MW	Ward
Mr	J	Warland
Mr	J	Warren
Mr	JL	Watson
Mr	EA	Watson
Mr	M	Webber
Mr	J	Weir
Mr	K	Wheatley
Mr	T	Whitchurch
Dr	A	Whitehead
Mr	RH	Wiggins
Dr	A	Wilkie
MR	**MA**	**WILKINS**
The late MR H WILLIAMS		
MR	**M**	**WILSON**
Mr	J	Wilson
Sq Ldr	JH	Wilson
Mr	P	Wixey
Mrs	R	Woodell
Mr	G	Wren
Mr	M	Wright
Mr	V	Wright
Mrs	M	Wright
Mr	BJ	Wyatt
Mr	RG	Wyatt
Mr	T	Young

Participants on the Kingston Hill Farm CBC plot
The Children of Horspath CP School

Appendix 7

Some useful addresses.

Banbury Ornithological Society (BOS)
25 Main Road, Middleton Cheney, Banbury, Oxfordshire, OX17 2ND.

Berkshire, Buckinghamshire and Oxfordshire Naturalists' Trust (BBONT)
3 Church Cowley Road, Rose Hill, Oxford, OX4 3JR.

British Trust for Ornithology (BTO)
The Nunnery, Nunnery Place, Thetford, Norfolk, IP24 2PU.

Council for the Protection of Rural England (CPRE)
Oxfordshire Branch, Priestley's Loft, The Barn House, Church Hanborough, Oxford, OX7 2AB.

English Nature
Foxhold House, Crookham Common, Newbury, Berkshire, RG15 8EL.

National Rivers Authority (NRA)
Thames Region, PO Box 214, Reading, Berkshire, RG1 8HQ.

National Rivers Authority, Conservation Manager, Kings Meadow House, Kings Meadow Road, Reading, Berkshire, RG1 8DQ.

Oxfordshire Biological Recording Scheme
c/o Oxfordshire County Museum, Fletchers House, Woodstock, Oxfordshire,

Oxfordshire County Ecologist
Department of Planning and Property Services, Speedwell House, Speedwell Street, Oxford, OX1 1SD.

Oxfordshire Farming and Wildlife Advisory Group (FWAG)
MAFF, Government Buildings, Marston Road, New Marston, Oxford, OX3 0TP

Oxford Ornithological Society (OOS)
c/o Edward Grey Institute, Department of Zoology, South Parks Road, Oxford, OX1 3PS.

Royal Society for the Protection of Birds (RSPB)
Thames and Chiltern Region, The Lodge, Sandy, Bedfordshire, SG19 2DL.

Thames Water Utilities
Conservation Manager, Water and Environmental Science, Nugent House (RBH2), Vastern Road, Reading, Berkshire, RG1 8DB.

Index of birds

Gadwall, 27, 34, 86
Gallinago gallinago, 128
    media, 129
Gallinula chloropus, 113
Gannet, 72
Garganey, 29, 88-89
Garrulus glandarius, 230
Gavia arctica, 63
    immer, 63
    stellata, 63
Gaviidae, 63-64
Godwit, Bar-tailed, 131
    Black-tailed, 131
Goldcrest, 21, 26, 34, 53, 211-212, 213
Goldeneye, 28, 93
Goldfinch, 25, 34, 58, 242-244, 246
Goosander, 28, 94-95
Goose, Barnacle, 83
    Bean, 82
    Brent, 83
    Canada, 4, 12, 27, 28, 34, 36, 40, 83-84, 256
    Egyptian, 34, 83
    Greylag, 34, 83
    Pink-footed, 82
    Snow, 34
    White-fronted, 82-83
Goshawk, 34, 98-99
Grebe, Black-necked, 67-68
    Great Crested, 27, 28, 34, 39, 65, 66-67, 184, 256
    Little, 27, 28, 34, 36, 39, 65-66
    Red-necked, 67
    Slavonian, 67
Greenfinch, 22, 24, 25, 27, 34, 58, 155, 242
Greenshank, 134
Grouse, Black, 108
Gruidae, 116
Grus grus, 116
Guillemot, 147
Gull, Black-headed, 22, 28, 34, 138-140
    Common, 139, 140-141
    Glaucous, 139, 142
    Great Black-backed, 139, 142-143
    Herring, 28, 34, 139, 141-142
    Iceland, 142
    Lesser Black-backed, 28, 139, 141, 143
    Little, 138
    Mediterranean, 138

Haematopodidae, 117
Haematopus ostralegus, 117
Haliaeetus albicilla 96
Harrier, Hen, 3, 10, 23, 97
    Marsh, 97
    Montagu's, 21, 34, 97-98, 257
Hawfinch, 25, 34, 59, 248-249
Heron, Grey, 28, 34, 37, 39, 75, 76-77
    Night, 75
    Purple, 77
    Squacco, 75
Hippolais icterina, 206
Hirundinidae, 177-180
Hirundo rustica, 178
Hobby, 24, 34, 36, 105-107
Hoopoe, 170

Hydrobates pelagicus, 71
Hydrobatidae, 71

Ibis, Glossy, 79
Ixobrychus minutus, 75

Jackdaw, 22, 23, 25, 34, 56, 157, 197, 232
Jay, 25, 34, 56, 197, 230-231
Jynx torquilla, 171

Kestrel, 23, 24, 34, 41, 104-105, 256
Kingfisher, 13, 27, 28, 34, 36, 46, 166-167, 238
Kite, Red, 3, 96, 109, 257
Kittiwake, 143
Knot, 126

Laniidae, 228-229
Lanius collurio, 228
    excubitor, 228
    minor, 228
    senator, 229
Lapwing, 3, 19, 22, 23, 28, 29, 34, 42, 123-125, 140, 235, 256
Laridae, 138-143
Larus argentatus, 141
    canus, 140
    fuscus, 141
    glaucoides, 142
    hyperboreus, 142
    marinus, 142
    melanocephalus, 138
    minutus, 138
    ridibundus, 138
Limosa lapponica, 131
    limosa, 131
Linnet, 26, 34, 59, 105, 155, 245-246, 255
Locustella naevia, 202
Lophura nycthemera, 111
Loxia curvirostra, 245
Lullula arborea, 175
Luscinia megarhynchos, 192
    svecica, 193
Lymnocryptes minimus, 128

Magpie, 24, 25, 34, 56, 104, 106, 108, 109, 121, 197, 200, 231
Mallard, 27, 28, 34, 40, 66, 87-88
Mandarin, 34, 85
Martin, House, 25, 28, 34, 48, 106, 179-180, 237
    Sand, 14, 27, 28, 34, 36, 47, 177-178, 235, 238
Melanitta fusca, 93
    nigra, 92
Merganser, Red-breasted, 94
Mergus albellus, 93
    merganser, 94
    serrator, 94
Merlin, 10, 105
Meropidae, 168
Merops apiaster, 168
Miliaria calandra, 253
Milvus milvus, 96